INTERNATIONAL SERIES OF MONOGRAPHS IN CHEMICAL ENGINEERING

GENERAL EDITOR: P. V. DANCKWERTS

VOLUME 8

INDUSTRIAL GAS CLEANING

INDUSTRIAL
GAS CLEANING

The principles and practice of the control of gaseous
and particulate emissions

W. STRAUSS

Reader in Industrial Science
University of Melbourne

PERGAMON PRESS

OXFORD · NEW YORK · TORONTO · SYDNEY

Pergamon Press Ltd., Headington Hill Hall, Oxford
Pergamon Press Inc., Maxwell House, Fairview Park, Elmsford,
New York 10523
Pergamon of Canada Ltd., 207 Queen's Quay West, Toronto 1
Pergamon Press (Aust.) Pty. Ltd., 19a Boundary Street,
Rushcutters Bay, N.S.W. 2011, Australia

First edition 1966
Reprinted 1974
Library of Congress Catalog Card No. 64–14803

Printed in Great Britain by A. Wheaton & Co., Exeter

ISBN 0 08 010569 6

Pig Legislation?

CONTENT

PREFACE

THE control of air pollution at its major and most varied source, the industrial process, is a task confronting an increasing number of engineers and applied scientists. When starting his post-graduate studies some years ago the author was set the problem of finding a new method of reducing the fumes from steel making processes, with particular emphasis on the fine orange–brown fumes from the then recently introduced oxygen lancing in the open-hearth and the pneumatic steel making processes. The new process was to be cheaper than the conventional methods used — electrostatic precipitation or venturi scrubbing — although the efficiency requirements were not quite as rigorous. Subsequently a pebble bed type filter was developed and found to be over 90 per cent efficient in some circumstances.[474]

At the beginning of the program of research no details of fume emission at the various stages of open-hearth steel making could be found in the published literature, and even if the fume characteristics had been defined, the possible mechanisms of collection were not set down in a textbook or monograph, together with the relevant equations which could be used to test the applicability of a particular mechanism. The author found further that gas cleaning was treated by its practitioners largely as an art based on practical experience and rule of thumb. Although the basic theory of gas cleaning mechanisms was published in scattered papers, no integrated account of these was available to engineers who wished to use them in "scale-up" calculations or in predicting the effect of a change in one of the process variables, such as gas velocity through a cleaning system. Even now only two aspects of gas cleaning, absorption and electrostatic precipitation, have received extensive treatment, while the gas cleaning methods involving particle mechanics generally have not been comprehensively reviewed. The author hopes that this book will go some way towards filling this gap, and that it will prove useful to the engineer designing or specifying gas cleaning plant as well as to the applied scientist developing new methods of gas cleaning.

The author wishes to acknowledge the assistance and encouragement he received from Prof. M. W. Thring, who first directed his interests towards this field, and from his colleagues, in particular, Mr. R. S. Yost, who is responsible for Appendix 1, Mr. C. H. Johnson, who read and made many helpful suggestions with respect to Chapters 4 and 7, and Mr. J. B. Agnew, who similarly assisted with parts of Chapter 3. The author is particularly indebted to the Engineering Librarian, Mr. J. Greig, and his staff, for their help with references and diagrams, and Mrs. F. M. Beissel, for her careful typing of the manuscript.

WERNER STRAUSS

University of Melbourne

LIST OF SYMBOLS

Latin Letters

a constant
interfacial or surface area per unit volume
height of cyclone entrance line
distance from node

A surface area
aggregate surface area of particles in unit volume

A_p external surface area of a porous solid

$\mathscr{A}$ area of plates in electrostatic precipitator
amplitude of sound vibrations

b constant
time fraction wind is in a 45° sector
entrance width of cyclone
(ab = cross-sectional area of cyclone entry)

B breadth of settling chamber
diameter of opening at cone apex in cyclone

c constant
concentration (mass or volume) of particles in gas

c_0 number of particles at zero time

C Cunningham correction factor

C_D drag coefficient

C_{DA} drag coefficient for accelerating particles

C_0 function of applied voltage $\mathscr{V}$ and electrode geometry ($\mathscr{V}/\ln R_2/R_1$)

C_p specific heat, constant pressure

C_v specific heat, constant volume

C_y generalized eddy diffusion coefficient – cross wind (Sutton[480])

C_z generalized eddy diffusion coefficient – vertical (Sutton[480])

$\mathscr{C}$ constant

d diameter of spherical particle

d' diameter of sphere of influence

d_A area diameter (diameter of circle with same projected area as that of particle)

d_c diameter of cloud

d_e drag diameter

d_s surface diameter (diameter of sphere with same surface area as particle

d_v volume diameter (diameter of sphere with same volume as particle)

d_{crit} diameter of smallest particle 100 per cent collected

d_{50} diameter of particle 50 per cent collected

D diameter of cyclone
      diameter of collecting body (fibre, droplet, rod or sphere)
      diameter of sampling probe

D_C diameter of core

D_e diameter of exit pipe in cyclone

$\mathscr{D}$ diffusivity

e electronic charge
      charge on an ion

$\mathbf{e}$ turbine efficiency

E strength of heat source relative to surrounding atmosphere (B.t.u./sec)
      field strength of electric field (V/cm)

E' strength of charging field

$\bar{E}$ energy intensity (sonic) (ergs/cm^3)

E_c critical field strength for electrical breakdown of gases

f free falling speed of particles

F fluid resistance force on particle

F_a hydrodynamic attractive force in sonic field

F_r radiation pressure in a sonic field (dynes)

F_t thermal force

F_c fluid resistance to clouds

F_E electrostatic force

F_{EI} electrostatic image force (image of collector induced on particle)

F_{EM} electrostatic image force (image of particle induced on collector)

F_{EC} coulombic force

F_{ES} space charge force

F_W fluid resistance corrected for wall effects

g gravity acceleration

g_c gravity acceleration constant

G potential temperature gradient in the atmosphere (°C/ft)
      force on a particle
      friction constant (Stairmand) for cyclones

$\mathscr{G}$ gravitational settling parameter

h height of cylindrical section of cyclone

H total height of smoke plume (effective stack height)
      height of settling chamber
      height of cyclone (or length, if cyclone body curved)

$\mathbf{H}$ field strength of magnetic field (oersted)

H_S chimney stack height

H_t height of a transfer unit (gas absorption)

H_T buoyancy rise of plume

H_V momentum rise of plume (velocity rise)

$\mathscr{H}$ Henry's law constant

i ionic current per unit length of conductor

I light intensity

     index of agglomeration (sonic)

$\mathscr{I}$ sound intensity

J variable in Bosanquet buoyancy rise equation

k orifice coefficient

     extinction coefficient

$\mathbf{k}$ Boltzmann's constant

k_f mass transfer coefficient – gas to solid surface

k_G gas film mass transfer coefficient

k_L liquid film mass transfer coefficient

K correction factor

K_G overall mass transfer coefficient (pressure units)

K_L overall mass transfer coefficient (concentration units)

l distance between two particles

     distance for absorption

l distance between enclosing walls

L rate of liquid flow

     depth of filter bed

     length of settling chamber

     distance between wire and plate in electrostatic precipitator

     distance moved by particle in sonic field

L_1 rate of liquid flow in scrubber (gal/1000 ft^3)

m mass flow

     mass of particle

     irregularity factor – a function of wire condition

M molecular weight

M' weight of a molecule

$\mathbf{M}$ rate of deposition (tons/(mile)^2 year)

$\mathscr{M}$ function of weights of particles and ions

n turbulence index (Sutton)

$\mathbf{n}$ number of times greater than the force of gravity

N molecules per unit volume

     number of points

N_1 ions per unit volume

$\mathbf{N}$ number of revolutions

$\mathscr{N}$ number of revolutions of gas stream in cyclone

N_A rate of molecular transfer of species A

p_A partial pressure of component

p_{AM} logarithmic mean partial pressure of component A

p_i partial pressure at interface

P total gas pressure

P_c cyclone gas pressure (average)

P_i cyclone inlet gas pressure

Pe   Peclet number

$\mathscr{P}$ power

$\boldsymbol{P}$ probability of collection

Δp pressure drop

Δp_{CF} pressure drop with constant gas flow

q charge on a particle (subscript I refers to particle I)

Q gas flow rate (ft³/sec)
      charge on a collecting body

Q' rate of emission of pollutant gas

r radius of particle
      distance between centre of particle and centre of collector

$\mathbf{r}$ resistivity of dust layer

$\bar{r}$ average pore radius

R universal gas constant
      radius of a circle
      radius of precipitator wire and tube
      interception parameter (d/D)

R_A drag on accelerating particles

Re   Reynold's number ($u\varrho D/\mu$ – pipes, $ud\varrho/\mu$ – particles)

Re_c Reynold's number – collecting body ($v_0D\varrho/\mu$)

R_h half distance between sphere centres for hexagonal particle arrangement

S cross-sectional area of absorption tower
      retentivity of charcoal (Turk's equation 3.50)
      width of corona layer on discharge electrode
      influence factor (ratio of diameter of sphere of influence of particle and actual particle diameter)
      depth of cyclone exit pipe within cyclone

Sc   Schmidt number ($\mu/\varrho\mathscr{D}$)

$\mathscr{S}$ collection surface in electrostatic precipitator per unit volume gas flow

t time

T absolute temperature

T_s stack exit gas temperature

T_1 absolute temperature at which density of stack gases equals density of atmosphere (°K)

u gas velocity
      wind velocity
      molecular velocity

$\bar{u}$ average velocity
      average velocity of gas molecules

u_g velocity amplitude of gas

u_H axial velocity

u_i inlet velocity
       ionic mobility in a field of unit strength
u_p velocity amplitude of particle
u_R radial velocity
u_s superficial velocity
u_t terminal velocity
u_T tangential velocity
U average gas velocity
U_S velocity of sound
v velocity
       stack exit velocity
v_0 undisturbed upstream fluid velocity
Δv relative velocity of two particles
V rate of gas flow (absorption)
       volume of settling chamber
V_a swept volume
V_A volume of species A at normal boiling point
$\mathscr{V}$ voltage, potential difference
V_1 voltage of collecting body
$\mathscr{V}_c$ corona starting voltage
V_d potential across deposited dust layer
w thickness of refractory
W rate of solids emission
       weight of adsorbing solid
       distance between successive wires in electrostatic precipitator
x downwind distance from stack (plume dispersion)
       mole fraction
       downstream distance in precipitator
       thickness of boundary layer
       thickness of dust layer
       dust content of filter cloth
       exponent in voltage/corona current equation
x_e equilibrium dust content of filter cloth
X function in Bosanquet buoyancy equation
X_g amplitude of gas vibration
X_p amplitude of particle vibration
y cross wind distance (plume dispersion)
       mole fraction
Z function in Bosanquet equation
       height of absorption tower
       diffusion collection parameter

Greek Letters

α constant
blade angle
entrance loss coefficient for cyclone
packing density

β constant
loss constant
volume concentration correction factor

γ specific heat ratio (C_p/C_v)

ϵ porosity or voidage of a packed bed or porous solid
dielectric constant of an aerosol particle

ϵ_0 specific inductive capacity of space: 8·85 coulomb^2/(dyne) (cm^2)

ε loss number

ζ dimensionless pressure loss factor

η efficiency

η_C interception collection efficiency

η_D diffusion collection efficiency

η_I inertial impaction collection efficiency

η_0 overall efficiency

η_{ICD} combined efficiency

θ angle of particle movement
parameter for cylindrical co-ordinate

$\varkappa$ permeability coefficient
thermal conductivity
coagulation constant

$\varkappa_g$ thermal conductivity of gas

$\varkappa_p$ thermal conductivity of particle

$\varkappa_{gtr}$ translational part of thermal conductivity of gas

λ mean free path of gas molecules
wave length of sound waves

μ viscosity of gas

μ_d viscosity of droplet

ν frequency

ξ constant for free vortex formula

ϱ gas density

ϱ_F fibre bed density

ϱ_L density of liquid

ϱ_V density of vapour

ϱ_p density of particle

σ molecular diameter
surface tension
space charge per unit volume

σ_{AB} sum of radii of two interacting molecules or ions (distance between centres)

τ dimensionless time parameter
time constant
dimensionless precipitator length $(x/L\,f(\mathscr{D}))$
period of vibration
T parameter $(= mu_T^2/3\pi\mu dR_2)$
φ friction factor for cyclones (Stairmand formula)
Φ current density (amp/cm^2)
dimensionless drift velocity parameter
χ internal porosity of solid granules
circularity of particles
ψ inertial impaction parameter
Ψ sphericity
ω drift velocity
ω' effective migration velocity

INTRODUCTION

I.1. WHY CLEAN GASES?

There are two fundamental reasons for the cleaning of gases in industry, particularly waste gases: profit and protection. For example, profits may result from the utilization of blast furnace gases for heating and power generation, but particulate impurities have to be removed from the gases before they can be burned satisfactorily. On the other hand, sulphur dioxide can be extracted from flue gases and economically converted into sulphur,[549] or germanium can be recovered from the fly ash of certain coals.

Protection, of the individual working in industry, the public in general, and of property, is the other reason for cleaning gases in certain cases. For example, waste gases which contain toxic constituents such as arsenic or lead fumes constitute a serious danger to the health of plant operatives and the surrounding population.[207] Other waste gases such as those containing fluorine compounds or sulphur dioxide, although not normally endangering health in the concentrations encountered may kill plants,[489] damage paintwork and buildings or merely discolour wallpaper and curtains, making an industrial town a less pleasant place to live in.[302]

The extent to which industries can clean their gases remains primarily a question of economics. In some instances provision of one type of plant may prevent profitable operation, or require major reconstruction, while another type of plant, although not quite as effective, will mean continued production. When the material to be collected constitutes the major process product, as for example the particles from a spray drying operation, an economic balance of loss of product against cost of increased efficiency of collection will decide the optimum type of collector.

Since, in practice, the most extensive gas cleaning is undertaken to prevent atmospheric pollution, the nature of such pollutants will be discussed here.

I.2. NATURE OF AIR POLLUTANTS

Air pollution may be either natural or man-made. Natural pollution may arise from soil erosion or volcanic explosions, the most famous of the latter being the eruption of Krakatoa in Indonesia in 1883, which caused sky-darkening hundreds of miles away. Man-made pollution originates either from combustion of carbonaceous materials — coal and coal products, oil and wood — or from certain industries: the manufacture of chemicals and cement or the processes of metallurgy, mining and quarrying. Figure I.1 shows the chief sources and the main constituents of air pollution.[350]

The most important of these from the point of quantity are the products of combustion: both gaseous; such as carbon monoxide, carbon dioxide, sulphur dioxide and sulphur trioxide, and particulate matter; such as fly ash, which is largely inorganic material, and unburned carbon. The collection of particulate matter is today incorporated into standard power station practice, while maintaining a minimum carbon monoxide concentration in the effluent gases is the aim of efficient operation. Thus, although exposure to cold undiluted flue gases, which may contain about 0·2 per cent carbon monoxide, is very dangerous, the concentrations which occur near power stations never present a hazard, whereas the cumulative effect of motor car exhausts in a road tunnel traffic jam may lead to harmful concentrations and long road tunnels should be monitored against this risk.

The removal of sulphur dioxide from flue gases, where it may be present in concentrations up to 0·4 per cent, depending on the sulphur in the fuel, remains one of the most difficult air pollution problems. The maximum allowable concentration (M.A.C.), which is the recommended maximum eight hour exposure limit for a normal person, is ten parts per million (ppm) for sulphur dioxide, but concentrations as low as 0·2 ppm will cause damage to pine trees, clovers and lucerne, although other plants, for example cabbage types, are somewhat more resistant.[552] Nonhebel[350] has pointed out that the potential sulphur dioxide–sulphuric acid emission from a modern base load 1000 megawatt power station is 550 tons/day and so particular care has to be taken to remove the sulphur dioxide before emission, or to ensure that the emission does not cause ground level pollution above 0·1 ppm even when atmospheric conditions are extremely unfavourable for dispersion.

Fluorides, which harm plants in concentrations as low as five parts per thousand million (5 pptm) are found in appreciable concentrations in waste gases from fertilizer manufacture, aluminium smelting and other processes where fluoride compounds form part of the raw materials or fluxing agents.

Apart from gaseous pollutants, small particles and mist droplets are the major problem in industrial gas cleaning and air pollution control. The fumes from the processing and purification of low melting point metals such as lead, arsenic, beryllium and zinc are extremely toxic, and a high degree of efficiency is necessary in their collection. Acid mists, for example from sulphuric or phosphoric acid manufacture, are often controlled by law, and effective collection equipment is generally installed.

Particles and droplets are variously described as grit, dust, fume, smoke, mist, aerosol or smog. The meanings generally given to these terms, and

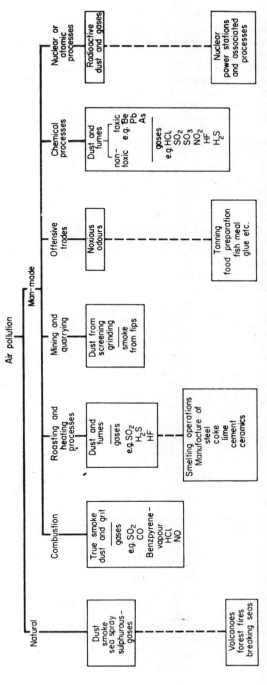

Fig. I.1. The sources of air pollution.[350]

TABLE I.1. CLASSIFICATION OF TERMS

Grit: Coarse particles, greater than 76 microns which is the size of the opening in the 200 mesh sieve.

Dust: Particles smaller than 76 microns (i.e. able to pass through a 200 mesh sieve) and larger than 1 micron.

Fume: Solid particles smaller than 1 micron.

Mist: Liquid particles, generally smaller than 10 microns.

Fogs: Mists are sometimes called fogs when they are sufficiently dense to obscure vision.

Smoke: This is the term used generally to describe the waste products from combustion, and may either be fly ash or the products of incomplete combustion, or both. The particles can be liquid or solid.

Smog: This portmanteau word—a combination of smoke and fog—is used to describe any objectionable air pollution. There are two kinds, known as the Los Angeles and the London type. The Los Angeles smog is photo-chemical and comes from motor car exhausts. The London type comes from the incomplete combustion of coal and is characterized by its relatively high sulphur dioxide concentration and particle content.

Soot: Soot is the aggregated particles of unburned carbon produced by incomplete combustion.

Aerosols: Initially this term was used for the fine relatively stable aerial suspensions. In recent years the term has been generally applied to all air-borne suspensions.

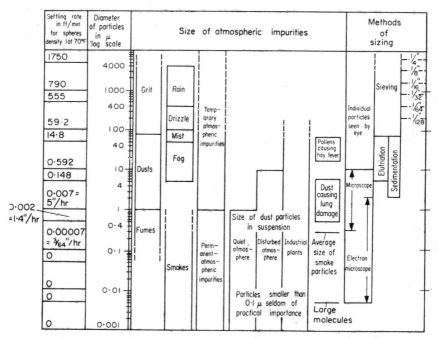

FIG. I.2. Size classification of atmospheric impurities, and the chief methods of particle sizing.[449]

those adhered to here, are listed in Table I.1. The grouping of particles in the various categories, their approximate size ranges, the chief methods of sizing and particle visibility are shown in Fig. I.2.

I.3. HOW CAN GASES BE CLEANED?

All process gases, whether waste gases or those about to undergo further treatment, flow along a duct or pipe which can be interrupted by the proposed method of cleaning. The method adopted depends of course on the nature of the material to be removed. If this is a gas, two alternatives are possible. The gas can either be passed through or brought into contact with a medium which will absorb the required gas in a preferred way, or it can be changed chemically. Gas absorption in liquids is widely used on such gases as hydrochloric acid vapour, ammonia, sulphur dioxide and carbon dioxide which form an appreciable part of the gas stream, while adsorption on a solid is more common with small quantities or traces of gases such as water vapour on silica gel, carbon dioxide on lime or organic vapours on active carbon.

Changing the chemical nature of the gases usually implies combustion or catalytic processing, particularly catalytic oxidation of organic materials, but of course also applies to such techniques as gas retention in a holding chamber to allow a process to go to completion instead of "freezing" it by immediate expulsion to the atmosphere.

The processes of removing gases are therefore chemical reaction, absorption or adsorption. In nearly all cases only one of these acts at any one time. Standard chemical engineering methods can therefore be applied to the design of plant.

The removal of small particles and droplets is however much more complex and a rigid physical classification is not possible as several mechanisms may, and often must, occur in combination. The basic mechanisms that can be employed are:

  (a) Gravity separation.
  (b) Centrifugal separation.
  (c) Inertial impaction.
  (d) Direct interception.
  (e) Brownian diffusion.
  (f) Eddy diffusion.
  (g) Thermal precipitation.
  (h) Electrostatic precipitation.
  (i) Magnetic precipitation.
  (j) Brownian agglomeration.
  (k) Sonic agglomeration.

In most cleaning plants more than one of the above mechanisms is usually responsible for the cleaning action, although in the majority of cases one is the controlling mechanism for the particular types of particles considered.

Thus, in filtration, inertial impaction, direct interception and Brownian diffusion are responsible, but Brownian diffusion is of major importance for particles in the sub-micron ranges, while impaction and interception are the collection mechanisms in the micron sizes. Electrostatic forces can also play a vital part here, partly because of the charges induced by charged particles on uncharged filtration media.

I.4. TACKLING A GAS CLEANING PROBLEM

Before a suitable plant can be recommended and designed, it is first necessary to know what has to be removed from the gas stream, the extent of the gas stream and its condition. Thus an analysis of the gas stream and its contents must be undertaken. The most important items of information required are:

(1) Gas flow rate.
(2) Gas temperature.
(3) Gas composition.
(4) Nature of material to be removed.
(5) Degree of removal required.

The degree of removal required will be discussed in Chapter 1, while the methods of obtaining items (1–4) will be outlined in Chapter 2. It may be possible, and in the case of exceptionally difficult problems may become economic necessity, to avoid gas cleaning altogether either by changing the basic process, by removing the plant to a more suitable site or simply by putting up a higher chimney.

If the cleaning plant is to be used on a new process, an estimate of the factors (1–3) must be made, while some information about the nature of the material can often be found in the literature concerning the process or from tests on similar processes operating elsewhere. In the case of gas cleaning plant over-design can prove very expensive and laboratory investigations may be warranted.

When the problem has been adequately analysed it is possible to carry out a series of calculations on the removal of gaseous constituents or particles which will indicate the type of cleaning mechanism that is possible, and the approximate dimensions and complexity of the required plant. From this an economic evaluation of the methods of gas cleaning will indicate the most suitable method and its approximate cost. As methods of costing vary so much these will not be dealt with here.

Another aim of the detailed analysis of cleaning mechanisms in this book is that it may help those who have found a new technique to analyse its principles, and so assist them in scale-up calculations.

CHAPTER 1

TO WHAT EXTENT MUST GASES BE CLEANED?

1.1. INTRODUCTION

If gases are used for chemical processing, and any constituent, either gaseous or particulate, is deleterious to the process, it must be removed. For example, carbon monoxide acts as a catalyst poison in ammonia synthesis, and has to be reduced to an acceptably low concentration before the hydrogen and nitrogen can be passed to the catalyst tower. The degree of removal required is set by the upper concentration limit that can be tolerated by the process. The cost of gas cleaning here is an integral part of the economics of the whole process.

Other gases, mainly natural, refinery or coal gases, are produced in very large quantities for sale for industrial and domestic heating and cooking, and these contain appreciable quantities of hydrogen sulphide which corrodes pipelines when the gases are cooled below their dew points. They also give off an unpleasant odour on combustion, and can affect certain processes such as steel re-heating. It is therefore necessary to reduce the hydrogen sulphide to a limit acceptable by the consumer.

Waste gases from processes such as combustion, metallurgical and chemical operations are usually emitted to the atmosphere, and these may contain constituents which could be harmful, such as arsenic oxides or radioactive materials, or merely unpleasant, like clouds of smoke. Limits are imposed on these emissions by three main considerations:

  (i) The concentrations which will harm plant and animal life.
  (ii) Legal limitations, imposed by the country, state, county or city.
  (iii) Reducing air pollution to establish civic goodwill.

These are not independent, as for example the legal limits on emissions are governed by the concentrations which damage the life of animals and plants.

Sections of this chapter will discuss what are harmful concentrations of air pollutants, and what concentrations are likely to be produced at ground level when the gases are emitted from a tall stack. Geographical factors which are likely to influence these concentrations are briefly mentioned. A further section will deal with legislative control of air pollution in some of the major industrial countries.

1.2. HARMFUL CONCENTRATIONS OF POLLUTANTS

The determination of what are harmful concentrations of gases and particles is extremely difficult, as much depends on the person, animal or plant exposed. The most extensive tables available are the recommended maximum allowable concentrations (M.A.C. values) for eight hour exposure for human beings issued by the American Conference of Governmental Industrial Hygienists (A.C.G.I.H.). Similar values recommended by Imperial Chemical Industries are widely used in the United Kingdom. These are listed in Table 1.1, together with suggested values recommended by Elkins.[134]

TABLE 1.1. MAXIMUM ALLOWABLE CONCENTRATIONS OF
IMPURITIES IN SOME COMMON INDUSTRIAL WASTE GASES[134]

Substance (gas)	A.C.G.I.H.* ppm	I.C.I.† ppm	Suggested ppm
Aniline	5	10	5
Benzene	25	50	25
Bromine	1	0·5	0·5
Carbon dioxide	5000	5000	5000
Carbon disulphide	20	10	20
Carbon monoxide	100	50	100
Carbon tetrachloride	25	50	25
Chloroform	100	50	100
Chlorine	1	1	1
Ethanol	1000	1000	1000
Fluorine	0·1		
Formic acid			10
Hydrogen bromide	5		5
Hydrogen chloride	5	10	5
Hydrogen cyanide	10	10	10
Hydrogen fluoride	3	2	1·5
Hydrogen peroxide 90%	1		2
Hydrogen sulphide	20	20	10
Ozone	0·1		0·2
Pyridine	10		5
Sulphur dioxide	5	10	5
Toluene	200	100	200

* A.C.G.I.H.—Recommendations of the threshold limits committee of the American Conference of Governmental Industrial Hygienists (1957).

† I.C.I.—Values recommended by Imperial Chemical Industries and widely used in the United Kingdom.

Substance dust and fume	A.C.G.I.H. mg/m³	I.C.I. mg/m³	Suggested mg/m³
Aluminium (fume)			15
Antimony	0·5	0·5	0·5
Arsenic	0·5	0·5	0·25
Beryllium	0·002		0·002
D.D.T.	1		2
Diphenyl		2	2
Iron oxide fume	15		15
Lead tetraethyl			0·1
Lindane	0·5		0·5
Mercury	0·1	0·1	0·1
Pyrethrum	2	1	1
Sulphuric acid	1	1	1
Titanium dioxide	15		
Vanadium pentoxide	0·1		0·1
Zinc oxide	15		15

Mineral dusts	millions of particles/ft³ air
Aluminium oxide (alumina)	50
Asbestos	5
Mica	20
Portland cement	50
Silica > 50% free SiO_2	5
5% < free SiO_2 < 50%	20
< 5% free SiO_2	50
Silicon Carbide	50

Radio-isotopes	½ life	M.A.C. in air[98] $\mu c/m^3$
Carbon[14]	5568 years	3·5
Cobalt[60]	5·3 years	0·35
Tritium (H^3)	12·4 years	22
Iodine[131]	8·1 days	0·013
Strontium[90]	19·9 years	0·00013
Sulphur[35]	87 days	0·27
Zinc[65]	250 days	0·11

Other countries suggest other limits. The lowest are those permissible in the U.S.S.R. where not only eight hour exposure values, but also maximum concentrations for continuous exposure, are specified. For example, the A.C.G.I.H. M.A.C. for sulphur dioxide is 5 ppm (parts per million) while Soviet authorities only allow 0·187 ppm (0·50 mg/m³) for eight hour exposure or 5·6 pphm (parts per hundred million) (0·15 mg/m^3) for continuous exposure.

The concentration of sulphur dioxide during the 1952 London smog averaged 0·7 ppm and rose to a maximum of 1·7 ppm, both values well below the M.A.C. value recommended in the United States, but still caused numerous deaths and illness, particularly among those with chronic bronchitis and other lung ailments. It appears therefore that the M.A.C. values may be applied to healthy people, but not generally to all, and much lower concentrations will have to be specified in new regulations for air pollution control.

Plants are adversely affected by much lower concentrations of pollutants than men or animals. Table 1.2 lists the maximum tolerances of various plants to sulphur dioxide, exposure times of 150 hours being used.[552] Damage to certain trees, particularly conifers, occurs with concentrations as low as 0·2 ppm,[201,552] but others are able to resist concentrations up to 1 ppm. The other major gaseous pollutants which damage plants and animals are fluorides, particularly hydrogen fluoride and silicon tetrafluoride. These compounds occur in the waste gases from superphosphate plants and certain smelting operations (particularly of aluminium) and so are not as widespread as sulphur dioxide. However, fluorides can damage some plants in concentrations as low as 0·1 pptm (parts per thousand million) and can accumulate on forage plants to cause subsequent fluorosis of cattle and sheep.

TABLE 1.2. EXPERIMENTAL UPPER TOLERANCE CONCENTRATIONS OF PLANTS TO SULPHUR DIOXIDE FOR AN EXPOSURE PERIOD OF 150 HOURS.[552]

Type of plant	Maximum concentration range ppm
Lucerne and clovers	0·15–0·3
Summer wheat, spinach	0·2–0·3
Beans, lettuce	0·2–0·4
Strawberries, roses	0·2–0·8
Potatoes, radishes	0·3–0·8
Beet sugar, cauliflower	0·4–0·8

There is little general information as to the effect of dusts on plants. In most cases dusts are chemically inert and cause little damage, except when concentrations are very high and the deposits exclude sunlight from leaves and flowers until such time when they are washed clean by rain. Cement dusts however are not inert chemically[109] and their effect on vegetation has been studied extensively. The cement dust from cement works forms a hard crystalline crust when deposited on the leaves. Calcium hydroxide solution is liberated from these crystals by atmospheric moisture and this penetrates through the leaf epidermis destroying the cells.

For radio-isotopes, a table of maximum exposures recommended in the report of the Committees on Permissible Doses for Internal Radiation (1958 revision) may be used as a guide. Here, however, concentrations which are absorbed by plants may be much lower than this, but will still be a problem when eaten by cows resulting in radioactive milk. In general, emissions of radioactive materials must be kept as low as possible.

1.3. GROUND LEVEL CONCENTRATIONS FROM ELEVATED POINT SOURCE EMISSIONS

The concentrations to which plants and animals are exposed at ground level can be reduced by emitting the gases from a process at great heights, from a tall chimney, so that the gases are dispersed over a very large area. This is often the cheapest way of dealing with an air pollution problem. In other cases, where it is not technically or economically possible to reduce the concentrations of certain gases to an acceptable value, this method enables a low effective ground level concentration to be maintained, even with adverse meteorological conditions such as persistent atmospheric inversions.

Normally, the temperature of the atmosphere decreases with increasing height (lapse conditions) and the warm gas emitted by a chimney will rise to great heights. Under certain conditions it is possible that a warm layer of air lies on top of a colder layer next to the ground. This is an inversion layer, and chimney plumes have difficulty in penetrating it, unless their temperature is greater than that of the layer. The waste gases from chimneys then collect in the restricted region below the inversion layer, and concentrations at ground level increase until winds and changed conditions disperse the accumulated gases. These ground level concentrations depend on the nature of the material being emitted, the gas temperature and velocity of emission, the actual stack height, wind velocity and the atmospheric temperature conditions. Observations have shown and calculations have indicated that at low wind velocities the buoyancy rise due to the gas temperature is likely to carry the waste gases to great heights, while at high wind velocities turbulence will rapidly disperse the waste gases. It is at moderate wind velocities of 15–20 m.p.h., or about 20–30 ft/sec, that the highest ground level concentrations are likely to occur.

The problem of estimating ground level concentrations may be considered in two sections. First the path of the plume and the maximum height reached (called the effective stack height, H) is calculated, and then the diffusion of the gases from this point must be considered. As a *first approximation*, the effective stack height can be considered as the sum of the actual height of the stack, H_S, the rise of the plume due to the velocity of the issuing gases, H_V, and the buoyancy rise H_T, which is a function of the temperature of the gases being emitted and the atmospheric conditions:

$$H = H_S + H_V + H_T \qquad (1.1)$$

For the velocity of the issuing gases to be effective in increasing the height of the plume, "downwash" at the chimney exit must be prevented by keeping the stack exit velocity above a critical value which has been found experimentally as a function of the wind velocity[439] (Fig. 1.1).

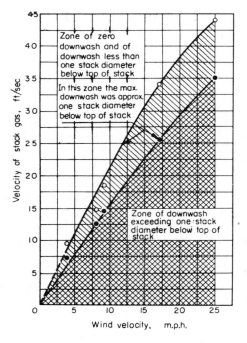

FIG. 1.1. Correlation of stack exit velocity and wind velocity for avoiding "downwash" of smoke plume.[439]

To achieve a stack exit velocity above the critical value in order to avoid downwash it may be necessary to remodel the stack exit, and a venturi nozzle design has been found most effective, as well as minimizing pressure losses.

The buoyancy rise effect H_T depends on atmospheric conditions, and in carrying out calculations of the type described here it is assumed that atmospheric conditions are stable over great heights and distances, an assumption that is only rarely justified in practice. When the temperature of the atmosphere decreases with increasing height at a rate greater than the adiabatic lapse rate (i.e. when the atmospheric temperature decreases by more than 3 °C per 1000 ft height) then the hot plume of gases emitted from a stack will rise to great heights, and no ground level pollution will occur. However, under mild lapse conditions (when the atmospheric temperature gradient G is less than 3 °C per 1000 ft) or when there is a temperature inversion, H_T tends to a maximum value.

– The rise of a plume can be calculated in a large number of ways, which give predictions of various degrees of accuracy. These have been reviewed in detail by Strohm[477] and only two methods will be presented here. These are the method of Bosanquet, Carey and Halton[59], which gives a conservative estimate of the plume rise for H_T and H_V, and a modification of the method by Priestley[378] for the buoyancy rise H_T, which gives a value which has been confirmed experimentally to within three per cent.

The formulae by Bosanquet, Carey and Halton are:

(1) for the stack exit velocity rise H_V

$$H_V = H_{V_{max}}\left(1 - \frac{0.8 H_{V_{max}}}{x}\right) \quad \text{when} \quad x > 2H_{V_{max}} \quad (1.2)$$

and

$$H_{V_{max}} = \frac{4.77}{1 + 0.43u/v} \frac{\sqrt{(Qv)}}{u} \quad (1.3)$$

where $H_{V_{max}}$ = maximum momentum rise of plume (ft)
x = distance downwind (ft)
u = wind velocity (ft/sec)
v = stack exit velocity (ft/sec)
Q = gas flow rate from stack (ft³/sec) measured at the temperature at which the density of the stack gases would be equal that of the ambient atmosphere.

(2) for the buoyancy rise H_T

$$H_T = \frac{6.37 g_c Q}{u^3 T_1}\left(\ln J^2 + \frac{2}{J} - 2\right) \quad (1.4)$$

where g_c = gravity acceleration constant (32.2 ft/sec²)
T_1 = absolute temperature at which density of stack gases equals the density of the atmosphere (°K)

and

$$J = \frac{u^2}{\sqrt{(Qv)}}\left(0.43\sqrt{\left(\frac{T_1}{g_c G}\right)} - 0.28\frac{v}{g_c}\frac{T_1}{(T_s - T_1)}\right) + 1 \quad (1.5)$$

where G = potential temperature gradient of the atmosphere (°C/ft)
T_s = stack exit gas temperature (°K).

The calculation can be simplified by replacing $(\ln J^2 + 2/J - 2)$ by Z in equation 1.4, and finding Z as a function of X from Fig. 1.2. where

$$X = \frac{ux}{3 \cdot 57 \sqrt{(Qv)}} \qquad (1.6)$$

A nomographic solution to these equations (1.2–1.6) drawn up by Strauss and Woodhouse[476] gives an answer of sufficient accuracy for practical cases.

The method by Priestley[378] is based on the assumption that the rising gas is in turbulent motion generated by the plume itself, and an allowance

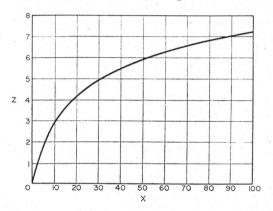

Fig. 1.2. Correlation for buoyancy rise of smoke plume between functions X and Z.[59]

is made for the entrainment of air in the plume, the spreading of the plume and its loss of momentum and heat by lateral diffusion as well as for the buoyancy of the plume. This self generated turbulence by the plume is additional to the atmospheric turbulence due to wind, and is generally the predominant factor in the initial plume rise.

This work also shows that the buoyancy and velocity rises are not strictly additive, the assumption made in equation (1.1), but that the combined rise is less than the sum of the two considered separately. Although Priestley's theory does not lead to a single formula covering all conditions, explicit approximate formulae can be derived for important ranges of conditions. Thus, for strong inversion conditions with light winds (less than 6 ft/sec), which in practice often combine to give maximum ground level concentrations, the buoyancy rise can be found from

$$H_T = 3 \cdot 01 u^{-\frac{1}{4}} \left(\frac{g_c G}{T_1} \right)^{-\frac{3}{8}} \left(\frac{E g_c}{C_p \pi \varrho T_1} \right)^{\frac{1}{4}} \qquad (1.7)$$

where E = strength of the heat source relative to the surrounding atmosphere (B.t.u./sec)

C_p = specific heat of the gas at constant pressure (B.t.u./lb)

ϱ = density of the stack exit gases.

This equation emphasises the importances of the heat in the exit gases in obtaining a large buoyancy rise.

The two methods of calculating ground level concentrations arising from the release of gases from a point source, those by Bosanquet and Pearson[45,60] and by Sutton[480] give similar answers, and only the Sutton equation, which is the more widely used, is given here. The calculation requires the selection of appropriate eddy diffusion coefficients C_y and C_z which are functions of the mean wind velocity profile, the degree of turbulence and other factors. They can be selected for the appropriate atmospheric conditions and plume height from Table 1.3. The coefficients assume an aerodynamically smooth surface, a condition only rarely met in practice, and so tend generally to give over-estimates in the ground level concentration.

TABLE 1.3. GENERALIZED EDDY DIFFUSION COEFFICIENTS[181] C_y, C_z AND TURBULENCE INDEX n

Height of source above ground (ft)	Large lapse		Zero or Small lapse		Moderate Inversion		Large Inversion	
	C_y	C_z	C_y	C_z	C_y	C_z	C_y	C_z
0	0·42	0·24	0·24	0·14	0·15	0·09	0·12	0·07
32	0·42	0·24	0·24	0·14	0·15	0·09	0·12	0·07
82		0·24		0·14		0·090		0·070
100		0·23		0·13		0·085		0·065
150		0·21		0·12		0·075		0·060
200		0·19		0·11		0·070		0·055
250		0·18		0·10		0·065		0·050
300		0·16		0·09		0·055		0·045
350		0·13		0·07		0·045		0·035
n	0·20		0·25		0·33		0·50	

Sutton's equation for the ground level concentrations of a gaseous pollutant, in parts per million by volume (ppm) at a distance x ft downwind and y ft crosswind from the source is:

$$c = \frac{2 \times 10^6 Q'}{\pi C_z C_y u x^{2-n}} \exp\left[-\frac{1}{x^{2-n}}\left(\frac{y^2}{C_y^2} + \frac{H^2}{C_z^2}\right)\right] \text{ ppm} \qquad (1.8)$$

where Q' = rate of emission of pollutant gas (ft³/sec)

n = turbulence index (dimensionless).

This gives a maximum value at a distance downwind x_{max} of:

$$C_{max} = 2 \cdot 35 \times 10^5 \cdot \frac{Q'}{uH^2} \cdot \frac{C_z}{C_y} \text{ ppm} \qquad (1.9)$$

where

$$x_{max} = \left(\frac{H}{C_z}\right)^{2/(2-n)} \text{ft} \qquad (1.10)$$

In practice the maximum concentration occurs approximately 10 to 15 times the effective height of the plume downwind from the source, which is approximately 25–35 times the actual stack height in the case of a hot gas emission. When the emissions consist of particles which are so small that they are carried along like gas molecules (i.e. if they are in the sub-micron size ranges) then the calculation will give ground level concentrations in mg/ft^3 instead of ppm by volume if the stack emission value in equation (1.8) which is in (ft^3/sec) is replaced by (kg/sec).

The average rate of deposition of particulate emissions can be found from[59]

$$\mathbf{M} = 2 \cdot 75 \times 10^6 \frac{Wb}{H^2} \left[\frac{\left(\dfrac{20H}{x}\right)^{20f/u+2}}{\Gamma\left(\dfrac{20f}{u}\right)} \exp\left(-\frac{20H}{x}\right) \right] \qquad (1.11)$$

where $\mathbf{M}$ = deposition rate (tons/(mile)^2 year).
  W = rate of solid matter emission (grams/sec)
  b = fraction of time wind is in 45° sector under consideration
  f = free falling speed of particles (ft/sec).

This may be written as:

$$\mathbf{M} = \frac{Wb \times 10^6}{H^2} \; \mathscr{F}\left(\frac{f}{u}, \frac{x}{H}\right) \qquad (1.12)$$

where $\mathscr{F}(f/u, x/H)$ represents the function in the diaresis in equation (1.11). This function has been plotted for various values of f/u and x/H (Fig. 1.3). In practice, particles of different sizes are emitted into a rising plume in a wind of varying velocity. It is then necessary to calculate the rate of deposition of particles in different size groups, with different wind velocities at a series of distances from the source to obtain an accurate picture. It is usually possible to assume an average wind velocity of 20 ft/sec for an approximate calculation.

For particles with diameters less than 20 microns (density unity), a simpler equation by Hawkins and Nonhebel[351] can be used.

$$\mathbf{M} = 3 \cdot 02 \times 10^7 \frac{Wbf}{uH^2} \qquad (1.13)$$

The estimates obtained by these calculations do not allow for some important practical phenomenon frequently connected with uneven temperature distributions in the atmosphere. These include "looping", in which a plume as a whole eddies up and down through considerable vertical distances, and "fumigation" in which a high concentration built up clear of

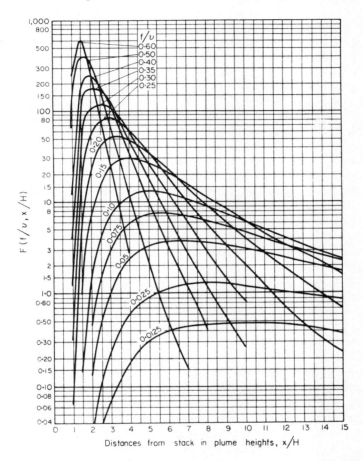

FIG. 1.3. Variation of rate of deposition of solid pollutant particles from a plume with distance from stack, based on falling speed and wind velocity.[59]

the ground overnight is quite suddenly brought down to the surface in the early morning with the onset of convection. Nor is any allowance made for the complex behaviour of plumes rising from rows or groups of chimneys. The above formulae do, however, give a guide to the concentrations and deposition rates that may be expected.

1.4. GEOGRAPHICAL FACTORS
IN AIR POLLUTION CONTROL

The estimates of ground level concentrations of pollutant materials obtained by calculations (section 1.3) are based on stable weather conditions in flat open country. However these geographical features may not exist at the place where a works is situated. For example, important economic factors in siting heavy industry are the sources of raw materials, such as the proximity of a coal or iron ore deposit for a steel works, or a river valley where barges and ships provide a cheap means of transport. Another factor is availability of land and closeness of a town for a labour supply. Therefore a plant may be situated where geographical features are not favourable to the dispersion of pollutants. The most common problems of this type arise where there is an accumulation of heavy industrial and domestic sources of pollution. The Meuse Valley between Huy and Liege, Monongahela Valley at Donora in Pennsylvania, 30 miles from Pittsburg are both centres of metallurgical industry, and have been sites of major air pollution disasters. The Thames river plain in London is another example of a river plain where heavy air pollution occurs, but here largely from domestic sources. Air pollution from the heavy industry in the Don river basin in Sheffield, England, has been investigated in considerable detail.[170]

High stacks alone are not a solution. The Trail (British Columbia) Smelter is located on a terrace 180 ft above the Columbia river bed, and has stacks 409 ft high. At certain periods this is not enough to obtain adequate dispersal of the smelter gases, because of the geographical feature of the Columbia river valley which is one-third to half a mile wide and bounded by mountains 1500–3000 ft high. Sintering operations at the smelter are controlled by the sulphur dioxide concentration observed some miles away at Columbia Gardens near the United States border. Maximum allowable concentrations are 0·3 ppm for 40 min in summer and 0·5 ppm for 60 min in winter. At Ducktown (Tennessee) two copper smelters created considerable local damage because of sulphur dioxide emissions. High stacks, in fact, extended the damage over a distance of 30 miles, and an acid plant was eventually erected to utilize the gases, after a U.S. Supreme Court investigation. The Anaconda smelter erected 300 ft stacks on a spur of the Rocky Mountains, 700 ft above the furnaces and 1100 ft above the valley floor, but arsenic poisoning due to arsenic trioxide particles, formed because of the condensation to small particles below 190 °C, could be traced over a distance of 35 miles along the path of the prevailing winds.

These examples illustrate how geographic features — prevailing winds, incidence of fogs and topographical features — can determine the extent to which it is necessary to clean the gases before releasing them to the atmosphere.

1.5. AIR POLLUTION CONTROL LEGISLATION

Clean air legislation has been written into the statute books of a number of countries, while in others control is exercised under health acts, regulations regarding nuisance, and also by common law. The legislation may cover a whole country, as in the United Kingdom, France and Germany, individual states as in Australia, or it may vary from county to county within the same s.ate, as in parts of the United States. Because of the widespread damage that can be caused by air pollution, which can even affect two countries, as in the case of the Trail smelter, the most widespread uniform legislative control is desirable. Some of the specific air pollution control legislation in the United Kingdom, United States, U.S.S.R., Germany, France, Netherlands, Belgium, Scandinavia, Italy, Australia and New Zealand will be given here.

1.5.1. United Kingdom

The three relevant Acts of Parliament governing the control of sources of pollution in England and Wales are:

  (i) The Alkali, etc. Works Regulation Act (1906).
 (ii) The Public Health Act (1936).
(iii) The Clean Air Act (1956).

Other acts, such as the Smoke Nuisance (Scotland) Acts (1857 and 1865) and the Public Health (Scotland) Act (1897–1939) are used in Scotland, and are in some ways similar.

The Public Health Act (1936) had important provisions which enabled local authorities to make by-laws, subject to the confirmation of the Minister of Housing and Local Government, to regulate the emission of smoke from industrial sources. The usual regulation prohibited the discharge of smoke for more than 2 min within a continuous period of 30 min. These regulations have however been more effectively covered by the Clean Air Act (1956)[169] which gives local authorities much wider powers. This act has provisions regarding the limiting of emission of dark smoke, which is defined as being as dark as, or darker than, shade 2 on the Ringelmann Chart (Fig. 1.4), except when lighting up a furnace, or as a result of unforseeable plant failure.

The Clean Air Act requires that new furnaces should be as far as possible smokeless, and be equipped with approved grit and dust arrestment equipment if they burn more than one ton per hour. The height of chimneys is also controlled, and in all cases, to prevent down draught, the recommended height is two and a half times that of adjoining buildings or 120 ft.

In any case, the chimneys have to be approved by the local authorities, and the topography of the surrounding buildings and land would be considered. The Act also empowers local authorities to set up smoke control areas or "smokeless zones" in residential and commercial areas, and other suitable areas such as new industrial estates. These areas may prohibit the installation of processes which cause smoke or fume, even if dust and fume recovery plant is installed to minimise the emissions. Other provisions of the Act permit the Minister of Housing and Local Government to exempt certain industries whose processes present special problems in air pollution

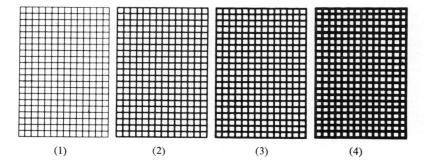

(1)   (2)   (3)   (4)

FIG. 1.4. Ringelmann smoke chart for classification of smoke density.[278]

1. Equivalent to 20 per cent black.
2. Equivalent to 40 per cent black.
3. Equivalent to 60 per cent black.
4. Equivalent to 80 per cent black.

control, as in the case of metallurgical fumes, and places these under the provision of the Alkali Act, which is also under his direction.

The Alkali, etc. Works Regulation Act of 1906 arose out of earlier legislation (1863) which regulated the emission of hydrochloric acid gas from the manufacture of sodium carbonate by the Leblanc or "saltcake" process. The Alkali Act today, through its list of scheduled processes, covers nearly all industrial processes which are actual, or may appear to be potential emitters of noxious gases. The operators of these scheduled processes are required to register the process, and a condition of the registration is that the Chief Alkali Inspector, who administrates the act, must be satisfied that the "best practicable means" of reducing the discharges of noxious or offensive gases are employed. The scheduled processes are subject to inspection, and provision must be made for sampling and flow measurements by the inspectors. Certain statutory limits are prescribed in the act, examples of which are given in Table 1.4, together with other values for maximum emissions recommended by the Alkali Inspectorate.

TABLE 1.4. STATUTORY LIMITS FOR EMISSIONS UNDER THE ALKALI, ETC.
WORKS REGULATION ACT (1906)

Hydrochloric acid in gases from Alkali (Salt cake) process	0.2 gr./ft^3
Sulphuric acid (chamber process) SO_3	4 gr./ft^3
Sulphuric acid (contact process) SO_3	1.5 gr./ft^3

Other emission limits recommended by the Alkali Inspectorate

Fluorine compounds	0.1 gr./ft^3
Sulphur dioxide (as SO_3)	0.5 gr./ft^3 (up to 100 ft)
(depending on the height of discharge)	1.0 gr./ft^3 (over 100 ft)
Chlorine	0.1 gr./ft^3
Hydrogen sulphide	5 ppm
Nitrogen oxides (nitric acid by ammonia oxidation)	3 gr./ft^3 (as SO_3)
(other processes, e.g. nitrogen)	1 gr./ft^3 (as SO_3)
Cement works	0.4 gr./ft^3 (S.T.P)

Lead works	Max. conc. gr/ft^3	Max. total loss of lead/week lb
Small works $<$ 3000 ft^3/min	0.1	200
Medium works 3000–10,000 ft^3/min	0.05	400
Large works $>$ 10,000 ft^3/min	0.01	1,000

1.5.2. United States

Air pollution legislation in the United States is very complex, because it is a matter for the individual states.[398] By 1962 sixteen states had adopted specific air pollution legislation, while fifteen states have some form of air pollution legislation on their statute books, enabling counties to pass local ordinances. In addition, Congress passed an act in 1955 to provide technical assistance and research for controlling air pollution.

The most comprehensive legislation is in California, and applies particularly to the Los Angeles County Air Pollution Control District (L.A.C.A. P.C.D.) and the Bay Area (B.A.A.P.C.D.). Emissions are divided into visible, particulate and gaseous categories, and where these overlap all regulations can be applied. In Los Angeles and the Bay Area, smoke of any colour darker than Ringelmann 2 for more than 3 min/hr is prohibited. Other regions are even more stringent, for example Utica (N.Y.) (population approx. 100,000 in 1950) permits only Ringelmann 1, (20 per cent obscuration) while in contrast to this Albany (N.Y.) and Boston (Mass.) will permit Ringelmann 3 (60 per cent obscuration).[428]

Particulate emissions permitted by L.A.C.A.P.C.D. and B.A.A.P.C.D. are limited to 0.3 gr./ft^3, while in Pennsylvania the Allegheny County Control Agency applies standards to open-hearth furnaces, cupolas and other metallurgical operations varying between 0·2–0·5 lb/1000 lb gas (0·16 to 0·26 gr./ft³). Other rules used relate the size of the operating unit to the amount of particulate matter that can be produced. The amount of gaseous material that may be permitted depends on the type of gas. Sulphur dioxide is generally limited to 0·2 per cent by weight in most counties, although B.A.A.P.C.D. uses the resulting ground level concentration instead of the emission as a basis for control. Limits are also set for emissions of fluorides, carbon monoxide, hydrocarbons and odorous gases. The trend in legislative control is that it is tending to become a multi-county or state-wide matter, rather than of local concern only, and the regulations will tend to become more restrictive.[531]

1.5.3. U.S.S.R.

In the U.S.S.R. air pollution is controlled through the "Office of Inspection and Technical Control of Gas Purifying Installations in Industrial Plants". This office supervises:

(i) The performance of gas purifying and dust collection equipment.

(ii) The enforcement of maximum allowable concentration levels (M.A.C. values) for industrial plant.

(iii) The implementation of government policy with respect to clean air.

TABLE 1.5. MAXIMUM ALLOWABLE CONCENTRATIONS OF ATMOSPHERIC POLLUTANTS PERMITTED IN THE U.S.S.R.[361]

Pollutant	Maximum permissible concentration			
	At any one time		24 hour average	
	mg/m³	pphm	mg/m³	pphm
Sulphur dioxide	0·50	18·7	0·15	5·6
Chlorine	0·10	3·3	0·03	1·0
Hydrogen sulphide	0·03	2·0	0·01	0·7
Carbon disulphide	0·50	6·8	0·15	2·0
Carbon dioxide	6·00	330	2·00	110
Oxides of nitrogen	0·50	40	0·15	12
Soot	0·15	—	0·05	—
Phosphorus pentoxide	0·15	2·5	0·05	8·5
Manganese and compounds	0·03	—	0·01	- -
Fluorine compounds	0·03	—	0·01	—
Sulphuric acid	0·30	7·3	0·10	2·5
Phenol	0·30	7·7	0·10	2·6
Arsenic compounds except arsine	—	—	0·003	—
Lead compounds except tetraethyl lead	—	—	0·0007	—
Metallic mercury	—	—	0·0003	0·0036

Supervisors of emissions from plants are the officers of the State Sanitary Inspectorate in the case of plants subordinate to the republics, or regions, or the local stations of the Sanitary and Epidemological Department in the case of cities. Supervision of air pollution control facilities in the construction of new plants is exercised at the stages when the works are being located and designed, and inspections are frequently carried out by the local authorities. An order issued in 1949 stipulated that no electric power station could be built without dust collection plant, and similar regulations regarding collection equipment are applied to non-ferrous metallurgical works, blast furnaces in steel works, and to organic solvent recovery plants.

Very strict regulations regarding M.A.C. values, not only for 8 hour periods, but also for continuous exposure are prescribed, these being much lower than those prescribed in the United States or suggested by I.C.I. in the United Kingdom. These values are listed in Table 1.5.

1.5.4. German Federal Republic

Recent legislation (1st June, 1960) in the German Federal Republic[333] is paving the way for federal control and supervision of industries, power plants, etc., which may cause air pollution (or noise). This legislation aiters sections 16 and 25 of the law affecting trades and section 906 of the Civil Code. Previous legislation varied with the administrative "Länder" divisions, but the new section 16 of the law affecting trades requires the registration of trades and industries which may cause air pollution, and sets up a committee of local and federal government, technical and economic experts to advise the controlling authorities of the technical and economic limitations of pollution (and noise) control. Section 25 of the legislation limits the registration period and also empowers the authorities to supervise emissions from the industries at the industries' cost. The authorities can also require industries to establish pollution control plant as far as is economically feasible.

The alteration of section 906 of the German Civil Code which was enacted at the same time departs from the previous point of view that if an industry producing noxious gas was indigenous, no claims as to damages to the surrounding population or property could be admitted. Now, although there can be no injunction preventing the noxious process, the operator of the process may be liable for damages.

Previous regulations under the health acts of the administrative "Länder" and municipalities will stand until detailed Federal regulations covering these industries are gazetted. At present German industry has greater latitude as regards the official control of pollution than the United Kingdom or parts of the United States or Canada, but control along the lines of the U.K. Alkali Inspectorate seems indicated.

In the meantime emission standards have been suggested by the Verein Deutscher Ingenieure (VDI) for different industries as a guide. Some of these are listed in Table 1.6.

TABLE 1.6. PROCESS EMISSION STANDARDS OF THE VEREIN DEUTSCHER INGENIEURE[468]

Process	VDI Standard	Emission	
		g/m³	gr./ft³
Ore sintering	VDI 2095	0·7	0·30
Flared blast furnace gas	VDI 2099	0·05	0·02
Coke screening, crushing and grinding	VDI 2100	0·3	0·13
Primary copper smelting	VDI 2101	0·5	0·20
Secondary copper smelting	VDI 2102	0·5	0·20

More detailed standards qualify permissible emissions from cement plants by stack height, topography, production and works location factors.[468]

1.5.5. France

French legislation dates from the law of Morizet[24] (1932) and involves two principles.

(i) If stack emissions are toxic, or even dangerous, then precautions must be taken for minimizing these before permission is granted for the process to be carried out.

(ii) For non-toxic material, the maximum solids concentration emitted is limited to 1·5 gr./Nm³ and the maximum emission to 300 kg/hr (660 lb/hr). This last figure is most conservative and cannot be applied to modern power houses, where, even with efficient equipment the solids output from an 800,000 lb/hr steaming capacity will be 10 times the legal limit.

The department of the Seine limits smoke to densities of Ringelmann 1 or less, except for about 5 per cent of the normal working time of the furnace. Also specified for the waste gases are maximum concentrations of sulphur dioxide (2 per cent) and carbon monoxide (1 per cent).

1.5.6. Holland

In the Netherlands a plant cannot be built without permission of the Inspector of Works. In the case of possible air pollution, a measure for controlling this is recommended and can be enforced by the local authority.

For new medium capacity boilers the recommendations follow the "code of good practice" which was proposed by a committee in 1950. This code suggests:[309]

(i) That the dust content of the gases leaving the stacks must be less than $(H/50)^2$ g/Nm^3, where H is the chimney height in metres. This means that for a 50 m (164 ft) stack, the maximum dust concentration may be 1 g/Nm^3 while for a 100 m (328 ft) stack the concentration may rise as high as 4 g/Nm^3.

(ii) The content of coarse particles, greater than 50 microns diameter, must be restricted to $0.025\,(H/50)^2$ g/Nm^3 or one-fortieth of the total emission.

(iii) The height of the stack should be at least 1·5 times the height of the highest neighbouring building.

The rules (i-iii) are suggested only for installations in flat open country. In built-up areas and for large power stations more stringent rules should apply.

1.5.7. Belgium

The height of chimneys that carry smoke and flue gases containing sulphur dioxide is prescribed, and based on the concentration of sulphur dioxide present.

1.5.8. Sweden and Denmark

No special legislation for the control of air pollution exists, but control over plants can be exercised by either local or central health authorities.

1.5.9. Italy

Italian air pollution legislation dates from the early 1930s and is contained in the unified sanitary laws of 1934. Those factories producing unhealthy vapours must be situated in the country, while a second category deals with those industries which require some protective measures for the surrounding population. In many instances, however, population has in fact grown up around the industries of the first group and special precautions must be adhered to if the plant is to be kept in operation.

1.5.10. Australia

Clean air legislation is a matter for the individual states, and two, New South Wales and Victoria, have passed specific Clean Air Acts while the others, including the Federal Government Territories, rely on the existing legislation to prevent nuisance to control possible sources of air pollution.

The New South Wales Clean Air Act (1961) empowers the Department of Health, which has an Air Pollution Control Branch to license scheduled industries, and charge a licence fee. Its officers can enter the scheduled premises and conduct tests and require the installation or alteration of existing equipment for controlling pollution. The department may also prohibit scheduled processes in certain areas, and has very wide advisory powers. To assist with this, the Act requires an advisory body of twelve members drawn from industry, trade unions, government departments and the universities to be set up.

Scheduled industries are those which present particularly difficult air pollution control problems, such as the iron and steel industry. Non-scheduled industries, such as small boilers, are controlled by the local authorities.

The Victorian Clean Air Act of 1957 has as its basis the Clean Air Act (England and Wales) of 1956 and specifically prohibits the emission of dark smoke from industrial chimneys. Other aspects of the legislation include the control of plans for new industrial establishments to ensure the fullest precautionary measures to prevent pollution, and the establishment of a Clean Air Committee which has powers to advise the Minister as to the abatement of pollution from power stations, locomotives, ships, aircraft and motor vehicles. A Clean Air Division within the Health Department administers the Act, and has powers of entry into premises and the investigation of pollution.

1.5.11. Canada

Here, as in Australia, clean air legislation is a state matter, and Ontario passed an Air Pollution Control Act in 1958. This legislation enables municipalities to pass by-laws, and gives them power to administer and enforce the air pollution abatement policy. In 1955 the Windsor area in this state, which is heavily industrialized had an ordinance which did not define the prohibited smoke density.[428] Detailed information regarding air pollution control in a particular area must be obtained from the local authorities.

1.5.12. New Zealand

The New Zealand Health Act (1956) has many similarities to the United Kingdom Alkali, etc. Works Regulation Act (1906), and in fact was drafted after a visit from the Chief Alkali Inspector. Plants which produce gases termed "noxious and offensive" must have effective means of preventing their discharge, and the emissions from sulphuric acid plants are restricted. "Chemical Inspectors" have been appointed with right of entry, inspection and investigation to supervise these processes.

CHAPTER 2

BASIC DATA REQUIREMENTS

2.1. INTRODUCTION

Before it is possible to specify suitable gas cleaning plant, the characteristics of the gases and the quantity of gas to be treated must be known. The temperature and chemical nature of the gases and the types of particles to be collected will determine the type and size of plant as well as the materials of construction. Consideration should also be given to the dew point of the gases. This may be surprisingly high if sulphur trioxide is present, and sets a minimum operating temperature in some cases, such as bag filters. A high dew point may be an advantage in other cases as it indicates very often a favourable operating temperature for electrostatic precipitators collecting fume with high electrical resistance. Here sulphur trioxide is sometimes added to the gases to achieve the dew point elevation, and the quantity required has to be known.

If a constituent gas is to be scrubbed out into solution, the rate of mass transfer of the gas to the scrubbing liquor must be known, while the removal of small particles requires an understanding of the physical characteristics of the particles: size distribution, density, and shape. Whether the particles are good conductors, or whether they are magnetic, may also be of importance.

This chapter will discuss the measurement of gas temperature and the measurement and calculation of gas flow rate and dew point and the methods of sampling of gases and particles. Also the chief methods of particle size determination will be outlined, although a detailed treatment is beyond the scope of the present volume.

2.2. DETERMINATION OF GAS FLOWS

The volumes of gas to be treated can be found either by direct measurement of the gas flow in a duct, pipe or chimney, or by calculation, if the gas composition is known, from the quantity and composition of reactant materials and the chemical nature of the process which is usually combustion.

2.2.1. Measurement of gas flows

Gas flows are most frequently measured with a differential head device — orifice plates, venturi tubes or pitot tubes — although for work at ambient temperatures in non-toxic gases particularly air conditioning, a vane anemometer is also frequently employed. For very low rates of flow, when a pitot tube response is very small and may not be stable a thermo-anemometer, which depends on the resistance change with variable loss of heat from a hot wire placed in the gas stream, can be very useful, but the instrument is not very robust and has not yet found wide industrial application.

Orifice plates and venturi tubes are usually permanently installed in a plant. Orifice plates require a straight run of duct of at least 9 duct diameters (D.D) — 6 before and 3 after the plate — for ordinary conditions, although the introduction of very turbulent conditions may require longer calming sections. Venturi tubes require even longer straight duct sections to allow for the long diffuser section and are more complex to construct than simple orifice plates, but have the advantage of a much lower pressure loss. Details of construction and the limitations of these devices may be obtained from British Standard No. 1042 or the appropriate American Standard.

Pitot tubes are very versatile. They do not require a long calming section in a duct as they measure local velocities: they are small so that they can be inserted through a small hole in the side of the duct without causing plant shut down and do not cause any appreciable pressure loss in the gas stream. Their chief disadvantage in finding a total gas flow is that a number of velocity measurements have to be made to establish the velocity profile of the gas stream. This is then integrated, usually graphically. Consequently if there are sudden fluctuations in the gas stream, erroneous flow rates may be deduced.

Essentially pitot tubes consist of an impact and a static pressure tube. In its simplest form (Fig. 2.1), the "hook" type, these may be separate tubes with the static pressure being measured at the duct wall. This may be used for very small ducts, where multiple wall tubes may be too large and cause flow pattern deformation or where a standard pattern tube is not available. The tube nose is best tapered with an 8° total cone angle, but it may be square ended as shown.

Usually the impact and static pressure tubes are combined into a single unit. The British Standard (British Standard No. 1042)[74] patterns are shown in Fig. 2.2. The ellipsoidal head shown in Fig. 2.2b. is to be recommended at low flow velocities. It is more robust than the N.P.L. sharp ended tube shown in earlier editions of the standard.

When using the pitot, velocity measurements must be made at a number of points, preferably in a straight section of the duct. Circular ducts are usually divided into a number of annuli of equal area and the velocity measured on two diameters intersecting at right angles giving four velocities for each annulus. When it is difficult to measure the flow near the wall, this may be estimated from a plot of velocity against distance from wall on

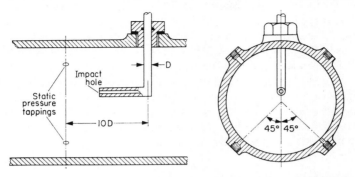

Fig. 2.1. Hook type Pitot tube for measuring impact pressure with separate static pressure tapping in pipe or duct wall.[105]

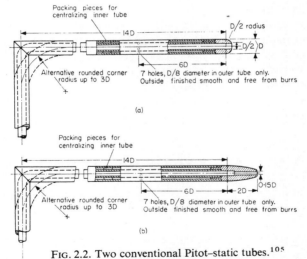

Fig. 2.2. Two conventional Pitot–static tubes.[105]

(a) Hemispherical head Pitot–static tube.
(b) Ellipsoidal head Pitot–static tube.

a log–log scale. In rectangular ducts, or ducts of odd shapes, the duct cross-section is divided into a number of small rectangles and the velocity measured in the centre of each. This is most conveniently carried out from a number of traverse entry points either in one wall of the duct, or preferably, in two adjacent walls. With fluctuating gas flows it is best to measure the variation in gas flow at one point only. If the flow is in the streamline region, the velocity at the centre of a circular duct is twice the average velocity. Alternately it is possible to measure the velocity at a radial position of 0·762 times the pipe radius from the axis of the pipe.

For relatively small gas flows a number of other meters are used, such as displacement type wet gas meters or the bellows type which is universal for town gas. Piston, fan and variable aperture type meters ("Rotameters") are also used for moderate gas flow measurement, particularly for process control. These require the whole of the gas flow to pass through the meter, and are therefore normally used to measure the volumes of gas sampled in a sampling train rather than the total flow in a duct.

Comprehensive details of flow measurement equipment may be obtained from specialized books such as "Flow Measurement and Control"[105] and from the appropriate standards and handbooks.

2.2.2. Calculation of flow rates

Very frequently a gas cleaning plant has to be designed before the process to which it is to be attached is in operation. In the most common case the process is combustion of coal or fuel oil, the compositions of which are known. The composition of the waste gases can either be calculated, assuming complete or partial combustion and representative fuel–air ratio or determined by gas analysis on the plant itself or a similar one. The calculation of the mass flow of the gases then becomes a problem in material balances. If the gas temperature is also known or is estimated from an energy–heat balance, then the gas volume can be calculated. A typical example is shown in Appendix I.

2.3. MEASUREMENT OF GAS TEMPERATURE

The determination of actual gas temperatures to a reasonable degree of accuracy is essential to a proper choice of cleaning mechanism and cleaning medium.

When the gases to be cleaned are in a vessel, or flowing along a duct, the walls of which are not at the same temperature as the gas, the method of measuring the temperature of the gas must allow for the thermal radiation effects inherent in the system. Thus, when the gases are colder than the enclosing walls, the walls will radiate heat to the temperature measuring element, and the temperature recorded will be warmer than the actual gas temperature. Conversely, for hot gases flowing in a colder duct, the temperature measuring element will radiate heat to the enclosing walls, and so will be unable to reach the actual gas temperature. This radiant heat transfer results in a temperature difference and increases very rapidly with temperature and at 1500°C it may be of the order of 200–300°C. In a well insulated vessel or duct, where the inside wall temperature is close to that of the gases, the temperature measured by the temperature sensing element will be virtually that of the gas.

The temperature sensing elements:

Thermometers: The ordinary mercury in glass thermometer will cover the temperature range from below 0°C to about 350°C. An alcohol in glass thermometer extends the lower end of this range to −80°C.

Platinum resistance thermometers are very accurate, and have a range from −200 to +600°C and sometimes higher.

Thermocouples: Copper–constantan thermocouples cover the range from −200 to about +400°C, while other base metal thermocouples, the most common being the chromel–alumel couple, have an upper limit of 1200°C.

Noble metal thermocouples can now be used to temperatures as high as 2500°C continuously, or 2800°C intermittently (e.g. a tungsten–rhenium couple). The most common thermocouples and their characteristics are given in Table 2.1 and Fig. 2.3, which gives their temperature–EMF curves.

For use in corrosive atmospheres, thermocouples must be sheathed for protection. Metal sheaths are satisfactory below 1000°C, while silica sheaths

TABLE 2.1. MATERIALS FOR THERMOCOUPLES FOR USE AT TEMPERATURES UP TO 2800°C*

Material	Temperature range†		Comments
Copper vs. constantan	− 200–400°C	(500°C)	
Iron vs. constantan	0–800°C	(1100°C)	
Chromel vs. alumel	0–1100°C	(1300°C)	
Platinum vs. Pt 8·7–13% Rh	0–1600°C	(1700°C)	
Pt 20% Rh vs. Pt 60–40% Rh	0–1800°C	(1850°C)	
Iridium vs. Ir 40–60% Rh	1400–2000°C	(2100°C)	(neutral atmosphere)
Iridium vs. tungsten	1000–2200°C	(2300°C)	(vacuum, neutral atmosphere or reducing conditions)
Tungsten vs. W–Re	up to 2500°C**	(2800°C)	(neutral atmosphere)

Ir = Iridium, Pt = Platinum, Re = Rhenium, Rh = Rhodium, W = Tungsten

* Some of the data were obtained from[17]; others are quoted by courtesy of Engelhard Industries Ltd.[138]

† Figures in brackets are extreme temperatures which can be attained for "spot" readings.

** Temperature–EMF relation (non linear) calibration is provided for each batch supplied by the makers.

The calibration of these thermocouples has been described by Lachman.[279]

can be used to slightly higher temperatures, but are themselves corrosive with respect to noble metal thermocouples. Re-crystallized alumina sheaths may be used to about 1850 °C. Beryllium oxide can be used to higher temperatures.

Calibration of temperature sensing elements: The primary standards of temperature are the melting point of ice (0 °C) the boiling point of water (100·0 °C) the boiling point of sulphur (444·60 °C) and the melting points of silver (960·5 °C) and gold (1063 °C). The melting point of palladium, at

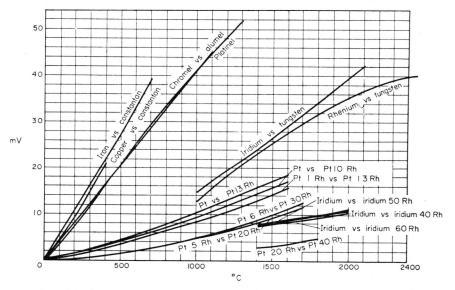

Fig. 2.3. Temperature–Millivolt graphs showing the characteristics of the usual common and noble metal thermocouples.[138]

1555·0 °C is a secondary standard, while the melting point of nickel (1452·0 °C) can also be used. Platinum melts at 1773·5 °C. The melting points of some other metals (thorium, niobium, etc.) can be used to extend the scale upwards. Lachman[279] used a standardized micro-optical pyrometer when calibrating noble metal thermocouples to 2200 °C in a high temperature research furnace.

The radiation losses from temperature sensing elements can be reduced in several ways.

(a) Thermocouples of different sizes: The radiation heat loss from a thermocouple is proportional to the surface area of the head formed where the two wires are joined. Thus, the losses will be less with smaller thermocouples. If then a series of thermocouples of different sizes are used, and the temperatures measured plotted graphically against the surface areas of the thermocouples, the curve obtained (which is usually virtually a straight

line), can be extrapolated to the temperature ordinate at zero surface area. This temperature is then a measure of the actual gas temperature.[490] The method is particularly useful in closed systems, or where withdrawal of the large quantities of gases required for suction and pneumatic pyrometers would interfere with the gases to a marked degree.

(b) Suction pyrometers: Another way of finding the actual gas temperature is to shield the temperature measuring element from the radiation of the walls by surrounding it with so called "radiation shields" and aspirating the gases past the element (usually a thermocouple) at high velocities in order to increase convective heat transfer to the element. The number of shields required is a function of the gas temperature, while the construction of the shields depends on the chemical properties of the gases as well as on the temperature.

Thus, Inconel (75–80 per cent nickel, 15–20 per cent chromium, rest iron) is satisfactory to temperatures of 1100–1200 °C when only a little sulphur dioxide is present in the gases. For gases with a high sulphur dioxide content, a high chromium stainless steel is preferable and may be used to about the same temperature. At higher temperatures the sheaths are made of refractory cements (mullite, alundum).

The thermocouple itself is usually sheathed to protect it against oxidation from the gases. The assembly of thermocouple, sheath and radiation shields is mounted on the end of a stainless steel probe which must be water cooled if it is to be used at temperatures exceeding 900 °C. A typical suction pyrometer is shown in Fig. 2.4 together with three types of radiation shields. The gas flow is provided by an ejector and measured with an orifice plate.

Since the refractory multiple shields are very fragile, they have been modified for mounting within the walls of the suction pyrometer, as is shown in Fig. 2.4. The shields extend 6 in. back from the tip of the pyrometer. It has been shown experimentally[31] that the best position for the thermocouple in this type of suction pyrometer is about one and a half inches from the end; further forward the couple tends to receive some radiation from the walls through the gas entry, while somewhat further back the water cooled walls of the probe radiate cold to the couple.

The accuracy of a temperature measured by a suction pyrometer is a function of the actual gas temperature, the temperature of the surroundings and the velocity at which the gases are being drawn past the thermocouple. If no gas is sucked past the thermocouple, the reading obtained has a certain error, but when the gas velocity is increased, the amount of the error will be reduced. The fraction of this reduction in error is called the "efficiency" of the pyrometer. The efficiency of a suction pyrometer operating at 500 ft/sec has been found for a series of temperatures to 1600 °C and with up to 10 radiation shields (Table 2.2).

The effect on the efficiency of using velocities other than 500 ft/sec can be obtained by multiplying the actual number of radiation shields by a

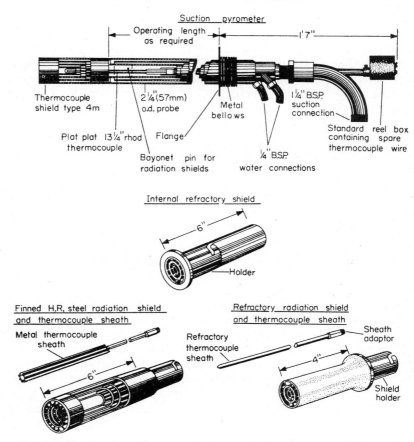

Fig. 2.4. Suction pyrometer design, showing general arrangement and three types of radiation shield.[287]

TABLE 2.2. Efficiency per cent for Sheathed Thermocouples with Blackened Metal Multiple Radiation Shields. Gas velocity 500 ft/sec.[285]

Tempera-ture °C	Number of radiation shields									
	1	2	3	4	5	6	7	8	9	10
400	98									
600	88	98								
800	71	93	98							
1000	54	81	93	97	99					
1200	39	69	85	92	95	98	99			
1400	28	55	74	83	91	95	97	99	99	
1600	20	43	62	73	83	90	94	96	97	98

TABLE 2.3. The Effect of Using Gas Velocities other than 500 ft/sec with Multiple Shield Suction Pyrometers[285]

Velocity (ft/sec)	10	20	50	100	200	300	400	500	600	700
Equivalent number of shields at 500 ft/sec	0·21	0·28	0·40	0·52	0·69	0·82	0·93	1·00	1·07	1·14

factor obtained from Table 2.3 which gives the equivalent number of shields at 500 ft/sec.

An allowance has also to be made for the cooling effect of aspirating the gases past the thermocouple. This is given in Table 2.4, and is of the order of 20 °C at velocities of 700 ft/sec.

TABLE 2.4. Cooling of Gases due to Aspirating at High Speeds[285]

Velocity (ft/sec)	100	200	300	400	500	600	700	800
Temperature drop °C	$\frac{1}{2}$	$1\frac{1}{2}$	$3\frac{1}{2}$	$6\frac{1}{2}$	10	14	19	25

As the gases at high temperatures have lower density than at ambient temperatures, and the mass flow is measured after the gases have been cooled in the water jacketed probe, a density correction must be applied to the flow measurement at the orifice plate when estimating the gas velocity past the thermocouple. The values for the mass flow of air, given in Table 2.5 enable the gas velocity past the thermocouple to be estimated from the orifice plate gauge reading.

If metal radiation shields are used, these soon become blackened and act as black body emitters (emissivity = 1) but if refractory radiation shields are used, these glow at high temperatures, and have an emissivity of less than 1. The data in Tables 2.2 and 2.3 assume the use of black shields.

TABLE 2.5. Mass Flow of Air[285] lb/(hr)(in²)

Temperature °C	Velocity ft/sec								
	100	200	300	400	500	600	700	800	900
200	116	232	348	464	580	696	812	928	1043
400	84	168	252	335	419	503	587	670	755
600	63	126	188	251	314	377	440	502	565
800	51	102	153	204	255	306	357	408	460
1000	43	86	129	172	215	258	301	344	387
1200	37	74	112	149	186	223	260	298	335
1400	33	66	98	131	164	197	230	262	295
1600	29	59	88	117	146	176	205	234	264

The equivalent number of other types of shields can be calculated by the use of a factor "f" which is a function of the ratio of the thickness of the refractory tube w and its thermal conductivity $\varkappa$, where:

$$f = 4aT^3 \frac{w}{\varkappa} \tag{2.1}$$

w = refractory thickness – cm
$\varkappa$ = refractory thermal conductivity cal/(°C) (cm) (sec)
T = absolute temperature – °C
a = constant.

TABLE 2.6. VALUES OF f FOR VARIOUS VALUES OF $w/\varkappa$[285]
(C.G.S. UNITS)

Temperature °C	$w/\varkappa$			
	10	20	50	100
1000	0·1	0·2	0·6	1·1
1200	0·2	0·3	0·9	1·8
1400	0·3	0·5	1·3	2·6
1600	0·4	0·7	1·8	3·6

The values of f in terms of the ratio $w/\varkappa$ can be obtained from Table 2.6. From the known emissivity of the refractory and the value of f the effective number of single metallic shields for which each refractory shield is equivalent can be read from Table 2.7.

TABLE 2.7. EFFECTIVE NUMBER OF SIMPLE METALLIC SHIELDS TO WHICH EACH REFRACTORY SHIELD IS EQUIVALENT[286]

f \ Emissivity	1	0·8	0·6	0·4	0·2
0	1·0	1·2	1·5	2·0	3·0
1	1·4	1·6	1·8	2·2	3·2
2	1·7	1·9	2·1	2·4	3·3
3	2·0	2·1	2·3	2·6	3·5
4	2·2	2·3	2·5	2·8	3·6

The refractory shields may require a fin allowance which is equal to $\sqrt{2}$, thus multiplying the equivalent number of shields by 1·41. If the refractory shields are of the packed tube pattern (Schack type) this allowance is a factor of 2·5. An example illustrating this is given in Appendix II.

Instead of using Tables 2.2 and 2.3 to calculate the suction pyrometer efficiency, a more rapid method for obtaining an estimate of the actual gas temperature is based on the fact that the efficiency of the instrument increases very rapidly (from zero) when the gas is first speeded up, and less rapidly with further increases in velocity. The shape of the velocity–temperature curve from zero to the actual flow rate can therefore be used to indicate the efficiency at the flow rate. An index suggested for specifying the curve shape is based on the temperature $T_{1/4}$ shown by the instrument at a quarter of the specified maximum flow:

$$\text{Shape factor} = \frac{T_{max} - T_0}{T_{max} - T_{1/4}} \tag{2.2}$$

where T_0 = indicated temperature with zero flow velocity
T_{max} = indicated temperature with maximum flow velocity.

Table 2.8 gives the efficiency at the maximum measured flow rate for a number of shape factors.

TABLE 2.8. EFFICIENCY FOR VARIOUS SHAPE FACTORS[285]

Shape Factor	2	$2\frac{1}{2}$	3	4	6	8	11
Efficiency %	63	80	87	93	97	98	99

The response of suction pyrometers is relatively fast and depends on the material of the head. Thus metal heads take about 2 min to reach equilibrium temperature, while zircon heads take twice as long.

(c) The pneumatic pyrometer: If a gas is drawn through a restriction in a pipe, the pressure drop across the restriction is a function of the geometry of the restriction, the mass flow of the gas, and its density. The density, in turn, is a function of the absolute pressure of the gas, its absolute temperature, and its composition. In the pneumatic pyrometer a continuous sample of the hot gases are drawn through a restriction, cooled and then drawn through a second restriction, where the temperature of the gases is also measured. The hot gas temperature is calculated from the pressure losses at the two restrictions and the temperature at the second (cold) restriction. In the most fully developed of these instruments, the calculation is carried out automatically by means of a simple analogue computer.

Basically, for a non-compressible gas, the pressure loss Δp, across a constriction in the tube is related to mass flow m, by the equation:

$$\Delta p = km^2/\varrho \tag{2.3}$$

where k is the orifice coefficient and ϱ is the gas density.
From the perfect gas law,

$$\varrho = MP/RT \tag{2.4}$$

where M = molecular weight of the gas

       P = total gas pressure

       R = universal gas constant.

In the pneumatic pyrometer, the two constrictions are in series, so the mass flows are the same for both restrictions. If subscript 1 refers to the hot restriction and subscript 2 to the cold restriction, then

$$\frac{P_1 \Delta p_1 M_1}{k_1 R T_1} = \frac{P_2 \Delta p_2 M_2}{k_2 R T_2} \tag{2.5}$$

If the pressure loss between the two restrictions is negligible, $P_1 = P_2$. Furthermore, since the dissociation of gas molecules, e.g. in flue gas, is

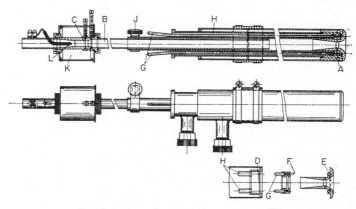

FIG. 2.5. Venturi pneumatic pyrometer.[231]

A — Hot venturi throat. F — Upstream pressure tapping point.
B — Gas tube. G — Pressure line.
C — Cold venturi throat. H — Pressure lines.
D — Position for sealing ring. L — Temperature sensing element.
E — Hot venturi insert.

negligible up to 2000 °C, $M_1 = M_2$. Even at 2500 °C the effect is calculated to be only about 5 per cent for a typical flue gas composition.[231] It is also important that no condensation occurs between the restrictions and that the flow is in the turbulent range.

Equation (2.5) can then be simplified to give:

$$T_1 = k \frac{\Delta p_2}{\Delta p_1} T_2 \tag{2.6}$$

where $k = k_2/k_1$.

An instrument developed largely by the B.C.U.R.A.[231] uses this principle in the venturi pneumatic pyrometer, shown in Fig. 2.5.

The probe, of $2\frac{1}{4}$ in. dia., is water cooled and made either of brass or of stainless steel. Its length depends on the particular application. The design of the hot venturi presented many problems. It is made of corrosion resistant steel and is easily replaced owing to the use of rubber O rings to seal the connection of the pressure tapping to two tubes in the water cooled jacket. A brass liner is provided for the water cooled tube to prevent condensation of the moisture in the gases. The cold end venturi is placed after the water cooled section, and the gas temperature is measured with a platinum resistance thermometer because these have a resistance change proportional to the absolute temperature in the required temperature range.

The measuring equipment[288] must automatically compute equation (2.6) The pressure differentials Δp_1 and Δp_2 are therefore converted to electric currents using pressure transducers. These are Beaudouin 0–50 millibar units supplied with 1 kc/s a.c. from a transistorized oscillator. The transducers each incorporate a differential transformer so that their output is proportional to the pressure differentials applied to them. The a.c. output is rectified with a silicon rectifier and then one current is passed through the resistance thermometer and the other to the slidewire of a potentiometer. The potential difference across the resistance is applied to the input of the potentiometer, which then indicates directly the absolute temperature of the hot gas.

This arrangement is much simpler than earlier methods which used a thermocouple instead of the resistance thermometer[232].

2.4. ESTIMATION OF DEW POINT

An accurate knowledge of the dew point of the gases to be cleaned is of primary importance, for collection below the dew point causes deposition of water droplets in which corrosive substances (e.g. sulphur trioxide) may be dissolved. These shorten the life of plant very considerably, and reduce that of some filter media to a few hours instead of some years of continuous operation. In addition, there may be corrosion of the materials of construction, both in the gas cleaning plant itself and in the process plant — e.g. the economizers in a boiler plant.

In combustion gases the moisture comes from the air used, as well as from hydrogen in the fuel. Consequently, on days with high atmospheric humidity, the waste gases, after cooling to ambient temperatures, will almost certainly be supersaturated and deposit moisture on collecting media, if these are below the dew point. If the fuel contains some sulphur, sulphur dioxide and sulphur trioxide will be present in the waste gases. Sulphur trioxide in very small quantities (0·005 per cent) with about 10 per cent water vapour will raise the dew point of the gases to about 150°C.[240]

The dew point can be found by an instrument which measures the temperature of a smooth, non-conducting surface set between two electrodes. When the material is dry, its resistance is infinite, but when a film of moisture condenses on the surface, the resistance is lowered, and a current passes between the electrodes. One of the earliest models was made by Johnstone[240] and a recent, more elaborate modification has been described by Bassa and Beer.[38]

Alternatively, the dew point can be estimated if the sulphur trioxide content of the gases is known. The sulphur trioxide determinations are

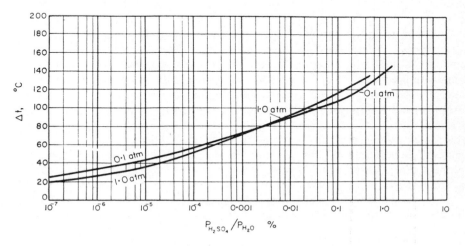

FIG. 2.6. Elevation of dew point by sulphur trioxide: Correlation of temperature elevation and partial pressure ratio $P_{H_2SO_4}/P_{H_2O}$.[346]

made more difficult by the fact that frequently about ten to one hundred times as much sulphur dioxide is present, and the sulphur dioxide slowly oxidizes to sulphur trioxide. This may be overcome by adding 6 per cent pure benzyl alcohol as an inhibitor to the absorbing (N/5 alkali) solution. Benzaldehyde, mannitol or p-amino phenol hydrochloride can also be used. The sulphur trioxide is estimated as the sulphate. Summaries of the standard methods of estimation have been given by Corbett and Crane.[100]

The estimation of dew point elevation can be made very simply from the ratio of the partial pressure of sulphuric acid, which may be taken to be the same as that of the sulphur trioxide (SO_3), and of the water vapour, using the graph derived by Müller[346] (Fig. 2.6). The curves are drawn for water vapour pressures of 0·1 and 1 atm, and the dew point elevation can be read off directly. The dew point of air and pure water vapour only may be found in standard tables, and the dew point of the mixture obtained by addition. For example, a flue gas with a 10 volume per cent water vapour and 0.01 volume per cent sulphur trioxide, will give

$$\frac{P_{H_2SO_4}}{P_{H_2O}} = \frac{0.01}{10} \times 100 = 0.1 \text{ per cent} \tag{2.8}$$

From Fig. 2.6, the dew point elevation for this ratio is given as $105\,^{\circ}\text{C}$. The dew point for $P_{H_2O} = 0.1$ is $45\,^{\circ}\text{C}$, and so the actual dew point temperature is $150\,^{\circ}\text{C}$. Müller found agreement to within about $5\,^{\circ}\text{C}$ between the calculated values and those found experimentally by various authors, so this method may be used with some confidence.

2.5. CLASSIFICATION OF SAMPLING

When sampling the gas stream for which gas cleaning plant is to be specified and designed it may be important to determine one or more of the following:

(i) The major gaseous constituents and their concentration.
(ii) The minor gaseous constituents, including trace quantities.
(iii) The composition and concentrations of liquid droplets and solid particles in the gas stream.

In some cases it is desirable, for control purposes, to measure a component continuously, for example oxygen in the flue gases from combustion or traces of dangerous materials, but mostly the gases are sampled as a

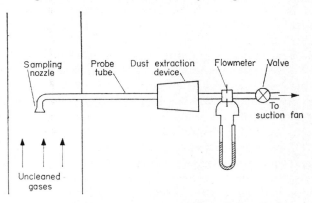

FIG. 2.7. General arrangement of sampling train.

preliminary step so that satisfactory techniques may be specified and adequate materials of construction may be selected.

In sampling, part of the gas stream is diverted through a sampling "train", of which a general arrangement is shown in Fig. 2.7. The train consists of a nozzle placed in the gas stream, usually facing upstream: a collection device: a volume measuring device, which may be either indicative or integrating, and some means of drawing the gases through the train, either a pump or an ejector. In detail, the methods depend on which of the three types of constituents are to be sampled.

2.6. COLLECTION AND ANALYSIS OF MAJOR GASEOUS CONSTITUENTS

When inserting a probe into a duct care must be taken that the sample is representative, and has not been collected from a "dead" zone where stagnation has taken place, or from a duct with stratified layers of gases. Leakage of air into the sample has also to be avoided. If the gases sampled are combustion or reaction gases, where the reaction is incomplete, care must be taken that the reaction does not progress in the sampling train, or the sampling tube act as a catalyst for further reaction. This can often be achieved by using a water cooled probe or similar device for "freezing" the reaction. Since undesirable condensation may result with the condensate absorbing one of the gas constituents preferentially, collection above the dew point is generally expedient. If dust is present it may have to be filtered out before collecting the sample.

The sampling probe in the case of gases is a simple tube. Mild steel can be used to about 300°C, ceramic lined to 500°C, and stainless steel of the 18 per cent chromium, 8 per cent nickel type to about 800°C. Water cooled probes can be used to much higher temperatures, (copper to 1250°C, stainless steel to 1600°C), while ceramic tubes have a very long life in the highest temperatures encountered commercially, those in metallurgical furnaces. Blockage of the sampling lines by high dust loads and condensation are common and special precautions may have to be taken, such as heated sampling lines and frequent or continuous replacement of the dust filter. To prevent corrosion of the sampling line, possibly due in combustion gases to sulphuric acid from sulphur trioxide and condensed water, special materials may be required, particularly when the sampling line is to be left in place for continuous sampling.

Those techniques where gas is sampled continuously for reaction control* can also be used for analysis of gases for plant design. The major techniques for analysis are density, thermal conductivity, infra-red absorption, differential absorption in solvents, change in electrical resistance of solvents and specific physical properties, such as the paramagnetic property of oxygen or the radioactivity of certain gases from radioactive sources.

Density instruments can be used to measure a component of higher molecular weight than the gas without this component. The most common

* The British Standards Institution has prepared a standard for the continuous automatic analysis of flue gases.[77]

example is carbon dioxide in flue gases. Carbon dioxide with a molecular weight of 44, has a considerably higher density than the other main components; oxygen (32), nitrogen (28) and carbon monoxide (28). The density meter is usually a comparison type instrument where two fast moving impellers immersed in air and gas respectively are driven in opposite directions and face two disks which are connected to a pointer on a scale. This instrument, known commercially as the Renarex or Pyrorex indicator could also be applied to other dense gases mixed with air.

Thermal conductivity is used in a balancing type instrument, built on the Wheatstone bridge principle. Carbon dioxide has about 60 per cent of the thermal conductivity of air, while carbon monoxide is only slightly lower than air. Unfortunately sulphur dioxide has only one third of the thermal conductivity of air, and so if flue gases contain several per cent sulphur dioxide (from high sulphur fuel) then the carbon dioxide reading will be much higher than if no sulphur dioxide were present.

Infra-red absorption presents a very elegant technique developed in recent years for routine industrial application[329] for gas mixtures whose molecules are dissimilar, e.g. SO_2, CO, CO_2, H_2O, N_2O, CH_4 and organic vapours. Some of these can be present together as long as the absorption bands do not overlap those of the gas being determined. Even then filter tubes containing the interfering gas can be placed in the optical paths so that the radiation emerging from these tubes will contain wavelengths which can be absorbed by the gas to be detected but none capable of being absorbed by the interfering gas in the sample.

Preferential absorption of one of the component gases is of course the classical method of gas analysis. Carbon dioxide is easily absorbed in caustic potash, oxygen in alkaline pyrogallol, and carbon monoxide in one of a number of solvents such as ammoniacal cuprous chloride. All of these are used in series in flue gas analysis in either the Orsat apparatus or one of its many modifications, where a sample of gas is progressively quantitatively reduced by successive absorption of the components. The process has been mechanised in such units as the "Mono Duplex" (made by James Gordon and Co. Ltd.) where the initial carbon dioxide absorption and volume reduction is followed by combustion of unburned gases (carbon monoxide and hydrogen), and a second carbon dioxide absorption, this volume reduction representing the proportion of unburned gases in the original sample. A more elegant technique also applicable to much smaller carbon dioxide concentrations is to measure the electrical conductivity of the caustic potash solution before and after carbon dioxide absorption has taken place.

Oxygen is *paramagnetic*, that is it seeks the strongest part of a magnetic field, while most common gases are diamagnetic, seeking the weakest part of a magnetic field. This is utilized in the instrument based on the magnetic wind principle devised by Lehrer and shown in Fig. 2.8.[336] The gas to be measured is drawn into the cell, traverses the annulus and leaves at the opposite side. The cell contains a horizontal tube which supports two identical platinum windings which are joined in a Wheatstone bridge circuit and become heated by the application of a potential across the bridge. A magnetic field is placed across part of the tube, the poles being arranged so that the magnetic flux is concentrated around one winding. The oxygen in

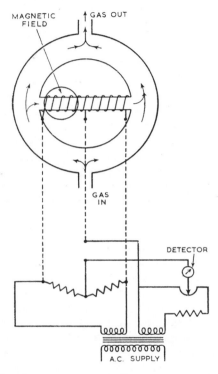

FIG. 2.8. Principle of oxygen concentration measurement using the paramagnetic property of oxygen ("magnetic wind" method).[336]

the gas is drawn into this field, enters the heated tube, and has its susceptibility reduced, thus allowing fresh oxygen to enter the tube, causing a continuous current of oxygen to pass along the tube from left to right. The left-hand platinum winding which heats the gas becomes cooler than the right-hand winding, and so unbalances the bridge, giving a measure of the oxygen in the gas. Detailed description of the commercial applications of this principle have been reviewed by Sterling and Ho.[467]

Gases with *radioactive components* are passed through special cells with Geiger–Müller or scintillation–photomultiplier unit tubes and connected to counting and recording equipment.

The methods described above all refer to continuous sampling and/or immediate analysis of the gas. However, in many cases this equipment is not available, nor is it possible to carry out the analysis at the point of sampling. It is then necessary to draw a sample of the gas into a gas sampling pipette, which may be of either glass or metal. Sampling pipettes are bulbs with a stopcock at both ends, and usually have a capacity between 25 and 500 ml. Before use, the pipettes are cleaned and filled with a liquid that will not absorb any of the gases to be sampled. For flue gases this is usually water with some strong acid added to minimize carbon dioxide absorption. In other cases mercury is often satisfactory, although heavy and more difficult to handle. During sampling the liquid is displaced by the gas, and if the pressure in the gas line is not too low, the liquid running out of the pipette can draw the gas sample in. Samples may also be collected in syringes, which is a favoured technique if gas chromatography is to be used for the analysis. If gas chromatography is unavailable or unsuitable for the gas, an absorption method*, either constant pressure (Orsat type) or constant volume (Bone and Wheeler type) apparatus, can be used. It should be noted that sulphur dioxide and carbon dioxide are usually absorbed together in alkaline solvents and differentiation of these components requires special precautions and techniques.

2.7. COLLECTION AND ANALYSIS OF MINOR GASEOUS CONSTITUENTS

Many of the techniques used for the major gaseous constituents, absorption, infra-red absorption, etc., can also be used for minor constituents but certain modifications may have to be applied. In addition to these, gas chromatography comes into its own for trace analysis, particularly of hydrocarbons.

Infra-red absorption will give full scale sensitivity for the tabled volume concentrations on a particular commercial instrument which is able to analyse continuously. (Table 2.9.)

When *gas chromatography* is used, spot samples of the gases are taken, and analysed subsequently. If a large number of samples are taken at close time intervals it becomes possible to find the variation in trace concentrations. The application of gas chromatography to these measurements is complex and cannot be simply described so reference should be made to one of the general textbooks and special papers such as Ettre's review of the application of gas chromatographic methods to air pollution studies.[143]

Most widely used are the *absorption methods*, where the gas stream sampled is passed through an absorbing solution (or in some cases a bed

---

* The methods to be used in the case of flue gases are covered by a British Standard Specification.[75]

of solids) and the volume sampled is measured in a flowmeter until enough material has accumulated for analysis. The main disadvantage is that only an average concentration for the sampling time can be obtained. The infrared absorption technique avoids this difficulty, while spot sampling for chromatography overcomes it at least in part, because of the speed of taking a spot sample.

Details of methods of analysis* have been fully surveyed in recent reviews by Kay[256] and a book by Jacobs.[233]

TABLE 2.9. FULL SCALE DEFLECTION
AT MAXIMUM SENSITIVITY

Gas	Vol. % for full scale
Carbon monoxide	0·05
Carbon dioxide	0·01
Nitrous oxide	0·01
Methane	0·1
Water vapour	0·25
Organic vapours	0·1 to 1

The air contaminant most frequently found in combustion waste gases is sulphur dioxide, and some of the most common methods of determination will be described here. In concentrations as low as 0·5 ppm sulphur dioxide can be absorbed in starch iodide solutions in a counter-current column. The light absorbed by the unchanged and partly decolourized reagent is compared by photoelectric cells coupled to a galvanometer.[107] Concentrations of the order of 5 ppm can be determined by a colourmetric comparison using p-roseaniline hydrochloride and formaldehyde which produces a red–violet compound.[214] A more complex method which entails hydrogen reduction of sulphur dioxide absorbed on silica gel, followed by molybdenum blue complex formation has also been suggested[1]. Other methods based on oxidation to sulphur trioxide with subsequent determination as sulphuric acid have been suggested, while in some cases a conductivity method may be applicable, but EDTA methods are the most common in use at present.

A method of determining sulphur trioxide in the presence of sulphur dioxide has recently been described by Seidman[429] but presents considerable difficulty because of the much greater proportion of sulphur dioxide and its continuous slow oxidation.

Hydrogen sulphide can be determined by passing the gases through a

* Analysis of minor constituents in flue gases is covered by a British Standard Specification.[78]

moistened strip of lead acetate paper. The darkening of the strip can be measured and related to a hydrogen sulphide concentration.

Traces of carbon dioxide are usually absorbed in alkali and the conductivity change measured. Carbon monoxide can be similarly determined by scrubbing the gas with alkali, oxidizing the carbon monoxide by passing it over a catalyst (heated copper oxide) and then treating as carbon dioxide.

2.8. ISOKINETIC SAMPLING AND PROBES FOR SOLID AND LIQUID PARTICLES

The method of sampling particles from a gas stream is essentially the same as that of sampling gases, but extra precautions have to be taken to ensure a representative sample. When particles are about 10 microns or larger, and the sampling velocity is lower than the velocity in the duct (Fig. 2.9b) some of the gases will be deflected around the probe, but some

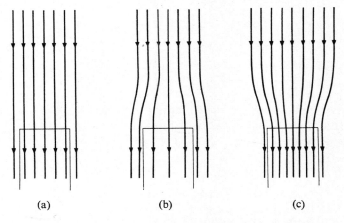

(a)   (b)   (c)

FIG. 2.9. Gas streamlines at the entrance to sampling probes.
(a) Isokinetic sampling.
(b) Sampling velocity too low.
(c) Sampling velocity too high.

of the particles, because of their inertia, will enter the probe and so a greater number of these larger particles will find their way into the sample. Conversely, if the sampling velocity is greater than the duct velocity (Fig. 2.9c) some of the larger particles will be deflected around the sampling nozzle. Only when the sampling and duct velocities are the same — that is, when the velocity is isokinetic — will a representative sample of the larger particles be collected by the probe (Fig. 2.9a). The actual error involved has been estimated by Badzioch[28] for a steady sampling velocity of

25 ft/sec, varying duct gas velocities, and 5 and 10 micron particles (with a density of 2). Figure 2.10 shows that, even with a duct velocity twice the sampling velocity, the error for 5 micron particles is only 3 per cent, but approaches 20 per cent for 10 micron particles.

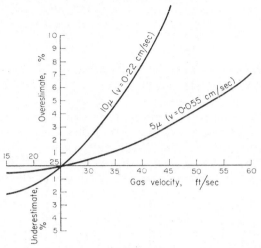

FIG. 2.10. Errors in concentrations of particles of 1 and 10 microns sampled at 25 ft/sec with a 1 in. dia. nozzle at ambient conditions.[28]

Davies[121] has suggested the following formula for estimating the sampling error for non-isokinetic conditions when using a sharp edged tube facing upstream.

$$\frac{c_s}{c_a} = \frac{u_a}{u_s} = \frac{u_a/u_s - 1}{(4\psi + 1)} \tag{2.9}$$

where c_s = concentration of particles in sample
c_a = concentration of particles in gas
u_a = velocity of gases in duct
u_s = velocity in probe
ψ = inertial impaction parameter (section 7.2)
$= d^2 C(\varrho_P - \varrho) u_a/18\mu D$ \hfill (7.6)

where D = diameter of probe
d = diameter of particle
ϱ = density of gas
ϱ_P = density of particle
μ = viscosity of gas.

As long as the velocity ratio u_s/u_a is between $\frac{1}{2}$ and 2, the concentration error is less than 20 per cent for $\psi < 0\cdot1$. A similar estimate is found from the equations given by Badzioch.[28]

Isokinetic sampling can be achieved in one of two ways: either by using a null-type sampling probe, or by measuring the velocity of the gas stream with a pitot tube as near to the probe as possible without interfering with the gas flow, and then adjusting the sampling velocity. In a null-type probe a static balance is maintained between the inner and outer tube walls. A typical design is shown in Fig. 2.11. The static tap lines are connected to both arms of a U-tube manometer and the sampling rate adjusted during sampling. However, it has been shown[124] that at the point of static balance, particularly with low gas flow rates (less than 20 ft/sec) the sampling velocity is not really isokinetic, and at these velocities even a small error in the static balance can introduce large errors in sampling. At greater gas flows the error is smaller (less than 5 per cent above 50 ft/sec) with the type of probe shown. If a null-type probe is to be used, calibration over the test range would be advisable.

Several types of sampling probes where the duct velocity is measured separately have been developed, particularly by research associations such as the British Iron and Steel Research Association[182] and the British Coal Utilization Research Association[205, 206] and are now produced commercially. The B.C.U.R.A. sampling train (Fig. 2.12) is particularly interesting because the problem of minimizing condensation in the probe and duct filter has been solved by mounting the dust extraction cyclone, backed up

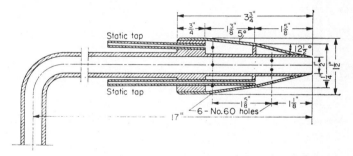

FIG. 2.11. Typical design of a null-type sampling nozzle.[524]

by a filter, on the end of the probe inside the duct. Several screw on nozzles with different entrance diameters are provided so that approximately constant volume sampling rates can be used over a wide range of velocities in the duct. The combination will withstand temperatures up to 350°C, but above this the filter must be mounted on the other end of the probe, outside the duct. The cyclone will operate up to 850°C within the duct, and also can be connected to the other probe end for work at higher temperatures. If, at these higher temperatures unreacted particles (e.g. unburned coal) are collected, they may continue to burn, and so a method of "freezing" the reaction may be necessary. This is achieved in the sampling head developed

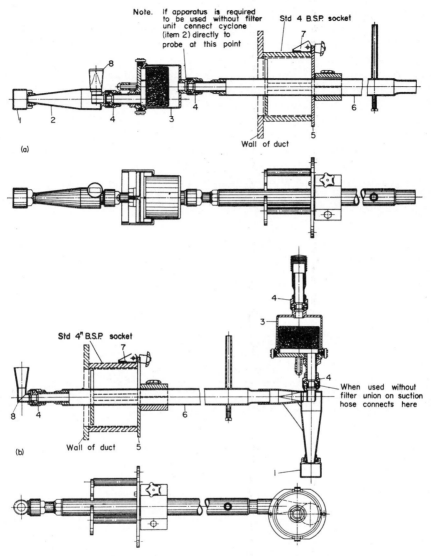

FIG. 2.12. B.C.U.R.A. Duct sampling apparatus with cyclone collector and filter.[206]

(a) Cyclone and filter positioned at end of probe, inside the duct (to 300°C).

(b) Cyclone and filter positioned outside duct
(for use at higher temperatures).

1. Hopper of cyclone.	5. Probe plug.
2. Cyclone.	6. Probe tube.
3. Filter housing.	7. Hinged clamping screw.
4. Union connection.	8. Detachable nozzle.

by the International Flame Research Foundation.[223] This is shown in Fig. 2.13. Here the collection device, a sintered brass or stainless steel thimble is mounted in the head of the water cooled probe. The nozzle, which is also water cooled, is fitted with a replaceable stainless steel liner and the material in the liner as well as the filter can be collected and analysed.

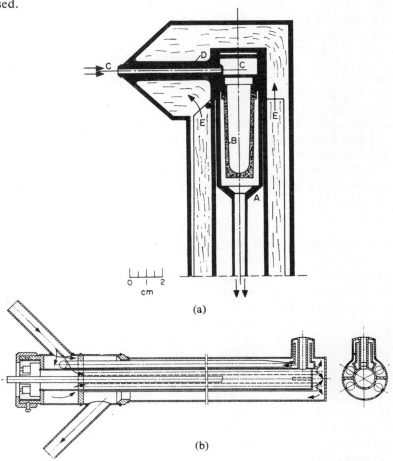

(a)

(b)

FIG. 2.13. Water cooled sampling probe for temperatures above 1100°C.

(a) Detail of sampling head.[275]

A — Holder for sintered metal thimble.
B — Sintered metal thimble.
C — Entrance to probe.
D — Sampling tube liner.
E — Water inlet lines.

(b) General arrangement of water-cooled probe.[223]

The flow pattern at the sampling nozzles has been studied[514] but in practice the actual shape of the probe was found to have little influence on the accuracy of sampling.[538] So long as a chamferred end was provided then the length of the end was not significant. The probes must be constructed so as to resist corrosion and oxidation. For flue gas analysis mild steel is satisfactory to about 400 °C, but oxidation may become a problem at higher temperatures. Stainless steel with welded construction is suitable to about 850 °C without water cooling. With water-cooled probes, copper is a possible material (for short probes) to about 1200 °C while stainless steel should be used for operation at higher temperatures. The cooling water may be introduced to the tip of the probe by running it through concentric tubes, in at one annulus and out through the other. At lower temperatures it is better to run the water in through the outer annulus, ensuring warmer water and less condensation in the probe. At higher temperatures the procedure should be reversed to allow cooler water to reach the tip. For sampling at the highest temperatures the cold water should be introduced in separate small tubes finishing close to and cooling the hottest parts of the probe tip and having the return flow in a single annulus.

2.9. SAMPLE COLLECTORS
FOR SOLID AND LIQUID PARTICLES

Some of these have been briefly mentioned in the previous section. The *cyclone collector* in the B.C.U.R.A. sampling train is of the Stairmand high efficiency pattern (section 6.7, Fig. 6.15) 1½ in. dia. and will collect all particles above about 5 microns dia. A similar pattern developed by Walter[512] appears to be satisfactory for particles above 2 microns. In the cyclones a fairly high rate of flow has to be maintained for maximum collection efficiency (about 5–10 ft³/min in the B.C.U.R.A. Stairmand pattern) so the system of interchangeable nozzles has to be used to cover a reasonable range of duct gas flows. In practice, a flow of 5 ft³/min measured in the flowmeter at ambient temperatures means a flow through the cyclone of 7¼ ft³/min at 120 °C and 9¼ ft³/min at 230 °C. At higher sampling temperatures the measured rate also has to be reduced to stay within the cyclone performance limits.

Thimble filters of sintered brass or stainless steel were mentioned as forming part of the I.F.R.F. sampling probe head. Filter thimbles may be of alundum, which is able to withstand considerable temperatures and so these may also be incorporated either in a filtering unit inside the duct[83] or in a heated filtering unit outside the duct. Alundum and porcelain filter tubes both have a very high gas flow resistance and block up quickly. Up to 350 °C, bags of fibre-glass cloth have been successfully used inside the duct. With colder gases paper filter thimbles become practicable, and these

have the advantage that they need only be used once and standard laboratory extractive methods can be applied to the recovery of the collected
material. A very neat internally heated collection unit with fibre glass or
cotton bags, able to operate at exceptionally high duct and fume concentrations has been described by Guthmann.[192] This unit can also be used at
low concentrations as provision has been made for substituting a filter
paper as the filtering medium.

The earliest units used laboratory filters papers but these are not normally very efficient collectors of fine aerosols in the sub-micron ranges. In
recent years asbestos bearing sheets and membrane filters made by the
Millipore Filter Corporation[85] have been shown to be virtually 100 per
cent efficient.[457] Equally efficient are deep, loosely packed glass fibre filters. The B.C.U.R.A. filter (Fig. 2.12) is usually filled with two layers of
glass wool: a superfine wool, fibre diameters 1–4 microns, about a $\frac{1}{4}$ in.
deep, followed by $1\frac{1}{2}$ in. layer of a coarser (6 microns dia.) glass fibre
pad. For work at higher temperatures quartz and aluminium silicate fibres
extend the operating range to the temperature limit of their metal containers. Glass containers with quartz fibres have been successfully used to
350 °C[474] for the collection of open hearth fume particles, which are almost
exclusively sub-micron sized. Quartz fibres are chemically stable to nearly
everything except hydrofluoric acid and this assists the subsequent leaching
of collected material.

Another technique of recovering collected material is the use of a filter
made of soluble material. Because of the water present in most gases it is
recommended, when no organic vapours are in the gas stream, that only
materials soluble in organic solvents be used. For example,[23] a tetrachlor-
naphthalene pad will retain two micron particles and is insoluble in water,
but dissolves in benzene, and will also sublime. The pad may be prepared
either by condensing a layer on paper or by dissolving tetrachlor-
naphthalene in ether, precipitating with ethanol and then filtering on to
a copper gauze support.

Electrostatic precipitators are not usually employed for collection of
samples from ducts, although a number of models are available for atmospheric sampling. Because of the low flow velocities normal in precipitators, a unit of impracticable size would be required to collect the relatively large volumes sampled from ducts. Moreover the necessary high voltage
direct current source equipment is invariably heavy and not readily transportable.

In selecting a collection technique, the subsequent treatment of the collected material must be considered. If only the overall weight is required,
nearly any of the above methods is satisfactory, as the collector can be
weighed before and after sampling, the net weight of the sample being obtained by difference. If the sample is to be analysed chemically it will have
to be removed from the filter, either by leaching or by the use of a soluble

filter medium. Perhaps of greatest importance is the sizing of the collected particles, and this presents the greatest technical difficulties. If liquid sedimentation or elutriation is to be used for sizing, leaching the filter with the sedimentation liquid is an acceptable method. However, for both liquid and air elutriation or sedimentation a major problem remains in redispersing the collected sample into the particles and agglomerates which existed in the gas stream.

Connecting a cascade impactor (see section 2.13) directly to the probe is possibly the only solution which gives a size classification of the particles

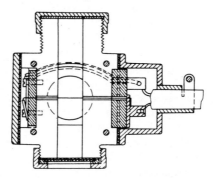

FIG. 2.14. Head of thermal precipitator for sampling very fine dusts.[89]

The sampling head is composed of two blocks of brass held together by screws to form a cube. The channel is formed between them by thin strips of insulating material which also isolate the resistance wire from the brass. Two holes in opposite faces accept the cover glasses which are kept in position by closely fitting brass plugs, for heating the wire a known current is passed through it from a battery. A shallow aspirator of 300 ml capacity fitted with a glass outlet jet, provides through the head a flow of air which is below the critical velocity.

as they are collected by the probe. This is particularly useful with droplets. If an optical or electron microscopic examination of the particles is to be undertaken, it is probably best to avoid the problem of dispersion of the bulk sample by collecting a special unagglomerated sample. This may be done by allowing the particles to settle in a chamber containing a sticky slide, or by drawing the particles in the gas through a thermal precipitator (Fig. 2.14). If the time for settling is known, an allowance for agglomeration during this period can be made.

2.10. SAMPLE VOLUMES

To find the volume of the gases sampled the collection system should be followed both by a means of measuring flow rate (either an orifice or an area flow meter) and by an integrating flow meter (frequently a bellows type gas meter). This last can be omitted if the flow rate is measured continuously and then integrated over the sampling time. It is important to cool the residual gases and to include in the train a catchpot, such as a conical flask, to remove excess water vapour, which will otherwise settle out in the flow measuring device. A thermometer or thermocouple pocket should also be provided at or near the flow measuring system so that the volumes can subsequently be related to a standard temperature. The pressure at this point should also be measured, usually by a mercury filled U-tube manometer, so that the volume at a standard pressure can be found.

The gases can be drawn through the sampling train by an ejector or a pump which may be driven electrically or pneumatically. If the gases sampled are explosive or combustible, electrical motors and other equipment must be suitably protected.*

2.11. CLASSIFICATION OF SIZE ANALYSIS METHODS

Size analysis methods fall into three groups:

(a) Those based on particle geometry.
(b) Those based on particle aero- and hydrodynamics.
(c) Those based on surface area.

Screen analyses and visual examination by microscope or electron microscope are the methods in the first group. The second comprises elutriation, sedimentation and impaction, while the third includes permeability, direct surface area (B.E.T.) measurements, β back scattering, etc.

In the design of gas cleaning plant one is principally concerned with the aerodynamic behaviour of particles, so those techniques which enable this to be predicted are most valuable. For larger particles in the regions above 75 microns (200 mesh) screen analyses and microscope analysis are easily carried out, but electron micrographs are often the only method of penetrating into the regions of sub-micron sized particles where aerodynamic methods are no longer feasible because of excessive Brownian motion. Surface area methods can sometimes be used, particularly permeability measurements which are very fast, but they give only an average size.

2.12. SIZE ANALYSES BASED ON PARTICLE GEOMETRY

Sieves are commonly used for particle size analyses down to 200 mesh screens, which have sieve openings of 74 microns (Tyler (U.S.) scale), 63 microns (Institute of Mining and Metallurgy (I.M.M.) (British) scale), or

* SPECIAL WARNING. If the gases sampled are toxic or likely to contain toxic constituents (e.g. blast furnace gases contain an appreciable fraction of carbon monoxide) great care must be taken as to the disposal of the residual gases expelled from the train during sampling.

76 microns (British Standard sieves). Tyler sieves are available down to 400 mesh (38 microns) and this represents the lower limit of ordinary screen analysis. Special electro-formed precision micromesh sieves[110] enable sieve analysis to be carried down as far as 5 micron particles. It should be remembered that sieves may pass irregular particles which are longer than the sieve opening if their two shorter axes are within the limits of that opening. Small fine particles tend to agglomerate and screening by shaking may take a very long time, so an air jet can be used to blow undersize particles through the sieve. This principle has been incorporated in the "air jet" sieve[300] in which a controlled air stream blows the fine particles through, giving rapid and accurate separation.

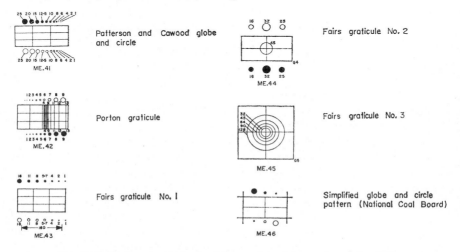

FIG. 2.15. Various graticules used for particle sizing and counting.[482]

Microscopic examination without determining the size distribution is rapid and gives an excellent idea of the appearance of the particles. Their chemical composition also may often be inferred from colour and from knowledge of their source. If only a bulk sample was collected, its re-dispersal for microscopic sizing will nearly always require the preparation of a suspension and subsequent evaporation of some drops thereof placed on a slide. A much better method is to avoid re-dispersion by collecting a sample on a sticky slide placed in the gas stream or in a settlement chamber. Coagulation during settling can be allowed for. Jet impactor slides are also suitable for microscopic examination. Here a particle count is usually all that is required, as the stages of the jet impactor (Fig. 2.17) have classified the particles. The use of a microscope for particle sizing has been explained elsewhere, for example by Fairs[144] and Green and Lane.[186] Special graticules, a selection of which is shown in Fig. 2.15, are available to simplify the counting and sizing. The spheres on the graticules are sized in a $\sqrt{2}$ progression, as in standard Tyler screens. Although particles as small as 0·14 microns can be detected under white light, 1 micron represents the practical minimum for normal sizing for the optical microscope. It should be remembered that when particles are observed under a microscope they are normally in their position of greatest stability, so if they are thin plates they will present their largest dimensions for measurement.

Electron microscopy is a highly specialized technique. Smoke and fume samples are usually collected with a thermal precipitator in which the material is deposited on a membrane on a cold slide near a heated wire. A thermal precipitator will not retain particles greater than 20 microns[523] but will readily collect all particles in the sub-micron ranges. Membrane (Millipore) filters are also suitable for sample collection. The resolution of simple electron microscopes is about 40 Å (Ångstroms) — about 1/250 micron — while high resolution models are able to improve on this by factor of ten. This is, however, well beyond the size of any particles normally encountered in industrial collection.

The tedious nature of particle sizing and counting, whether through a microscope or from electron micrographs, has been overcome by the development of two techniques for automatic particle sizing and counting. The first of these depends on mechanical scanning with photoelectric detection, coupled with high speed counting devices[342, 343]. The second involves scanning the sample with a flying spot from a cathode ray tube, picking up the scattered light pulses from the particles individually on a photocell,[167] and recording the pulses on counters.

2.13. PARTICLE ANALYSES BASED ON AERO- AND HYDRODYNAMICS

Sedimentation is the simplest method of particle size grouping utilizing the aero- or hydrodynamic behaviour of the particles. One of the earliest sedimentation pipettes, the Andreasen pipette,[15, 248] is still in use, sometimes in modified forms, such as the one developed by Stairmand,[458] a robust and easily used unit. The settling medium is usually water to which a peptizing agent may have been added. The particles are shaken up in the fluid and then allowed to settle, samples of the mixture near the bottom of the apparatus being taken at regular intervals. These are then evaporated and weighed. The size distribution therefore depends on the viscosity of the fluid, so that temperature uniformity during sedimentation is important. An adequate sample (approximately one gram) is required. The process has been made automatic by the development of the sedimentation balance[26, 40, 61, 166] where the increase in the load of a pan suspended in the bottom of a beaker containing the mixture is counteracted by some form of torsion arrangement, the changes in which are recorded on a time base. A very elegant technique of finding the rate of sedimentation is to measure the back-scattered β radiation from the deposited material at which a one millicurie ^{90}Sr source has been directed. Centrifugation can of course be used to speed up the gravity settling process.[127, 252]

Sedimentation in air can be used for particle size distribution measurement in apparatus of the settlement dust counter type[88] in which a volume

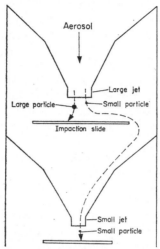

FIG. 2.16. Principle of the "cascade" impactor.[340]

of air is enclosed in a cylinder at the base of which is an arrangement for exposing a number of microscope cover glasses in sequence. By timing the exposures and counting the number of particles collected on each slide, a particle size distribution can be obtained.

The range for sedimentation is from approximately below 325 mesh (42 microns) to about 0·2 microns.

In elutriation the fluid is passed upwards counter-current to the sedimenting particles. To obtain steady flow requires careful control. Liquid elutriators, using both gravity and centrifugal forces (in miniature cyclones),[258] are available commercially. The particles separated in them are much coarser than in simple sedimentation. Fine particles can be separated by air elutriators. A simple model has been described by Stairmand[461] while the multi-stage Haultain "Infrasizer"[9] has been available for many years. The centrifugal elutriator developed by Gustavsson[191] and sold commercially as the Bahco air elutriator has proved very useful for particle size analysis of the type encountered industrially.[269] Except for the Bahco elutriator, elutriation methods are normally restricted to mineral particles which are comparatively coarse and where large samples are available.

Multi-stage or cascade impaction as a development of the impingement principle was first introduced in the Greenburg–Smith impinger[188] in which a stream of dust laden gases is passed through a nozzle and the resultant jet allowed to impact on a plate before being diverted. The multi-stage impactor was introduced by May[335] and the principle is shown in Fig. 2.16. The large jet with low velocity will deposit the larger particles on the slide, while the small high-velocity jet will deposit the smaller particles

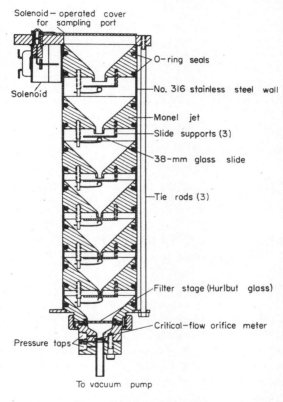

FIG. 2.17. General arrangement of six-stage cascade impactor developed by the Batelle Institute.[340]

on a subsequent slide. The design of a six stage model with after-filter developed by the Batelle Institute[340] is shown in Fig. 2.17. The efficiencies of collection on each stage vary considerably. As seen for May's four stage model (Fig. 2.18), the "cut-off" in each stage is not very sharp, and with six stages considerable overlapping will occur between the stages. However, the cascade impactor presents the only method of sampling droplets and obtaining an immediate size distribution with a minimum of coagulation.

In the same way the impactor will size particles while sampling as the agglomeration during passage through the impactor is very small. However, particles have less sharp "cut off" than droplets because of particle "bounce" and "shatter". Use of sticky coated slides will overcome this to some extent. Both for the four stage and six stage models the range is 0·5–15 microns, which probably represents the practical limits of impactors.

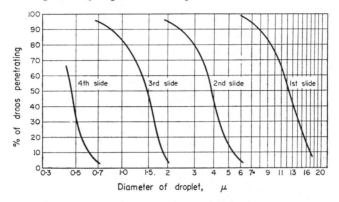

FIG. 2.18. Droplets penetrating past the various stages in a four-stage impactor.[335] (The range of the six stage unit is similar.)

2.14. AVERAGE PARTICLE SIZE BASED ON SURFACE AREA

Permeability has been widely used for finding the average sizing of particles in powders. The passage of a volume of air through a sample packed under standard conditions is timed. The specific surface A found by permeability[87, 301] can be related to average particle size by consideration of the porosity ϵ (fraction of free volume) which is found experimentally from the density of material and weight of sample tablet of known volume. The equivalent capillary theory[142] in simple form gives the particle diameter d as

$$d = \frac{3}{2}\left(\frac{1-\epsilon}{A}\right) \tag{2.10}$$

Specific surface area can also be found from absorption measurements either of gases (B.E.T. surface area determinations)[80] or of dyestuffs (particularly methylene blue), or by the heat of wetting of the surface.[189] Some of these later methods give the total specific surface area of the particles including their internal surfaces even if these are only pores a few millimicrons diameter. Their application to particles which may themselves be porous (for example carbon particles in smoke) can lead to incorrect surface areas.

2.15. OTHER METHODS OF PARTICLE SIZING

Two other methods of particle sizing which are not easily classified under the headings in section 2.11 are the electric gating technique and the light extinction method. The electric gating technique is incorporated in the Coulter counter in which a suspension of the particles in an electrically conducting liquid flows through a small aperture between two electrodes. If a relatively non-conducting particle passes between the electrodes, a voltage decrease occurs between the electrodes proportional to the size of the particle.[334] The apertures may be between 10 and 1000 microns diameter, and the minimum particle measured is about 0·3 microns, similar to the minimum for sedimentation.[44]

Particles in suspension in a gas or liquid absorb, reflect, or scatter light depending on their size, shape, and surface texture and on the wavelength of the incident light. This can be utilized for particle size analysis by applying the Lambert–Beer law[447] to a system where the particles are dispensed in a fluid medium.

$$I_i = I_0 \exp\left(-kcl/d\right) \tag{2.11}$$

where I_0 = intensity of the light in the absence of obscuring particles (i.e. the light transmitted by the pure fluid)

I_i = intensity of beam after passing through the suspension

k = the extinction coefficient (a constant)

c = mass concentration of particles/unit volume (g/cm^3)

l = length over which absorption takes place

d = diameter of particles (microns).

In practice, the extinction coefficient differs for particles of different sizes, so Rose[402] and Rose and Sullivan[403] give the equation for the apparent specific surface A' (in m^2/g):

$$A' = \frac{4}{cl} \ln I_0/I_i \tag{2.12}$$

The true specific surface A can then be found from empirical relations:

$A = 4{\cdot}5A'^{(0.77)}/\varrho_p^{1/4}$ for the range $600/\varrho_p < A' < 60{,}000/\varrho_p$ (2.13a)

and

$A = 120A'^{(1/2)}/\varrho_p^{1/2}$ for the range $60{,}000/\varrho_p < A' < 180{,}000/\varrho_p$ (2.13b)

where ϱ_p = density of the particle.

In a similar category are smoke density meters where a beam of light shining on a photoelectric cell across a duct is partially interrupted by particles moving along the duct. Although difficult to interpret in terms of particle size and concentration, smoke density meters will indicate fluctuations in particle numbers.

CHAPTER 3

THE REMOVAL OF A GASEOUS CONSTITUENT: ABSORPTION, ADSORPTION AND COMBUSTION

3.1. INTRODUCTION

It is often necessary to treat a gas stream for the removal of one or more of its gaseous constituents, which may be harmful, obnoxious, or commercially valuable. For example, it is important to remove carbon monoxide from the gases for ammonia synthesis before they enter the catalyst columns, as carbon monoxide is a catalyst poison.

It is essential in areas of dense or predominantly residential population, to remove the obnoxious odours, essentially organic nitrogen and sulphur compounds, produced by processes such as roasting coffee or rendering offal.

It would be very desirable to remove sulphur dioxide from flue gases, both because it contributes to atmospheric pollution, and because it can be converted to the commercial commodities, sulphuric acid and sulphur.

There are three methods of removing gaseous constituents; gases may be absorbed in a liquid, adsorbed on a solid surface, or changed chemically into a harmless gas. The last usually involves the combustion of the organic material, either directly or with the assistance of catalysts. The basic mechanism in all these is the diffusion of the particular gas either to the surface of an absorbing liquid or adsorbing solid or catalyst, or to the reaction zone of a chemical reaction. This is in contrast to the more complex collection of particles and droplets where a combination of mechanisms, inertial impaction, interception, settling, electrostatic and thermal forces, play a part, in addition to diffusion. A detailed discussion of adsorption, absorption and combustion processes is beyond the scope of the present book which is concerned with the application of these methods to gas purification and so it deals only briefly with the fundamental processes of these operations. A full treatment of these topics is given in specialized books on absorption,[344, 354, 441] adsorption[80, 326, 504] and combustion.[491] Those aspects which are of particular interest in the control of air pollution will be dealt with in some detail. These include the removal of sulphur dioxide from flue gases, the removal of hydrogen sulphide, fluorides and oxides of nitrogen from process waste gases, and the combustion, both direct and catalytic, of organic vapours and odours.

Absorption and adsorption of gases depend on the transfer of molecules from the bulk of the gas to the liquid or solid surface. In the case of the liquid, the gas molecules then diffuse to the bulk of the liquid, while at the solid surface they are held by physical (van der Waals) or chemical forces (chemisorption). When the solid or liquid surface is brought into contact with a stagnant gas, the diffusion of the gas molecules is by molecular diffusion, and the rate of this depends on the pressure and temperature of the gas and the molecular species in the gas. The rate of molecular transfer N_A, in molal units per unit area in unit time is given by Fick's law:

$$N_A = -\mathscr{D}\,\frac{\mathrm{d}c_A}{\mathrm{d}x} \tag{3.1}$$

where $\mathrm{d}c_A/\mathrm{d}x$ is the concentration gradient in the direction of diffusion (c_A being the concentration and x being the distance), and $\mathscr{D}$ is the molecular diffusivity, which has the dimensions $(\text{length})^2/(\text{time})$.

3.2. CALCULATION OF MOLECULAR DIFFUSIVITY

The diffusivity in the gas phase can be calculated from an equation based on the kinetic theory of gases; and for a single species, this is:

$$\mathscr{D}_G = \tfrac{1}{3}\lambda\bar{u} \tag{3.1a}$$

where λ = mean free path of gas molecules

$\bar{u}$ = average velocity of gas molecules.

From the kinetic theory, which considers the gas as a mixture of hard spheres without intermolecular forces of attraction and repulsion, the mean free path is given by

$$\lambda = 1/\sqrt{(2)}\pi N\sigma^2 \tag{3.2}$$

where N = number of molecules per unit volume

σ = diameter of a molecule

and the average velocity is given by

$$\bar{u} = \sqrt{(8RT/\pi M)} \tag{3.3}$$

where T = absolute temperature

R = universal gas constant

M = molecular weight.

For the interdiffusion of two species of molecules A and B of different molecular weights, M_A and M_B and different sizes, σ_A and σ_B, the diffusivity is

$$\mathscr{D}_{AB} = \frac{1}{3} \frac{N_A \lambda_A \bar{u}_A + N_B \lambda_B \bar{u}_B}{N_A + N_B} \tag{3.4}$$

where N_A and N_B are the numbers of molecules of each of the species A and B within a unit volume.

Using a mean molecular diameter, σ_{AB} instead of individual diameters, equation (3.4) can be simplified to give[236]

$$\mathscr{D}_{AB} = \frac{1}{3\pi N(\sigma_{AB})^2} \sqrt{(\bar{u}_A^2 + \bar{u}_B^2)} \tag{3.5}$$

$$= \frac{2\sqrt{(2)}\sqrt{(RT)}}{3\pi^{3/2} N(\sigma_{AB})^2} \sqrt{\left(\frac{1}{M_A} + \frac{1}{M_B}\right)} \tag{3.6}$$

using equation (3.3) for average velocities of the molecular species. As collision diameters are not easily obtained it is more convenient to use the molar volumes at the normal boiling points V_A and V_B, which are proportional to the cube of the collision diameter σ_{AB};

$$\mathscr{D}_{AB} = b \frac{T^{3/2}}{P(V_A^{1/3} + V_B^{1/3})^2} \sqrt{\left(\frac{1}{M_A} + \frac{1}{M_B}\right)} \tag{3.7}$$

where b is a constant. This constant could be calculated from the kinetic theory of gases, but more realistic diffusivities are obtained when using an empirical value of 0·0043 (in c.g.s. atm °K units)[175], 0·0166 (f.p.s. atm °K units) or 0·0069 (f.p.s. atm °R units). Molecular volumes can be found in tables or by adding together atomic volumes.[355]

More sophisticated values of molecular diffusivities, allowing for attractive and repulsive forces, using the Leonard-Jones 6:12 potential (i.e. the attractive force varies inversely as the sixth power, the repulsive force as the inverse twelfth power) can be obtained from the equation by Hirschfelder, et al.[217]

$$\mathscr{D}_{AB} = \frac{bT^{3/2}}{P(\sigma_{AB})^2 W^1} \sqrt{\left(\frac{1}{M_A} + \frac{1}{M_B}\right)} \quad \text{(cm)}^2/\text{sec} \tag{3.8}$$

where b is 0·002628 in c.g.s. units
and W^1 is the collision integral which is a function of the molecular potential energy parameter characteristic of the interaction, in °K and Ångstrom Units.

Details of this method of calculating the diffusivity may be obtained from reference [217].

Diffusivity in the liquid phase may be calculated from Einstein's suggestion that an osmotic force acts on molecules in the direction of decreasing solute concentration c:

$$F = -\frac{kT}{c} \cdot \frac{dc}{dx} \qquad (3.9)$$

where k = Boltzmann's constant

The resistance to the motion of the molecules, considered as spheres is given approximately by Stokes law (see section 4.1)

$$F = 3\pi\mu\sigma u \qquad (3.10)$$

where σ = diameter of molecule

   μ = viscosity of solution

   u = velocity of molecule

$$\therefore u = -\frac{kT}{3\pi\mu\sigma c} \cdot \frac{dc}{dx} \qquad (3.11)$$

The rate of diffusion N_A is the product of the velocity of the molecules and the concentration

$$N_A = uc = -\frac{kT}{3\pi\mu\sigma} \cdot \frac{dc}{dx} \qquad (3.12)$$

The diffusivity can now be calculated from Fick's law (equation 3.1) and is

$$\mathscr{D}_L = \frac{kT}{3\pi\mu\sigma} \qquad (3.13)$$

Values for diffusivity given by the Stokes–Einstein equation are very approximate, and in practice experimental values, such as are given by the *International Critical Tables*[228] or Landolt–Börnstein[292] should be used when these are available.

3.3. STEADY STATE DIFFUSION OF TWO GASES

When a gas is being continuously absorbed from a gas mixture, which is constantly renewed, an equilibrium is set up, with constant concentration gradients. The transport of the gas molecules no longer occurs by simple molecular diffusion, as is the case with a stagnant gas, but also by bulk transport of the gas, in order to replenish the concentration of the molecules being removed from the interface. If there are two species A and B, with molal concentrations c_A and c_B respectively, when the system is in equilibrium; at constant pressure

$$c_A + c_B = \text{constant} \qquad (3.14)$$

Differentiating with respect to x, the distance in the direction of the diffusion and bulk transport, perpendicular to the interface, gives a relation between the concentration gradients of the components:

$$\frac{dc_A}{dx} = \frac{-dc_B}{dx} \tag{3.15}$$

The bulk flow in the x direction carries components A and B in the proportion of their partial pressures p_A and p_B. So for component A, the total flow N_A is the sum of the bulk flow fraction $N_A p_A/P$ (P = total pressure) and the molecular diffusion, given by equation (3.1)

$$N_A = N_A \frac{p_A}{P} - \mathscr{D}_G \frac{dc_A}{dx} \tag{3.16}$$

For an ideal gas, the concentration c_B is related to the partial pressure p_B by

$$c_B = p_B/RT \tag{3.17}$$

Substituting (3.17) in (3.16), $(1 - p_B)$ for p_A, and using (3.15) this gives

$$N_A = N_A\left(1 - \frac{p_B}{P}\right) + \frac{\mathscr{D}_G}{RT} \cdot \frac{dp_B}{dx} \tag{3.18}$$

Rearranging:

$$N_A \frac{p_B}{P} = \frac{\mathscr{D}_G}{RT} \cdot \frac{dp_B}{dx} \tag{3.19a}$$

and

$$N_A \int_0^x dx = \frac{P\mathscr{D}_G}{RT} \int_{p_{B_1}}^{p_{B_2}} \frac{dp_B}{p_B} \tag{3.19b}$$

which on integration gives:

$$N_A = \frac{\mathscr{D}_G P}{RTx} \ln (p_{B_2}/p_{B_1}) \tag{3.20}$$

If the logarithmic mean partial pressure of component B across the distance through which the transport takes place, x, is defined as

$$p_{BM} = \frac{p_{B_2} - p_{B_1}}{\ln p_{B_2}/p_{B_1}} \tag{3.21}$$

Equation (3.20) can be written as:

$$N_A = \frac{\mathscr{D}_G}{RTx} \frac{P}{p_{BM}} (p_{B_2} - p_{B_1}) \tag{3.22a}$$

$$= \frac{\mathscr{D}_G}{RTx} \frac{P}{p_{BM}} (p_{A_1} - p_{A_2}) \tag{3.22b}$$

3.4. FILM THEORY OF ABSORPTION

When a gas stream is moving across a surface and the bulk of the gas is in turbulent motion (i. e. when the Reynolds number exceeds critical value of 2100), turbulent mixing maintains a homogeneous composition throughout this region. Close to the surface, the gas movement is slower and a laminar layer occurs, while at the interface it is usually assumed that the gas is stagnant. The depth of the surface layers depends on the flow characteristics of the gas. In gas absorption it is assumed that the concentration of the gas being absorbed is constant in the turbulent region, and a concentration gradient exists across the surface layers, or film, to the interface. When a liquid absorbent is used, a similar film exists on the liquid side, and it is assumed that the two phases are in equilibrium at the interface. The partial pressure at the interface p_i and the concentration at the interface, c_i, are then related. When steady state conditions of transfer have been reached, the rate of transfer N_A from the gas stream to the interface, and from the interface to the bulk of the liquid stream must be equal, and

$$N_A = k_G(p - p_i) = k_L(c_i - c) \tag{3.23}$$

where p = partial pressure of the transferring component in the bulk of the gas stream

   p_i = partial pressure at the interface

   c_i = concentration at the interface

   c = concentration in the bulk of the liquid

   k_G = gas film mass transfer coefficient

   k_L = liquid film mass transfer coefficient.

Comparison with equation (3.22b) shows that the gas film mass transfer coefficient can be calculated from:

$$k_G = \frac{\mathscr{D}_G}{RTx} \frac{P}{p_{BM}} \tag{3.24}$$

which is seen to be a function of the diffusivity, the log mean partial pressure of the non-absorbing component, and x, the distance through which diffusion is taking place, which is the film thickness. On the liquid film side the mass transfer coefficient may be calculated from

$$k_L = \mathscr{D}_L/x_L \tag{3.25}$$

where $\mathscr{D}_L$ = liquid phase diffusivity

   x_L = liquid film thickness.

Although, as has been shown, the diffusivities can be calculated, the film thickness cannot be found directly. It is, however possible to find the equivalent film thickness representing the combination of transfer mechanisms through laminar boundary layers from an experimental mass transfer coefficient and a calculated or experimental diffusivity. It is then possible to use the value for a similar type of absorption. This has been done by Gilliland and Sherwood,[176] who correlated the results of a number of experiments using a wetted wall column:

$$\frac{k_G RTD}{\mathscr{D}_v}\ \frac{p_{BM}}{P} = \frac{D}{x} = 0 \cdot 023\ \mathrm{Re}^{0 \cdot 83}\ \mathrm{Sc}^{0 \cdot 44} \qquad (3.27)$$

where D = diameter of the column

Re = Reynolds number $uD\varrho/\mu$

Sc = Schmidt number $\mu/\varrho\mathscr{D}_v$

$\mathscr{D}_v$ = gas phase diffusivity

Here u is the velocity of the gas relative to the column, while ϱ and μ are the density and viscosity of the gas.

This correlation is satisfactory where the rate of absorption is controlled by the rate of transfer through the gas film, but unfortunately the rippling which occurs in the liquid curtain surface makes this an unsatisfactory method of finding the equivalent film thickness for liquid film controlled absorption.

When the system is controlled by the liquid film resistance, the mass transfer coefficient can be measured in a disk column,[466] which gives a better correlation than the wetted wall column. The mass transfer coefficient for the liquid film k_L can be calculated from the equation.

$$\frac{k_L}{\mathscr{D}_v} = 21 \cdot 0 \left(\frac{4L}{\mu}\right)^{0 \cdot 7} \left(\frac{\mu}{\varrho\mathscr{D}_v}\right)^{0 \cdot 5} \qquad (3.28)$$

where L = the rate of liquid flow (e.g. lbs/hr) per unit width of surface (lbs/(hr)/ft).

However, even without detailed knowledge of equilibrium data and film coefficients, overall coefficients can be found, and these are defined by:

$$N_A = K_G(p - p^*) = K_L(c^* - c) \qquad (3.29)$$

where p^* = equilibrium partial pressure of solute over a solution having the same concentration c as the main liquid stream,

and c^* = concentration of a solution which would be in equilibrium with the solute partial pressure existing in the main gas stream.

These points are shown in the equilibrium diagram (Fig. 3.1).

The over-all coefficients K_G (using pressure units) and K_L (using concentration units) can be determined experimentally and used directly in the design equations.

The overall driving force is $(p - p^*)$ in pressure units and in $(c^* - c)$ concentration units. The point B on the equilibrium curve represents the compositions of the two phases at the interface, and the driving forces

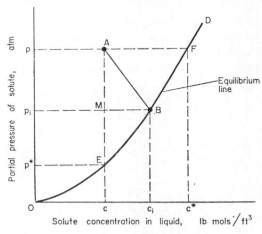

FIG. 3.1. The driving forces in gas absorption.

$p - p_i$ and $c_i - c$ are represented by the vertical distance AM and horizontal distance MB respectively. Thus, from (3.23)

$$\frac{p - p_i}{c_i - c} = \frac{k_L}{k_G} \tag{3.30}$$

and the ratio $-k_L/k_G$ represents the slope of the line AB.

Where the equilibrium relation is of the form

$$p^* = \mathcal{H}c \tag{3.31}$$

and $\mathcal{H}$ is a constant, then Henry's law applies. From equations (3.23) and (3.29) it can be deduced that

$$\frac{1}{K_G} = \frac{1}{k_G} + \frac{\mathcal{H}}{k_L} \tag{3.32a}$$

and

$$\frac{1}{K_L} = \frac{1}{k_L} + \frac{1}{\mathcal{H}k_G}. \tag{3.32b}$$

If $\mathcal{H}$ is small, $K_G = k_G$ and the absorption is gas film controlled: conversely, if $\mathcal{H}$ is large, $K_L = k_L$ and the absorption is liquid film controlled.

The equations (3.32) show also that for intermediate values of the coefficient $\mathscr{H}$ both films must be considered. Furthermore, if $\mathscr{H}$ is not a constant, i.e. if the equilibrium curve is not a straight line, then the overall coefficients will vary with the concentration dependence of $\mathscr{H}$.

3.5. DESIGN OF ABSORPTION SYSTEMS

A suitably designed unit for absorbing gases should be able to operate at the highest possible efficiencies, with maximum flexibility of throughput and with the lowest capital and operating charges. Absorption units can be classified into two groups. In the first, bubbles of gas are dispersed in the

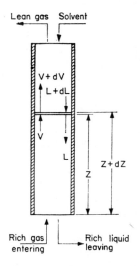

Fig. 3.2. Diagrammatic representation of a counterflow continuous absorption tower.

liquid in either a continuous or multi-stage system, while in the second, liquid drops are dispersed through the gas. In nearly all units except single stage absorbers, the operation of the plant is essentially a counter-current flow absorption operation of the type shown diagrammatically in Fig. 3.2, although some scrubbing plants operate with concurrent flow. Only continuous plant will be discussed here.

If

V = molar rate of flow of gas phase
L = molar rate of flow of liquid phase
y = mole fraction of gaseous component being absorbed
x = mole fraction of absorbed component in liquid

and subscript 1 = bottom of contacting tower
subscript 2 = top of contacting tower.

Then, for steady state operation, a material balance over a differential tower section is:

$$dV = dL \qquad (3.33)$$

and a component balance over the same section is:

$$d(Vy) = d(Lx). \qquad (3.34)$$

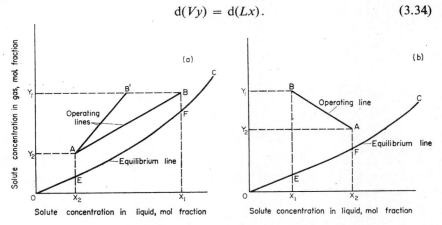

FIG. 3.3. (a) Operating and equilibrium lines in a counterflow column.
(b) Operating and equilibrium lines in a co-current contacting system.

On integration, using as one limit the bottom of the tower (subscript 1) and as the other any level within the tower, equation (3.34) becomes:

$$Vy - V_1 y_1 = Lx - L_1 x_1 \qquad (3.35a)$$

or

$$Vy + L_1 x_1 = Lx + V_1 y_1. \qquad (3.35b)$$

This is the equation of the operating line, and is valid for all values of x between x_1 and x_2 and all values of y between y_1 and y_2 (Fig. 3.3a).

In the general case, V and L vary at different points up the tower, and the operating line will be curved. In many gas cleaning problems, however, the component being absorbed constitutes only a small fraction of the gas and the absorbing liquid, and then the operating line is essentially linear.

In a differential section of the column, height dZ, the intersurface area is dA, and the rate of absorption is—from equations (3.23) and (3.29)

$$N_A \, dA = K_G(p - p^*) \, dA = K_L(c^* - c) \, dA$$

$$= k_G(p - p_i) \, dA$$

$$= k_L(c_i - c) \, dA. \qquad (3.36)$$

If a is the interfacial area per unit of tower volume, and S is the tower cross-section,

$$dA = aS \, dZ.\tag{3.37}$$

The value of a is not usually known accurately in practice, in the case of packed towers, where only a fraction of the available surface may be absorbing, or in the case of spray towers, where the surface area of the droplets is not known. It is therefore usual to combine the mass transfer coefficient with the area in a composite coefficient, k_Ga, k_La, K_Ga or K_La. Substituting (3.37) in equation (3.36):

$$d(Vy) = N_A \, dA = k_Ga(p - p_i) \, S \, dZ$$

$$= k_La(c_i - c)$$

$$= K_Ga(p - p^*) \, S \, dZ\tag{3.36a}$$

$$= K_La(c^* - c) \, S \, dZ$$

the mole fraction y of the soluble component in the gaseous phase is p/P and the mole fraction x in the liquid phase is c/ϱ_{mean}, then equation (3.36a) can be transformed to

$$d(Vy) = k_g aP(y - y_i) \, S \, dZ = k_L a\varrho_m(x_i - x) \, S \, dZ$$

$$= K_G aP(y - y^*) \, S \, dZ = K_L a\varrho_m(x^* - x) \, S \, dZ\tag{3.38}$$

$(y - y^*)$ is represented by the vertical lines BF at (x_1, y_1) and AE at (x_2, y_2) in Fig. 3.3a.

For gas absorption, where V and L are not constant, it can be shown that $d(Vy) = V \, dy/(1 - y)$. Combining this with equation (3.38) gives the equation for the height of the tower Z, with gas film coefficients.

$$\int_0^z dZ = \int_{y_1}^{y_2} \frac{V}{k_G aPS} \cdot \frac{dy}{(1 - y)(y_i - y)}$$

$$= \int_{y_1}^{y_2} \frac{V}{K_G aPS} \cdot \frac{dy}{(1 - y)(y^* - y)}\tag{3.39a}$$

or for liquid film coefficients:

$$\int_0^z dZ = \int_{x_1}^{x_2} \frac{L}{k_L a\varrho_m S} \cdot \frac{dx}{(1 - x)(x - x_i)}$$

$$= \int_{x_1}^{x_2} \frac{L}{K_L a\varrho_m S} \cdot \frac{dx}{(1 - x)(x - x^*)}\tag{3.39b}$$

Simplifying these equations by multiplying both terms in the integral by the logarithmic mean driving force:

$$(1 - y)_{LM} = \frac{y_2 - y_1}{\ln \dfrac{1 - y_1}{1 - y_2}} \quad \text{and} \quad (1 - x)_{LM} = \frac{x_2 - x_1}{\ln \dfrac{1 - x_1}{1 - x_2}}$$

and assuming that the product of this and the mass transfer coefficient is a constant; then

$$
\begin{aligned}
Z &= \frac{V_{av.}}{k_G a(1 - y)_{LM} PS} \int_{y_1}^{y_2} \frac{(1 - y)_{LM}}{(1 - y)(y_i - y)}\, dy \\[2ex]
&= \frac{V_{av.}}{K_G a(1 - y)_{LM} PS} \int_{y_1}^{y_2} \frac{(1 - y)_{LM}}{(1 - y)(y^* - y)}\, dy \\[2ex]
&= \frac{L_{av.}}{k_L a \varrho_m (1 - x)_{LM} S} \int_{x_1}^{x_2} \frac{(1 - x)_{LM}}{(1 - x)(x - x_i)}\, dx \\[2ex]
&= \frac{L_{av.}}{K_L a \varrho_m (1 - x)_{LM} S} \int_{x_1}^{x_2} \frac{(1 - x)_{LM}}{(1 - x)(x - x^*)}\, dx.
\end{aligned}
\tag{3.40}
$$

The group outside the integral sign is the height (H_t) of a transfer unit, while the group within the integral sign represents the number (N) of transfer units. The height of the tower is then

$$Z = H_t \times N. \tag{3.41}$$

The height of a transfer unit can be evaluated from the mass transfer coefficient, the characteristics of the system and the initial and final concentrations of absorbing gas or solute. The number of transfer units can be evaluated by the use of the equilibrium diagram for the system and one of the following methods:

(a) Graphical integration: If no relation between the variables y and x is available except an experimental equilibrium curve, it is necessary to evaluate the number of transfer units graphically, plotting

$$(1 - y)_{LM}/(1 - y)(y^* - y)$$

against y, if $K_G a$ is known, or against similar functions in the other cases.

(b) Simplified graphical integration of $1/(y^* - y)$ can be used if an arithmetic average of $(1 - y)$ and $(1 - y^*)$ can be substituted for $(1 - y)_{LM}$ without introducing any undue error. The complex integral from equation (3.40) then simplifies to

$$N = \int_{y_1}^{y_2} \frac{dy}{y^* - y} + \frac{1}{2} \ln \frac{1 - y_2}{1 - y_1} \tag{3.42}$$

(c) If the concentrations are very dilute, and both operating and equilibrium curve are linear, with the equation

$$y = mx + C \quad \text{for the equilibrium line},$$

then it can be shown that

$$N = \frac{y_2 - y_1}{(y^* - y)_{LM}} \tag{3.43}$$

where

$$(y^* - y)_{LM} = \frac{(y^* - y)_1 - (y^* - y)_2}{\ln \dfrac{(y^* - y)_1}{(y^* - y)_2}}.$$

When the liquid flow rate is large compared to the gas flow rate, the operating line, slope L/V, will be steep, and the driving forces large. With low L/V ratios, the driving force will be reduced until the operating and equilibrium lines touch, when equilibrium will be attained, and the minimum liquid rate can thus be found. This minimum could only be achieved in an absorber of infinite length.

Co-current flow is not usually used in packed towers or simple spray towers. It is common, however, in various scrubbers of the venturi or cyclonic spray types which are used for lean gas mixtures. The calculation of the number of transfer units in the co-current case is similar to that in the counter-current, except that the operating line has a slope in the opposite direction as shown by the operating line in Fig. 3.3b.

An empirical equation for the number of transfer units in a cyclonic spray scrubber (Fig. 9.7) absorbing sulphur dioxide has been derived by Johnstone and Silox.[244]

$$N = \frac{0 \cdot 088 \, nP}{V^{0 \cdot 8} S} \tag{3.44}$$

where n = number of nozzles in the scrubber

   S = cross-sectional area of gas inlet (ft²)

   P = total pressure of gas (atm)

   V = gas flow rate through entry: (lb moles)/(min) (ft²).

A more general correlation for scrubbers, based on the power consumption of the plant has been suggested by Lunde[317] which indicates that the number of transfer units in a spray tower is proportional directly to the power introduced in the liquid $\mathscr{P}_L$ and inversely to the power introduced by the gas $\mathscr{P}_V$.

$$N \propto \mathscr{P}_L / \mathscr{P}_V^{0 \cdot 1} \tag{3.45}$$

However, constants to be used in this equation have not been determined.

3.6. CONSTRUCTION OF ABSORPTION PLANT

Counter-current gas–liquid contacting may be carried out in the following ways:

(1) Bubbling the gas through a vessel containing the absorbing liquid. Vessels usually contain a pipe with holes emitting the gas, called a porous gas sparger, and the degree of gas dispersion may be assisted by agitating the liquid. This is not a usual method for industrial gas cleaning.

(2) The gas can be passed through a series of bubble cap plates or other types of plates in a plate column. The design of these columns is fully discussed in texts on the design of distillation columns. Plate columns are more expensive to construct than packed columns, but they have other advantages, such as the ability to handle very high liquid rates, being easier to clean, more amenable to interstage cooling or heating, and having a lower total weight. Turbogrid[43] and sieveplate columns can also be used for gas absorption. These are sometimes cheaper to construct than the traditional bubble cap type columns, and may be more effective.

(3) The gas can be passed through a simple packed column. This is the most common equipment used for absorption, and will be more fully discussed below.

(4) Spray towers: These are widely used for the collection of particles and their design for this purpose is discussed in Chapter 9. Contrary to what might be expected they are sometimes used for gas absorption where there is a high liquid film resistance,[442] because the circulation within the drops presents fresh surfaces for absorption to take place. In general, however, spray towers cannot be used for absorbing high concentrations because of the low liquid–gas ratio that can be maintained. They have the advantage that they do not easily block up because of their open construction, have a very low pressure drop and can be operated at high gas rates, particularly when a cyclonic spray eliminator is employed.

Packed columns are constructed very simply (Fig. 3.4) with the packing either randomly distributed or stacked in an empty tower. It is supported above the gas entry and the liquid runs down over it. The packing may simply be broken rock or stone, or take the form of rings (Raschig rings, Lessing rings, Pall or Dixon rings) saddles (Berl saddles, Intalox saddles, McMahon saddles), grids (wood or carbon) or a number of other types of tower filling packing such as wooden slats and Spraypack,[323] which consists of an expanded metal mesh structure filling the column. Rings smaller than 2 in. dia., and saddles are usually randomly poured into the column, while larger rings are carefully stacked, particularly if they are fragile. The packing rings can be metal, glass, ceramic or plastic, depending on the corrosive conditions in the tower. The liquid must be carefully distributed in order to wet all the packing, particularly near the top. Spray

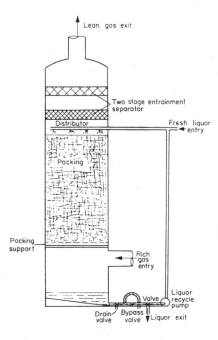

FIG. 3.4. Components in a packed tower.

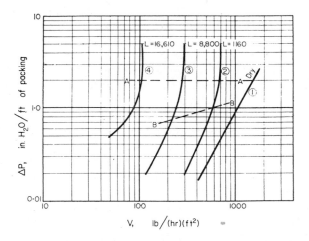

FIG. 3.5. Relation between gas flow rate (V), liquid flow rate (L), and pressure drop (Δp) in a packed column.[27]

AA — The flooding point line,
BB — The loading point line.

eliminators must also be provided. The packing support must be sufficiently strong mechanically to carry both the packing and liquid if this should fill the column during flooding, and its structure must also be more open than the packing so that it does not become flooded and hold up the gas or liquid.

The diameter of an absorption column is determined by two factors, the first being a satisfactory rate of relative liquid and gas flow, and the second

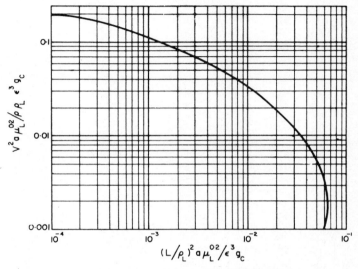

FIG. 3.6. Correlation of flooding rates.[313]

L = mass velocity of liquid (lb/hr. ft^2).
V = mass velocity of gas (lb/hr. ft^2).
μ_L = viscosity of liquid (centipoise).
ϱ = gas density (lb/ft^3).
ϱ_L = liquid density (lb/ft^3).
a = specific surface area of packing (ft^2/ft^3).
ϵ = porosity of packing (dimensionless).
g = 4·17 × 10^8 (ft. lb (mass)/lb (force). hr^2).

being the most economic tower dimensions. At low liquid and gas flow rates, an orderly trickling of the liquid over the packing is observed. When the gas rate increases, the pressure drop increases, and a point occurs when some of the liquid is held in the packing (liquid hold up). This is the *loading point*. At a higher gas rate *flooding* occurs, and the pressure rises very quickly as is shown in Fig. 3.5. The point where this happens is the *flooding point*, which has been shown to be a characteristic of the viscosity of liquid as well as of the density and mass flow rates of the liquid and gas. The flooding rates of a large number of fluids and packing materials have been correlated (Fig. 3.6),[313] and can be determined in a particular case by using

TABLE 3.1. CHARACTERISTICS OF SOME COMMON PACKINGS

Packing	Porosity $\in$%	Specific surface a (ft²)/(ft³)	Number per ft³	Dumped Wt. lb/ft³
Raschig rings (ceramic)— in.				
¼	73	250	88,000	48
½	64	111	10,500	52
1	73	58	1,350	45
2	74	28	162	40
Intalox saddles (ceramic)— in.				
¼	75	300	117,500	42
½	78	190	20,700	45
1	78	78	2,385	34
2	79	36	265	33
Pall rings (metal)— in.				
1	93·4	66·3	1,520	33
2	94·0	36·6	210	27·5

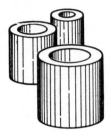

(a) Raschig rings

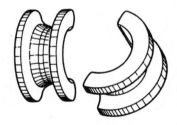

(b) Intalox saddles

(c) Pall rings

this curve. Appropriate data for some common packings are listed in Table 3.1.

It is usual to operate columns at gas flow rates less than 50-60 per cent of the flooding point rate; and this determines the minimum tower diameter. A more rapid graphical method for the minimum tower diameter is based on similar principles and has recently been published by Chen.[93] Here the tower diameter D (based on 50 per cent of flooding rate) can be found from

$$D = 16 \cdot 28 \left(\frac{V}{\varphi L} \right)^{0 \cdot 5} \left(\frac{\varrho_L}{\varrho} \right)^{0 \cdot 25} \tag{3.46}$$

where V = gas flow rate (lb/hr)

and the function φ can be obtained from Fig. 3.7.

Once the minimum tower diameter has been found, the design diameter has to be based on economic considerations, so long as these indicate that the most economical diameter is not less than this minimum.

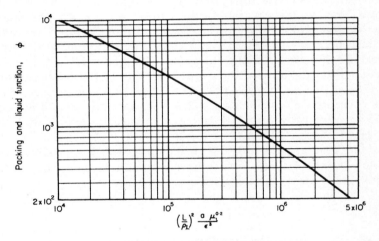

FIG. 3.7. Correlation for calculating tower diameter based on 50 per cent of flooding rate.[93]

φ = correlation parameter.
Other notation as in Fig. 3.6.

The type of packing has to be decided. This has to withstand corrosive conditions within the tower when they exist. The more complex packing materials with a larger effective surface area are more expensive, but require a smaller tower for the same duty. The cost of a tower shell is found to increase approximately with the square of the shell diameter. However, a wider tower requires a shallower packing, with a lower pressure loss for the gas flow, reducing fan power requirements. A balance of these factors will give the most economic tower diameter, and this should be chosen if it gives a gas rate of less than 50 per cent of the flooding rate. If the most economic diameter is less than this, the minimum applicable to the design requirements should be chosen.

✻ 3.7. GAS ABSORPTION PROCESSES ✻

3.7.1. Sulphur dioxide (SO₂)

Sulphur dioxide is the most common gaseous air pollutant because of the wide occurrence of sulphur in fuels and mineral ores. The problem has two aspects. In the treatment of sulphur bearing minerals (lead, zinc, copper, tin and other ores) sulphur constitutes a major part of the ore, and this is released during sintering and smelting as sulphur dioxide in high concentrations which causes considerable damage, even at a large distance from the point of release. This occurred in the state of Washington, the cause being the smelter gases from Trail in British Columbia, just across the United States border. Damages of over $ 420,000 were awarded against the Consolidated Mining and Smelting Co. of Canada Limited[262] up to 1937. In cases like these treatment of the smelter and sinter plant waste gases is imperative. Restrictions in many parts of the United States stipulate that the stack concentration of sulphur dioxide from a smelter should not exceed 0·75 per cent by volume, while the Los Angeles County specifies 0·20 per cent.[255]

Much more general is the problem of sulphur dioxide from combustion gases from power generation. Here the concentration of sulphur dioxide is much lower, as is shown in the values in Table 3.2.

TABLE 3.2. CONCENTRATIONS OF SULPHUR DIOXIDE
IN COMBUSTION WASTE GASES
(USING 15% EXCESS AIR IN COMBUSTION)

	% sulphur	SO₂ in flue gas %
Coal	1	0·11
Coal	4	0·35
Fuel oil	2	0·12
Fuel oil	5	0·31

The quantity of sulphur dioxide pr uced is however very large. A coal fired station burning 3,000 tons of coal with 2 per cent sulphur per day produces 120 tons of sulphur dioxide. The treatment of the enormous quantities of waste gases from power stations has been attempted in several cases, but no really satisfactory solution which is generally applicable has so far been found.

The absorption of sulphur dioxide from smelter gases has been satisfactorily tackled in several ways. Unfortunately sulphur dioxide is only slightly soluble in water (Fig. 3.8), but it is readily soluble in alkaline solutions. Those actually used contain ammonia, xylidine or dimethyl aniline,

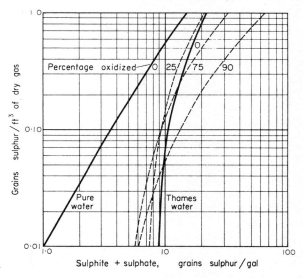

FIG. 3.8. Solubility of sulphur dioxide in water and in dilute alkaline solution such as Thames River water.[392(a)]

Solubility with various degrees of oxidation in alkaline solution are also given (broken lines).

Temperature: 40°C or 105°F.

Gas volumes have been reduced to N.T.P.

although numerous other amines have been suggested.[46] The Lurgi "Sulphidine Process" uses a 1:1 xylidine–water mixture as the absorbent and produces pure sulphur dioxide, which can be used in other processes such as sulphuric acid manufacture. Toluidine has also been tried, but not found as successful. Xylidine and water are normally immissible, but as sulphur dioxide reacts with the xylidine, some xylidine sulphate, which is water soluble, is formed, and when the concentration of sulphur dioxide approached 100 g/l. the mixture becomes homogeneous. An equilibrium curve for the sulphur dioxide–xylidine water system is shown in Fig. 3.9. Essentially the process consists of absorbing the sulphur dioxide in the xylidine–water mixture. Sodium carbonate (soda ash) solution is added to convert the xylidine sulphate formed to sodium sulphate, and the sulphur dioxide is stripped off in a column heated to 95–100 °C. This sulphur dioxide, with some xylidine, is water washed to produce pure sulphur dioxide. Some dilute sulphuric acid is used to recover xylidine vapours from the exhaust gases. When a gas containing 8 per cent sulphur dioxide is used, the concentration after

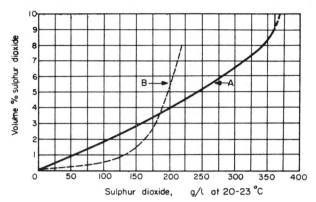

FIG. 3.9. Absorption isotherms for sulphur dioxide in
(A) Anhydrous dimethyl aniline.
(B) 1:1; xylidine–water mixture.[154]
(Basis of Sulphidine process.)

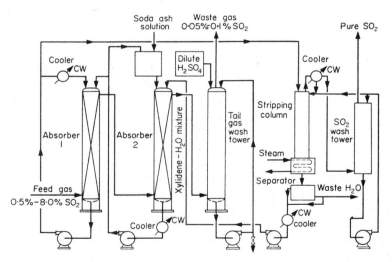

FIG. 3.10. Flow sheet of sulphidine process:[267] absorption of sulphur dioxide in xylidine–water mixtures.

scrubbing is reduced to 0·05–0·10 per cent sulphur dioxide. At low sulphur dioxide concentrations the process ceases to be economical because of the losses of xylidine. A flow sheet is shown in Fig. 3.10.

The dimethylaniline process, developed by the American Smelting and Refining Company, and known as the ASARCO process, also produces pure sulphur dioxide.[154] Particulate impurities are first removed from the gases, using electrostatic precipitation (Chapter 10) and the gases are then scrubbed with pure dimethylaniline. The equilibrium diagram (Fig. 3.9)

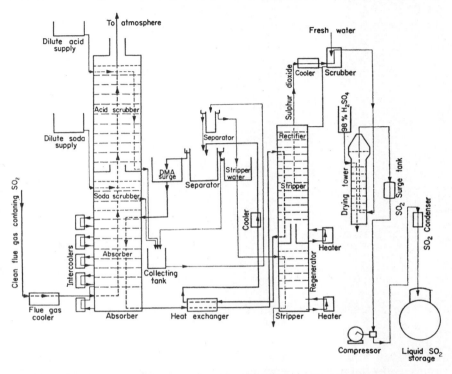

FIG. 3.11. Flow sheet of ASARCO process: absorption of sulphur dioxide in dimethyl aniline solution.[154]

shows that dimethylaniline is a more efficient absorber than the xylidine–water mixture for sulphur dioxide concentrations greater than about 3·5 per cent; although at lower concentrations the xylidine water mixtures have an economic advantage. The waste gases are scrubbed with sodium carbonate solution to remove traces of sulphur dioxide and dimethylaniline, and also with dilute sulphuric acid which absorbs the last traces of dimethylaniline. The sulphur dioxide rich liquors are passed to a steam distillation column which strips the sulphur dioxide from the liquors, and the gases are then passed to a scrubber, to remove the dimethylaniline, a drying tower to remove moisture, and then to a sulphur dioxide storage for further processing, such as acid manufacture.

A plant constructed at Selby, California, with a capacity of 20 tons/day (sulphur dioxide) recovers 99 per cent of the sulphur dioxide in the waste gases from a Dwight–Lloyd sintering machine which contains 5 per cent sulphur dioxide. It uses 1·1 lb dimethylaniline, 35 lb of sodium carbonate and 40 lb of sulphuric acid per ton of sulphur dioxide produced, as well as 2400 lb of steam and 145 kWh of power, and cooling water at the rate of 300 gal/min (65°F). A flow diagram of the process is shown in Fig. 3.11.

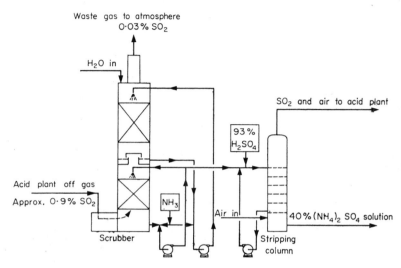

FIG. 3.12. Flow sheet of COMINCO process: absorption of sulphur dioxide in ammonia solution.[267]

Bubble cap columns have been used for both absorber and stripping columns, and a number of operations such as absorbing soda and acid scrubbing are combined in each tower, reducing the cost of the plant.

Ammonia is used by the Consolidated Mining and Smelting Company at Trail, and is known as the COMINCO process, a flow diagram being shown in Fig. 3.12. The gases are passed through a two stage column filled with wooden slat packing. The absorption is carried out in a dilute ammonium sulphate solution to which ammonia is added. The sulphur dioxide is stripped from the ammonium sulphite by adding concentrated (93 per cent) sulphuric acid, producing sulphur dioxide and ammonium sulphate. The sulphur dioxide is used in further acid manufacture.

Sulphur dioxide removal from flue gases is much more difficult because of the enormous quantities of gas that have to be handled. Ordinary river water is not suitable for scrubbing, but the Thames river water is slightly alkaline and has been used for scrubbing the flue gases at the Battersea and Bankside power stations. The process is limited because the discharge from the scrubbers into the river increases the calcium sulphate concentration which will form scale in heat exchangers, as well as affecting marine life in the river. Furthermore, since the flue gases after scrubbing are cold, they will not rise and disperse the residual sulphur dioxide over a wide area, but cause heavy local pollution.

At Bankside gases from a fuel oil fired station, using oil with 3·8 per cent sulphur are scrubbed, and 95 per cent of the sulphur dioxide is removed. A

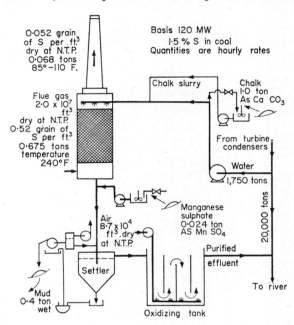

FIG. 3.13. Battersea process: absorption of sulphur dioxide in Thames River water to which an alkaline slurry has been added.[392(a)]

flow sheet of the process is shown in Fig. 3.13, and equilibrium data for sulphur dioxide Thames river water is included in Fig. 3.8. A chalk slurry is added in practice to make the river water more alkaline, and therefore more effective for scrubbing, and some manganese sulphate is added, together with air, to the effluent liquors as an oxidizing agent, so that the water can be passed back to the river as the sulphate and not the sulphite. The absorption tower consists of timber lined cast iron with grids of red cedar and teak. The aeration tanks and other parts of the plant are lined with acid resistant materials. There are, however, serious maintenance problems connected with the plant.[392(b)]

A process similar to the Battersea one, but not relying on a slightly alkaline river to provide the bulk of the alkali, is the I.C.I. — Howden Cyclic

Lime Process.[366] A lime or chalk slurry (5–10 per cent by weight) is circulated through a wooden grid absorption tower and calcium sulphite is formed, which then oxidizes to the sulphate with oxygen from the flue gases.

A flow sheet for the process is shown in Fig. 3.14. The problem of scaling which could occur with the supersaturated calcium sulphate solutions has been solved by passing the solution from the scrubber to a delay tank where

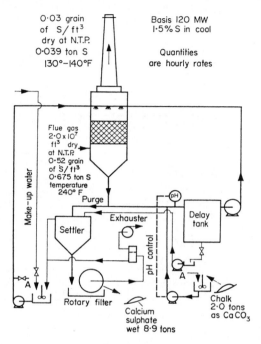

FIG. 3.14. Howden–I.C.I. cyclic lime process: absorption of sulphur dioxide in lime slurry liquor.[392(b), 366]

a slurry of lime, adjusted for pH is added. Here the excess calcium sulphate crystallizes on the existing crystals, before the solution is re-cycled back through the tower. Some of the crystalline slurry is passed to a settling tank and the crystals are removed. No use is made of these, because they are contaminated with fly ash, but an ammonium carbonate digestion, which would yield ammonium sulphate, has been suggested.[161]

The other process which has been applied on a large scale (flue gas rate 56,000 ft^3/min) is the Fulham–Simon–Carves process.[259, 511, 549] Here (Fig. 3.15) the flue gases are scrubbed with ammoniacal liquors from gas works. After scrubbing, some sulphuric acid (77 per cent) is added to the liquors and the mixture autoclaved at 200 psi and 170 °C for 3 hr. This produces sulphur and ammonium sulphate.

The overall equation is:

$$2\,NH_4HSO_3 + (NH_4)_2S_2O_3 = 2\,(NH_4)_2SO_4 + 2\,S + H_2O.$$

The first plant was installed at the Fulham power station in 1939, and a second large plant is at the North Wilford Power Station (Nottingham) where it was tested in 1957.

The relative economics of the three flue gas washing processes which have been operated indicate that the Howden–I.C.I. cyclic lime process is the

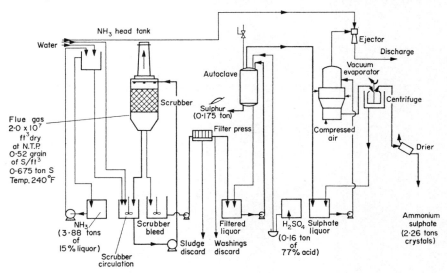

FIG. 3.15. Fulham–Simon–Carves process: absorption of sulphur dioxide in ammonia liquor from gas works or coke ovens, with production of sulphur and ammonium sulphate.[392(b), 259]

cheapest to operate if no suitable river or source of cheap ammonia is available. If ammonia is readily available, for example as a by-product from a gasworks, then the Fulham–Simon–Carves process is the most economic.

Other possible processes include contacting the flue gases with sodium sulphite and bisulphite, which increases the bisulphite content.

$$SO_2 + NaHSO_3 + Na_2SO_3 + H_2O = 3\,NaHSO_3$$

The solution is then reacted with zinc oxide, giving zinc sulphite.

$$NaHSO_3 + ZnO = ZnSO_3\,(ppte.) + NaOH.$$

This is then calcined to give zinc oxide and sulphur dioxide which can be used for other processes.[245]

$$ZnSO_3 = ZnO + SO_2.$$

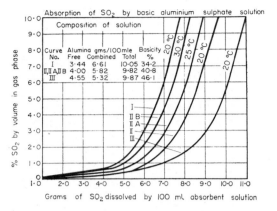

(a) Absorption isotherms of sulphur dioxide in basic aluminium sulphate solution.

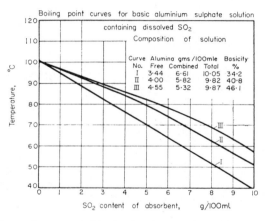

(b) Boiling point curves of basic aluminium sulphate solution containing dissolved sulphur dioxide (for steam stripping).

FIG. 3.16. I.C.I.—Basic aluminium sulphate process.[19]

Basic aluminium sulphate has also been used as an absorbent, with recovery of the sulphur dioxide, by stripping in a steam heated column (Fig. 3.16b).[19] The equilibrium diagram for the sulphur dioxide–basic aluminium sulphate system is shown in Fig. 3.16a. This process was developed by I.C.I. and put into operation at the Imatra Smelter of the Outokumpu Copper Company. The gases are first scrubbed with water to remove particulate impurities and then passed through 4 absorption towers, each with 35 ft of wooden grid packing, the liquid moving counter-currently as shown in Fig. 3.16c (where only 3 towers are shown). The saturated liquors, containing 60 g/l. of sulphur dioxide then passed to a pre-heater and on to the sulphur dioxide regenerator. To resist corrosion, the plant is constructed throughout of lead lined equipment, acid resisting brick covered with lead sheet, or wood for the grids in the absorption towers.

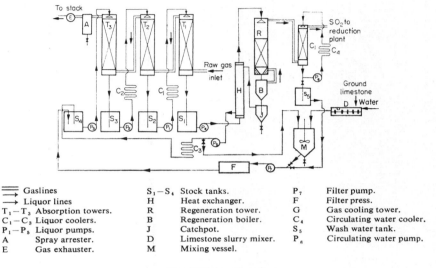

≡ Gaslines	$S_1 - S_4$ Stock tanks.	P_7	Filter pump.
→ Liquor lines	H	Heat exchanger.	F	Filter press.
$T_1 - T_3$ Absorption towers.	R	Regeneration tower.	G	Gas cooling tower.
$C_1 - C_3$ Liquor coolers.	B	Regeneration boiler.	C_4	Circulating water cooler.
$P_1 - P_5$ Liquor pumps.	J	Catchpot.	S_5	Wash water tank.
A	Spray arrester.	D	Limestone slurry mixer.	P_6	Circulating water pump.
E	Gas exhauster.	M	Mixing vessel.		

FIG. 3.16 (*continued*)

(c) Flow sheet for Outokumpu plant (only three absorption towers of the four erected are shown).

3.7.2. Fluorine and fluoride compounds (HF, SiF$_4$)

Hydrofluoric acid gas (HF), silicon tetrafluoride (SiF$_4$) and the combination of these, fluosilicic acid (H$_2$SiF$_6$) are emitted with the waste gases from superphosphate fertilizer manufacture, when the phosphate rock is treated with sulphuric acid in "dens"; in the smelting of aluminium when fluorspar (CaF$_2$) is used as a flux; in the electrolytic manufacture of aluminium, where aluminium oxide (alumina Al$_2$O$_3$) is fused in cryolite (Na$_3$AlF$_6$) at 900–1000 °C and electrolysed; and in calcium metaphosphate furnaces. As was seen in Chapter 2, very low concentrations of fluorides (of the order of one part per hundred million) may damage vegetation, and somewhat higher concentrations may lead to chronic fluoride poisoning of sheep and cattle, so fluorine emissions have to be carefully controlled. Fortunately, as is shown in the equilibrium diagrams (Figs. 3.17a and 3.17b) both hydrogen fluoride and fluosilic acid (with which silicon tetrafluoride is in equilibrium) are very readily soluble in water, and water scrubbing is

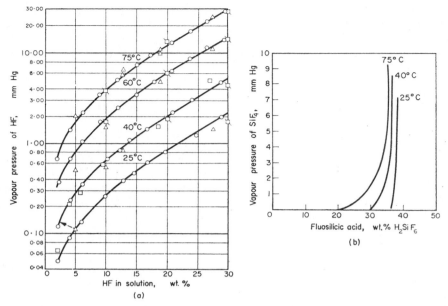

Fig. 3.17. Equilibrium diagrams for aqueous hydrofluoric and fluorsilicic acid solutions.[539]

(a) Partial pressure of hyorogen fluoride over hydrofluoric acid solutions.[539]

(b) Partial pressure of silicon tetrafluoride over aqueous solutions of fluorsilicic acid (H_2SiF_6).[539]

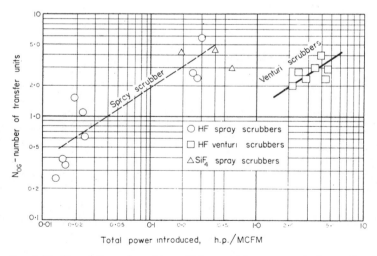

Fig. 3.18. Correlation of scrubber efficiency with respect to hydrogen fluoride with power input. Scrubber efficiency is given in transfer units.[317] Points for silicon tetrafluoride are based on data by Pettit and Sherwin.[267]

nearly always effective in reducing the fluoride concentration to an acceptable value.

Counter-current spray towers, co-current flow spray towers, venturi scrubbers, wet cell washers and packed towers have all been used in actual plants or pilot plants for treatment of these gases.

Lunde's correlations of power consumption with the number of transfer units, N, for spray scrubbers and venturi scrubbers is shown in Fig. 3.18. These can be converted into efficiencies (Appendix III). A simple counter-flow scrubber working on a nodulizing kiln was found to be 97 per cent efficient.[325] Other data on this particular plant are given in Table 3.3.

TABLE 3.3.[325] DATA FOR SIMPLE COUNTERFLOW SCRUBBER ON A NODULIZING KILN

Tower height	80 ft
Tower diameter	1 ft 6 ins
No. of spray injection points	6
Water flow	700 gal/min
Gas inlet temperature	300°C
Gas exit temperature	72°C
Gas inlet rate	52,000 ft³/min
Gas exit rate	26,500 ft³/min
Hydrogen fluoride inlet rate	4,000 lb fluorine/day
Hydrogen fluoride exit rate	97 lb fluorine/day
Hydrogen fluoride removal efficiency	97·6%
Sodium fluoride dust inlet rate	340 lb flourine/day
Sodium fluoride dust exit rate	14 lb fluorine/day
Sodium fluoride collection efficiency	96%
Hydrated lime (neutralizing agent) used	24,000 lb/day (1,000 lb/hr)

Wet cell washers, where the cells consist of coarse and fine fibres, have been tested by First *et al.*[153] One unit, shown in Fig. 3.19, consisted of three stages:

Stage 1. An 8 in. wet cell, with 255 micron Saran fibres using 9·2 gal water per minute.

Stage 2. A fibre glass (10 micron fibre) pad, 20 in. × 27 in., 2 in. deep, packed to 0·46 lb/ft³ (dry).

Stage 3. One wet cell and one dry pad in series.

The gas flow rate was 600 ft³/min and the pad resistance 2·46–2·77 in. W.G. (water gauge).

With concentrations of 50–200 mg/m³ of hydrofluoric acid, the cumulative efficiency of the stages was 94, 97 and 99·5 per cent. A unit using two similar wet cells, but with a lower gas rate of 108 ft³/min and water flows of 9·6 gal/min (cell) gave efficiencies of better than 99 per cent.

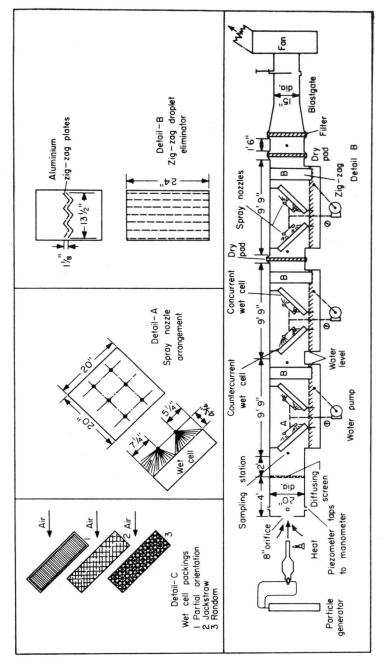

Fig. 3.19. Wet cell washer for hydrogen fluoride containing gases.[153]

A floating bed scrubber (section 9.6) where the bed consists of lightweight moulded plastic spheres has been used successfully on the fluoride containing waste gases from alumina electrolysis[260]: 95 per cent efficiency in fluoride removal has been obtained with a 1-ft deep bed of hollow polyethylene spheres and a superficial velocity of 500 ft/min, resulting in operating pressure drops of $3\frac{1}{2}$–4 in. W.G.

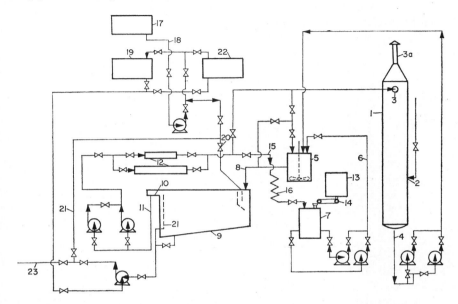

Fig. 3.20. Flowsheet for fluorine and hydrogen fluoride containing effluent gases.[291]

The fluorine-containing gases are introduced to a packed absorption tower, 1, through nozzle 2. The tower is fed with a counter-current stream of 5 – 10 per cent sodium hydroxide solution, which is introduced at the top of the tower through nozzle 3. Inert gas is vented through stack 3a. The effluent liquid from the tower, containing sodium fluoride in solution, is continuously withdrawn from the tower through line 4, and passed into a regeneration tank, 5, to which is supplied, through line 6, a small stream of lime slurry which enters from slaker 7. In the regeneration tank, 5, the sodium fluoride formed is converted to calcium fluoride by reaction with lime, under conditions of good agitation. The mixture flows through line 8 into a settling tank 9, wherein the calcium fluoride and excess lime are settled out. The clear, regenerated liquor overflows weir 10 and is discharged through line 11 back to the absorption tower 1.

In order to maintain temperature control on the tower, the discharge from settling tank 9 first passes through a heat exchange system, 12. This system is automatically regulated to maintain a constant temperature of 100 – 150° F on the tower feed.

The lime slurry is prepared by the addition of lime (quick or hydrated) from bin 13 to tank 7, using belt feeder 14. The slaking or slurrying medium is a portion of fresh tower feed recycled to tank 7 through line 15. This solution may be cooled by passage through exchanger 16.

Incoming 50 per cent sodium hydroxide solution is pumped from tank car 17 through line 18 to storage tank 19, which is partially filled with water to make a 25 per cent solution. Make-up alkali can be withdrawn from 19 as needed and pumped through line 20 to the settling tank, 9.

When sufficient solids have accumulated in the settling tank, the clear liquor is decanted off through a swing pipe and pumped through line 21 to decantation tank 22. After the settling tank has been cleaned, the clear liquor returned thereto from the decantation tank, 22.

Waste solids in the settling tank may be removed by adding sufficient water to make a slurry, and pumping through 23 to disposal.

When fluorine gas is present, the use of water should be avoided because the fluorine does not always react with water, and also because explosions have occurred in some systems. In this case sodium hydroxide in 5–10 per cent concentrations has been found to be a satisfactory absorbent. A flow sheet for a commercial fluorine and hydrogen fluoride disposal plant is shown in Fig. 3.20.[291]

The sodium hydroxide solutions are passed down through a packed column at 100–150 °F. Caustic concentrations below 2 per cent are avoided

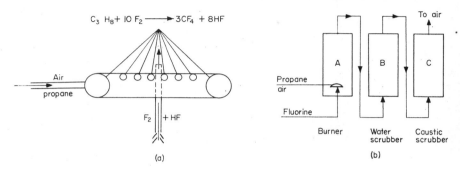

FIG. 3.21. Fluorine and hydrogen fluoride gas combustion and absorption.[498]

(a) Ring burner fed with air–propane mixture.
(b) Absorption process flow sheet.

as this leads to the formation of fluorine oxide (OF_2), which is extremely poisonous. This compound is also formed when the contact time between gas and caustic is about 1 sec, and minimum contact times of 1 min are recommended,[290] when the fluorine and hydrogen fluoride both react with caustic soda to form sodium fluoride (NaF):

$$F_2 + 2\,NaOH = \tfrac{1}{2}O_2 + 2\,NaF + H_2O$$

$$HF + NaOH = 2NaF + H_2O.$$

The sodium fluoride is then treated with lime to regenerate the sodium hydroxide.

$$2\,NaF + CaO + H_2O = CaF_2\,(ppte) + 2\,NaOH.$$

Other reasons for this regenerative stage are that sodium fluoride, which has limited solubility in the caustic system, is an objectionable contaminant leading to plugging and eroding of the equipment, and also because it is poisonous, and could not be discharged with the effluent water without further treatment.

This process can be used where there is residual fluorine and hydrogen fluoride after preparing fluorocarbons, before these are passed on to further treatment. The other possibility of removing fluorine, when this occurs in process waste gases, is to burn it with hydrocarbon gases, in particular hydrogen, to form hydrogen fluoride, which can then be absorbed in water. A system showing a special fluorine burner and a scrubber system incorporating this is shown in Figs. 3.21a and 3.21b.[498]

Materials of construction are a problem with fluorine hydrogen fluoride gas and other fluorides. Absorption columns are either of wood with wooden grid packing or moulded plastic. Carbon bricks have also been found to be a satisfactory lining for gases containing elemental fluorine. Nickel and nickel alloys such as Monel can be used because a nickel fluoride film forms which protects the metal. In the case of steel, the iron fluoride is a powdery, nonadhesive material, and so steels are not usually used in contact with these gases, particularly at elevated temperatures.

3.7.3. Chlorine and chlorides

The absorption of hydrochloric acid gas in water, in which it is very soluble, is a standard process in the manufacture of hydrochloric acid. Chlorides are found in the waste gases of smelting aluminium; from scrap where salt (NaCl) is used as a flux, and similar processes, while the absorption of elemental chlorine is an essential stage in the purification of this gas before further processing.

The absorption of hydrochloric acid vapour generates a considerable amount of heat, and so cooling has to be provided. The process is usually a two stage one,[104] where a cooler–absorber, frequently of carbon, is used in the first stage, and the tail gases are then passed through a packed tower with stoneware packing for the removal of the last traces of the acid gas. Equilibrium data for the system given in Table 3.4.

TABLE 3.4. EQUILIBRIUM DATA FOR HYDROGEN CHLORIDE GAS AND WATER[228]

Wts. of HCl per 100 weights of H_2O	Partial Pressure of HCl, mm Hg (Torr)				
	10°C	30°C	50°C	80°C	110°C
78·6	840	—	—	—	—
66.7	233	627	—	—	—
56·3	56·4	188	535	—	—
47·0	11·8	44·5	141	623	—
38·9	2·27	9·90	35·7	188	760
31·6	0·43	2·17	8·9	54·5	253
25·0	0·084	0·48	2·21	15·6	83
19·05	0·016	0·106	0·55	4·66	28
13·64	0·00305	0·0234	0·136	1·34	9·3
8·70	0·000583	0·00515	0·0344	0·39	3·10
4·17	0·000069	0·00077	0·0064	0·095	0·93
2·04	0·0000117	0·000151	0·00140	0·0245	0·280

The chlorides usually encountered from smelting and other processes are not gaseous but very fine crystals, which can be collected by methods such as scrubbing, settling or filtration of the gases, depending on the circumstances.

Chlorine itself may be collected by scrubbing the gases with water. The reactions which occur are complex, and are discussed in detail elsewhere.[443]

As with the fluorides materials of construction are a major problem. Carbon steels and stainless steels are not suitable, but at low temperatures rubber lined towers with stoneware packing may be used. Nickel, silver and tantalum metal alloys can also be used.

3.7.4. Hydrogen sulphide

Natural gas, refinery gas and coal gas, all of which are used for industrial and domestic heating as well as chemical processing, contain hydrogen sulphide as their major sulphur impurity. Depending on their source they may also contain smaller concentrations of carbon disulphide (CS_2), carbonyl sulphide (COS), thiophene (C_4H_4S) and thiols (mercaptans; RSH), pyridine bases, hydrogen cyanide, carbon dioxide and ammonia. Hydrogen sulphide also occurs in the waste gases from the evaporation of kraft pulping liquors and smelting operations. Process or fuel gases which contain hydrogen sulphide are corrosive when cooled below their dew point, have an objectionable odour, cause difficulties in steel making and heat treatment, and create other problems. It is therefore necessary to remove hydrogen sulphide and some of the other compounds from these gases. Some municipalities require hydrogen sulphide concentrations as low as 0·005 gr./ft³ for domestic gas, although concentrations of 0·15–0·30 gr./ft³ are often allowed. For metallurgical processes higher concentrations, of the order of 0·5 gr./ft³ are generally permissible.[180]

Because of the economic importance of hydrogen sulphide removal a large number of processes have been developed. As these have been fully described by Kohl and Riesenfeld[267] they will only be reviewed briefly here.

The most common process for purifying (or sweetening, as this is sometimes called) natural and refinery gases, which contain small quantities of carbon disulphide and carbonyl sulphide and no ammonia are the ethanolamine or Girbotol processes (named after the Girdler Corporation). Essentially, hydrogen sulphide and carbon dioxide, both of which are present, are absorbed in a bubble column in an aqueous solution of the ethanolamine, forming a complex at low temperatures, which is then passed to a stripping column where, on heating, the acid gases are regenerated and the ethanolamine solution returned to the absorption column (Fig. 3.22a). The first compound to be used was triethanolamine (TEA), but it was subsequently found that for the absorption of both carbon dioxide and hy-

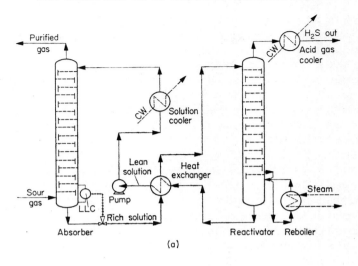

(a)

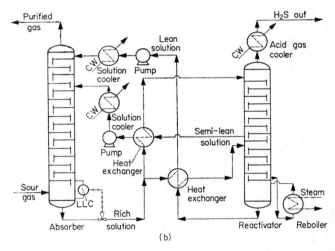

(b)

FIG. 3.22. Girbotol process.[391]

(a) Basic flow diagram.
(b) Modified Girbotol process, using split streams to reduce steam consumption.

drogen sulphide, a 15–20 per cent aqueous solution of monoethanolamine (MEA) was more suitable as it has a higher capacity per unit weight of solvent, a higher reactivity and is more easily regenerated. Its disadvantages are that it forms a heat stable compound with carbonyl sulphide, diethanolurea $(CO(NHCH_2CH_2)_2)$ resulting in loss of amine, and that it has a relatively high vapour pressure, requiring the scrubbing of the acid gas after stripping to remove entrained Monoethanolamide vapour. Monoethaol-amine is therefore commonly used for natural gas sweetening, while the diethanolamine (DEA), which does not form diethanolurea is used for refinery gases, where some carbonyl sulphide is present besides being less volatile and so reducing losses. Dipropanolamine is also used. Monoethanol-treatment of natural gas lowers the hydrogen sulphide concentration below 0·0025 gr./ft^3, which is a satisfactory level, even for the most stringent domestic requirements. When selective absorption of hydrogen sulphide in the presence of carbon dioxide is required, triethanolamine or methyldiethanolamine (MDEA) (30 per cent aqueous solutions) is used.

If dry hydrogen sulphide is required, scrubbing with water cannot be used to recover the volatilized amine, and diethylene glycol (or sometimes tri-ethylene glycol) is used instead as a scrubbing liquor. Owing to the large scale operation of these processes, it is economically advantageous to reduce steam requirements for stripping, and to improve the recovery of heat. This has been achieved by modifications such as carrying out the initial absorption in a heat exchanger and using a split stream stripping method where only a part of the solution is stripped to a low acid gas concentration, reducing the quantity of vapour rising through the stripping column (Fig. 3.22b).

Coal gas, made either in vertical continuous retorts, used primarily for gas making, or in horizontal retorts, for metallurgical coke, contains, a much greater range of impurities than natural or refinery gas. (Table 3.5).

TABLE 3.5. SULPHUR COMPOUNDS
IN COAL GAS[374]

Compound	Volume %
Hydrogen sulphide	0·3–3·0
Carbon disulphide	0·007–0·07
Thiols (RSH)	0·003
Thiophene (C_4H_4S)	0·010
Carbonyl sulphide	0·009
Hydrogen cyanide	0·10–0·25

The gases also contain about 1 per cent ammonia and 1·5–2 per cent carbon dioxide, and the presence of ammonia suggests that this could be used to give an alkaline solution in water for the absorption of hydrogen sulphide. Ammonia absorption is gas film controlled and very fast, hydrogen sulphide absorption into aqueous ammonia solutions is also gas film controlled, although not quite as rapid as the ammonia, while carbon dioxide absorp-tion into water or weakly alkaline solutions is liquid film controlled. This is therefore a process which will give the selective absorption of the two major impurities, ammonia and hydrogen sulphide, and also of some of the minor impurities such as carbonyl sulphide and hydrogen cyanide. The selective absorption, however, only results in the removal of about 90 per cent of the hydrogen sulphide, so a second scrubbing or final purification, probably with the dry iron oxide process, is necessary.

Usually the ammonia produced will not remove more than 30–50 per cent of the hydrogen sulphide, and it is necessary to strip some of the acid gas and re-cycle the aqueous ammonia. The removal of sulphide and ammonia, together with the re-cycle (in broken lines) is shown in Fig. 3.23.

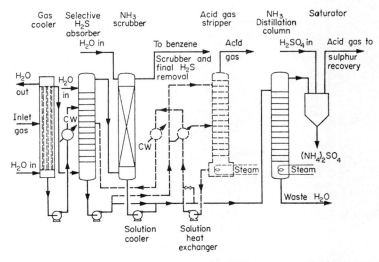

FIG. 3.23. Removal of hydrogen sulphide and ammonia.[267]

Typical flow diagram showing selective hydrogen sulphide removal process without solution re-cycle (solid lines) and with partial solution re-cycle (dotted lines); indirect ammonium sulphate recovery process.

The end product is ammonium sulphate, and hydrogen sulphide gas, which can be turned into the acid for adding in the process for ammonium sulphate, as well as sulphur.

There are a number of variants of this process; for example, it is possible, by using concentrated ammonia solutions, to absorb the hydrogen sulphate in the first stage, and then pass the ammonia on to a second absorber (Collin Process). The acid gas is then stripped from the concentrated ammonia solution (Fig. 3.24). The details of these processes are discussed elsewhere.[267]

Sodium carbonate (3–3½ per cent aqueous solution) is used to absorb hydrogen sulphide in a number of processes developed by the Koppers Co. Inc. These are based on the reaction

$$Na_2CO_3 + H_2S = NaHCO_3 + NaHS.$$

In the first of these processes, the Seaboard process, a large quantity of air is used to strip the hydrogen sulphide from the absorbent. The hydrogen sulphide cannot be recovered, and some of the sodium sulphide is oxidized to thiosulphate, leading to a weakening of the absorption liquors, which have to be replaced at intervals. The more recent development of these processes is the Vacuum Carbonate process, where the hydrogen sulphide

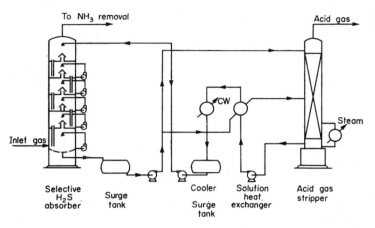

FIG. 3.24. Collin process:[267] selective absorption of hydrogen sulphide with total liquid re-cycle.

is stripped under reduced pressure (25 in. Hg), lowering the steam required for stripping by reducing the weight required for the removal of hydrogen sulphide. This reduces the sensible heat requirement, as the stripping can be at nearly the same temperature as the absorption, and also enables the use of low pressure steam for the reactivation stage. A flow sheet of this process is shown in Fig. 3.25.

An alternative to the Girbotol process is a process which was developed by Shell and uses a 40 per cent aqueous solution of potassium phosphate (K_3PO_4) as absorbent instead of the ethanolamines:

$$K_3PO_4 + H_2S = K_2HPO_4 + KHS.$$

This process has the advantage that the phosphate is more stable than the ethanolamines, the process is more selective towards hydrogen sulphide in the presence of carbon dioxide, and in addition live steam can be used to strip the hydrogen sulphide although steam consumption is somewhat greater.

The Alkacid processes, used in Germany on a large scale since before 1939, use an inorganic alkali combined with a weak, non-volatile, organic acid. Three solutions, designated "M", "Dik" and "S" are used, depending on the application. Solution M, which contains sodium alanine, is used for either hydrogen sulphide, carbon dioxide or both; Dik, which contains the potassium salt of dimethyl glycine, is used for hydrogen sulphide in the presence of carbon dioxide; while "S" which contains sodium phenolate, can be used when the gases contain hydrogen cyanide, ammonia, carbon disulphide, thiols and tars. The former reagents M and Dik, are very corrosive, while a similar phenolate process, developed by the Koppers Corporation, had severe operating difficulties.

Water itself can be used for hydroden sulphide absorption, but the rate of absorption is such that unless the size of the plant required for effective absorption were so large as to be uneconomic, the degree of removal would be inadequate.

In all of the above processes, the regeneration of the absorbing solution results in the production of hydrogen sulphide. However, a useful step would

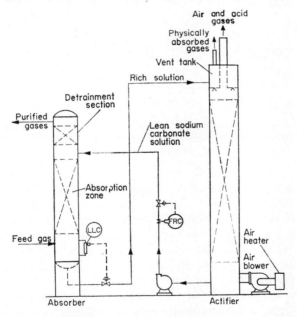

FIG. 3.25. Seabord process:[267] hydrogen sulphide recovery by absorption in dilute sodium carbonate solution and regeneration by air.

be the production of elemental sulphur by oxidation, particularly in the case of coal gas purification, where sulphuric acid is required to precipitate ammonium sulphate. This would have to be supplied by an external source, if no sulphur, which can be made into sulphuric acid, were available. The most important processes in this group use atmospheric oxygen as the oxidizing agent in the presence of a catalyst such as iron oxide, (Ferrox,

Gluud and Manchester Processes) nickel sulphate (Nickel process) sodium thioarsenate (Thylox process), iron cyanide (Fischer and Staatsmijnen–Otto processes) or organic oxidation catalysts such as hydroquinone (Perox process).

There are several iron oxide processes: the Ferrox, developed by Koppers Co. in the United States; the Gluud, in Germany; and the Manchester process, developed by the Manchester Corporation Gas Department in

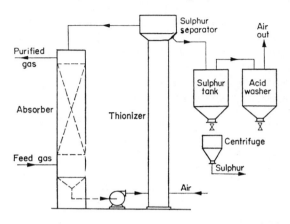

FIG. 3.26. Gluud process:[267] absorption of hydrogen sulphide in dilute ammonium carbonate solution, followed by atmospheric oxidation for sulphur recovery, using iron oxide catalyst.

England. These are all essentially the same, using sodium or ammonium carbonate solution (3 per cent) to absorb the hydrogen sulphide. The solution also contains a small concentration ($\frac{1}{2}$ per cent) of ferric oxide, which acts as a catalyst in the oxidation of the hydrogen sulphide in the regeneration stage which takes place, in the case of the Ferrox process, in a fairly shallow tank where very fine bubbles of air are bubbled through the solution, while in the case of the Gluud and Manchester processes, very tall aeration towers (60–100 ft) are used. The sulphur, on formation, clings to the rising air bubbles and is then scooped off as a froth. The essential difference between the Ferrox, Gluud and Manchester processes is that the first two use single stage contact, while multi-stage washing with fresh solution in each washing stage is used in the Manchester process, as well as separate delay vessels to ensure complete reaction. In these processes a considerable amount of iron oxide is collected together with the sulphur in the froth, leading to a poor sulphur product as well as reagent losses. A flow sheet of the Gluud process is shown in Fig. 3.26.

The Thylox process uses sodium thioarsenate as both absorbing and oxidizing solution. The sulphur yield from this process is larger, and the reagent losses lower than in the iron oxide catalysed processes. The main reactions are

(a) Absorption
$$H_2S + Na_4As_2S_5O_2 = Na_4As_2S_6O + H_2O$$

(b) Regeneration
$$2Na_4As_2S_6O + O_2 = 2Na_4As_2S_5O_2 + S.$$

The process equipment requirements are similar to the iron oxide processes, as is seen from the flow sheet (Fig. 3.27).

The processes using ferrocyanide complexes are fairly complicated chemically, and because of their limited utilization will not be discussed further here. The Perox process appears to be coming into favour, particularly in Germany, for large scale application, but it is essentially the same as the other oxidation processes discussed.

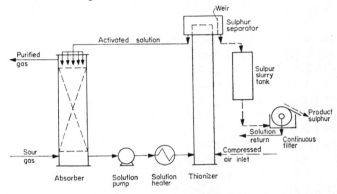

FIG. 3.27. Thylox process: absorption of hydrogen sulphide in sodium thio-arsenate, with atmospheric oxidation of the sodium thioarsenate complex $(Na_4As_2S_6O)$.[391]

In considering which process to use for removing hydrogen sulphide from process or waste gases, the initial concentration and the degree of removal required, the presence of other impurities, and whether or not carbon dioxide also has to be removed are first considerations. Power and steam costs, and the costs of reagents, as well as the capital costs, which depend on the complexity of the plant and the materials of construction demanded by the corrosive nature of the liquids, will require careful assessment for the various possible processes to determine the most economic one.

3.7.5. Nitrogen compounds

The removal of ammonia from coal gas has been discussed in connection with hydrogen sulphide, and these two gases are usually absorbed together (section 3.7.4). The more complex nitrogen compounds, often referred to as the pyridine bases (pyridene, picoline, collidine, aniline and quinoline) are removed in the same scrubbing process.

The oxides of nitrogen, nitric oxide and nitrogen dioxide, being the most common, which are formed in industrial processes such as nitric acid manufacture or the pickling of metals, are fortunately readily soluble in water. They are therefore collected either in bubble cap columns with cooled trays where dilute nitric acid is a suitable absorbent, or in venturi scrubbers using water. In these scrubbers where much air is entrained in the liquid, oxidation of the nitric oxide to the dioxide is also accomplished. These processes are discussed in detail by Sherwood and Pigford[441], while experimental data on the rates of absorption of nitrogen dioxide by water have been published by Decker, Snoek and Kramers.[123]

3.8. ADSORPTION OF GASES ON SOLIDS

Since the mechanism of adsorption of gas molecules on the surface of a solid is very complex, and depends on the physical and chemical nature of the gas and the solid in each particular case, it is more difficult to deduce a general approach to the design of adsorption equipment than countercurrent absorption plant. In practice most of the designs are based either on experience with other similar plants or on pilot plants. Nonetheless an understanding of the principles is of considerable assistance in deciding whether adsorption is the best process for the removal of certain gases, in the selection of suitable adsorbing materials and in scaling up designs.

When a gas molecule is adsorbed on the surface of a solid it settles on it very much like a condensing molecule, and is then held on the surface either by physical attractive forces, (London–van der Waals forces) or in certain cases, depending on the chemical nature of the molecule and the surface, by chemical forces (chemisorption). In a particular system both types of adsorption may occur as well as intermediate types. The solids best suited to adsorption are very porous, with very large effective surface areas, which are obtained with materials such as carbon, alumina or silica gel. Some surface characteristics, as for example crystal dislocations, or oxygen atoms with unshared electron pairs available for hydrogen bond formation, assist in chemisorbing specific molecules. The exact nature of these surface characteristics is imperfectly understood and more research is required to create surface characteristics which will assist in selective chemisorption of particular molecular types or groups of molecular types. Other desirable characteristics of the adsorbing solids are that the granules should be hard, so that they do not collapse under their own weight when packed into a tower, and that they should not powder or fracture easily, so that they can be transported and poured into containers without breakage. The three solids mentioned earlier all have these properties. It is frequently a requirement that the solid, after it has been saturated with the gas molecules, can be easily regenerated and re-used.

The adsorption of a gas on a solid takes place in several stages. The first is the movement of the gas molecules to the external surface of the solid, and this is the same as the diffusion of the gas molecules through a stationary layer to the liquid–gas interface in absorption (section 3.3).

The rate of transfer N_A for this stage is expressed by an equation similar to (3.23), with appropriate allowances for the granular condition of the adsorbing material:

$$N_A = k_f \frac{A_p \epsilon}{\varrho_B} (p - p_i) \tag{3.47}$$

where k_f = mass transfer coefficient (gas to solid surface)

A_p = external surface area of the solid

ϵ = voidage between granules

ϱ_B = bulk density of the packing

p, p_i = partial pressure in the bulk of the gas and at the surface, respectively.

The mass transfer coefficient can be found from an equation similar to (3.27).[543]

$$k_f = 1 \cdot 82U \left(\frac{DU\epsilon\varrho}{\mu} \right)^{-0 \cdot 51} \left(\frac{\mu}{\varrho\mathscr{D}} \right)^{-0 \cdot 67} \tag{3.48}$$

where U = mean linear velocity of gas relative to the solid

μ = gas viscosity

ϱ = gas density

$\mathscr{D}$ = diffusivity of gas molecules being adsorbed

D = equivalent spherical diameter of the granules, i.e. diameter of a sphere of the same volume as the granule.

The second stage in adsorption is the penetration of the molecules in to the pores of the solid; the third stage is the actual adsorption of the molecule on the site in the pore. Sometimes a molecule then penetrates through the solid by internal diffusion, but this last stage does not affect the rate of adsorption. The actual adsorption on the site is very fast compared to the first two stages, and it is these which determine the rate of adsorption. The rate of diffusion through the pore is given by the *pore diffusivity* $\mathscr{D}_{pore}$, which can be found from the following equation,[526] for cases where the pores are smaller than the mean free path of the gas molecules λ:

$$\mathscr{D}_{pore} = \frac{\mathscr{D}\chi}{2} \left\{ 1 - \exp(-2\bar{r}\bar{u}/3\mathscr{D}) \right\} \tag{3.49}$$

where $\bar{r}$ = average pore radius

   $\bar{u}$ = average molecular velocity (eqn. 3.3)

   χ = internal porosity of the solid granules.

Heat is evolved when molecules are adsorbed. When the adsorption is purely physical, then the heat evolved is the same as the latent heat in condensation. When the adsorption is a chemical reaction, the heat evolved is greater. The removal of molecules from the surface requires the heating of the surface to drive off (vapourize) the molecules. When the adsorption is chemisorption, this may mean removing some of the surface atoms with the desorbing molecule, thus changing the nature of the surface. This may decrease or increase its adsorptive capacity.

Equation (3.48) shows how the transfer of molecules from the bulk of the gas stream is a function of the size and shape of the particles, the bed voidage, and the driving force. This last function is the difference between the concentration in the bulk of the gas and at the surface, which in turn depends on the degree of saturation that has been reached. The equation (3.48) indicates how the mass transfer coefficient is a function of the gas velocity as well as of the carrier gas properties and the diffusivity of the gas being adsorbed, while the diffusivity in the pores (equation 3.49) is mostly a function of the pore voidage (χ) and the diffusivity. To decide whether stage 1 or 2 is the rate determining step requires a comprehensive knowledge of the system, and this is only rarely available. Empirical design procedures are therefore almost invariably used. Some of the most common adsorbents and the gases for which they are used are therefore discussed, together with a description of the type of plant in which they are used.

The adsorbents can be classified into three groups:

(a) Non polar solids, where the adsorption is mainly physical.

(b) Polar solids, where the adsorption is chemical, without changing the chemical structure of the molecules and the surface.

(c) Chemical adsorbing surfaces, which adsorb the molecules and then release them after reaction which may be either catalytic, leaving the surface unchanged or non-catalytic with the surface atoms, requiring their replacement.

The only important material in the group of non-polar solids is carbon, which consists almost wholly of neutral atoms of a single species, and presents a surface which is a generally homogeneous distribution of electrical charges at the molecular level, without potential gradients. Such a surface does not bind polar molecules in preference to non-polar ones at particular sites. Carbon is therefore very effective in adsorbing non-polar organic molecules, particularly near their normal boiling points. Even if there is water vapour in the gas stream, the organic molecules will be adsorbed preferentially because the polar water molecules are more strongly attracted to one another than to the non-polar carbon surface.

Thus large organic molecules are very readily adsorbed, smaller organic molecules and large inorganic ones less easily, smaller inorganic ones less still, and those which are permanent gases hardly at all. A list classifying substances into 4 groups is given in Table 3.6.[33]

TABLE 3.6. RELATIVE ADSORPTIVITY OF MOLECULES ON ACTIVE CARBON[33]*

2—Acetaldehyde	1—Carbon dioxide	3—Hydrogen sulphide
4—Acetic acid	1—Carbon monoxide	4—Isopropyl alcohol
3—Acetone	4—Carbon tetrachloride	4—Masking agents
3—Acrolein	3—Chlorine	4—Mercaptans
4—Alcohol	4—Chloropicrin	4—Ozone
2—Amines	4—Cigarette smoke	4—Perfumes, cosmetics
2—Ammonia	4—Cresol	4—Perspiration
3—Anaesthetics	3—Diesel fumes	4—Phenol
3—Animal odours	4—Disinfectants	2—Propane
4—Benzene	4—Ethyl acetate	4—Pyridine
4—Body odours	1—Ethylene	4—Ripening fruits
2—Butane	4—Essential oils	4—Smog
4—Butyl alcohol	2—Formaldehyde	3—Solvents
4—Butyric acid	4—Gasoline	4—Stuffiness
4—Cancer odour	4—Hospital odours	4—Toluene
4—Caprylic acid	4—Household smells	4—Turpentine

The capacity index has the following meaning:

4 — High capacity for all materials in this category. One pound takes up about 20 to 50 per cent of its own weight — average about $\frac{1}{3}$ ($33\frac{1}{3}$ per cent). This category includes most of the odour-causing substances.

3 — Satisfactory capacity for all items in this category. These constitute good applications but the capacity is not as high as for Category 4. Adsorbs about 10–25 per cent of its weight — average about $\frac{1}{6}$ (16·7 per cent).

2 — Includes substances which are not highly adsorbed but which might be taken up sufficiently to give good service under the particular conditions of operation. These require individual checking.

1 — Adsorption capacity is low for these materials. Activated charcoal cannot be satisfactorily used to remove them under ordinary circumstances.

* The carbon is a 50 min (chloropicrin test) activated coconut shell charcoal.

Activated carbon (frequently called charcoal—if the source is wood) is made by the pyrogenic decomposition of suitable coals and woods in special retorts. The raw materials may be lignites and bituminous coals, woods and nuts. Some of the purest carbon is made from Eucalyptus Marginata (Australian Jarrah) which is exceptionally low in mineral content, while good quality commercial activated charcoals with very large effective surface areas come from coconut shell, which has been charred at about

1150°C and subsequently "activated" by treatment with steam at about 600°C.

The basic parameters which determine the action of a carbon are the surface area available for adsorption and the diameters of the pores to determine whether the molecules being adsorbed can reach the micro-structure. The surface area is determined most accurately by the gas adsorption (B.E.T.) method.[135] The average pore diameter can be found from the pore volume, determined by the high pressure mercury injection technique[227] or electron microscopy.[14] Some typical data for adsorbent materials is shown in Table 3.7.[526]

TABLE 3.7. SURFACE AREA, PORE VOLUME AND MEAN PORE DIAMETER FOR ADSORBENT MATERIALS[526]

Material	Area (m²/g)	Pore volume (cm³/g)	Mean pore diameter (Ångstroms)
Activated carbon	500–1500	0·6–0·8	20–40
Silica gels	200–600	approx. 0·4	30–200
Activated alumina	175	0·39	90
Kieselguhr	4·2	1·14	22,000

The practical effectiveness of an active carbon is generally measured by testing the material by passing air, which was saturated with carbon tetrachloride vapour at 0°C, at 25°C and 760 mm pressure through a bed and measuring the amount adsorbed, expressing the amount as a percentage of the original weight. The retentivity is then tested by blowing dry air at 25°C for 6 hours through the bed.

TABLE 3.8. ADSORPTIVE CAPACITY AND RETENTIVITY OF ACTIVE CHARCOAL FOR ORGANIC MATERIALS[326]

Substance	Adsorptive capacity (weight %)	Retention after removal (weight %)
Carbon tetrachloride	80–110	27–30
Gasoline (motor spirit)	10–20	2–3
Benzene	45–55	5·9 (steam)
Methanol	50	1·2
Ethanol	50	1·05
Isopropanol	50	1·15 1 hour
Ethyl acetate	57·5	4·87 at
Acetone	51	3·0 150°C
Acetic acid	70	2·5

The test used for gas mask charcoals is the length of life of the bed when chloropicrin vapours are adsorbed in a thin bed under standardized conditions. Typical values for the adsorptive capacity and the retentivity of carbon tetrachloride and other organic materials are given in Table 3.8.[326]

Activated carbon is used for the recovery of hydrocarbon solvents, the removal and recovery of hydrocarbon gases from coal gas and natural gas, and the removal of odours and other trace impurities from gas streams. In the first two cases the recovery of the hydrocarbons is an economic project,

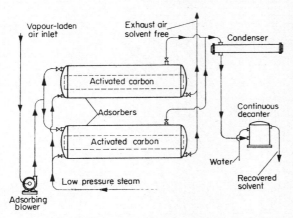

FIG. 3.28. Deep bed carbon adsorber for hydrocarbon recovery.[502]

as they can be used commercially. The plant consists of two deep beds of carbon housed in pressure vessels which are alternatively charged with the hydrocarbons and then steamed at 100–150°C to remove the adsorbed material (Fig. 3.28). The beds are 1–3 ft deep and velocities of 30–120 ft/min are used. The pressure drop through such beds is given by the graph in Fig. 3.29.

The control of odours with active charcoal is very effective. Thin beds with high flow rates and a life of 12–18 months or even longer are used continuously before replacement becomes necessary. The carbon is housed in canisters or in porous folds (Figs. 3.30a and 3.30b) and the flow rates used are similar to those in air conditioning filters, with which they are often combined. A suitable design value is 60 ft/min for a ½ in. bed of carbon. Reactivation of this carbon is more difficult than for solvent recovery systems, requiring temperatures of 600°C, and is therefore usually only carried out by the filter material manufacturer or a similar specialist organization.

The service life of such carbons can be estimated from an equation by Turk.[497]

$$t = 6\cdot43 \times 10^6 SW/Qc\eta M \qquad (3.50)$$

where t = life of unit − hours
    S = retentivity of gas (fraction) in adsorbing solid
    W = weight of adsorbing solid (lb)
    η = fraction efficiency of adsorption
    Q = flow through bed (ft³/min)
    c = inlet concentration − parts per million
    M = average molecular weight.

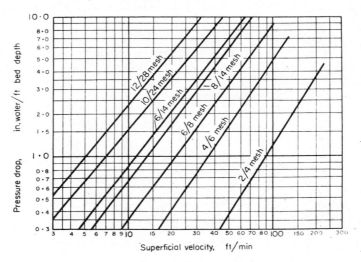

FIG. 3.29. Pressure drop through dry packed granular carbon beds.[502]
Air flowing downwards − 1 atm pressure, 70°F.

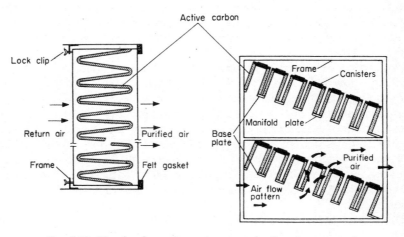

FIG. 3.30. Housing for active carbon granules for odour control,
operated without cooling period.[33]

Typical values for the retentivity S to be used in this equation are given in Table 3.9.[497]

Using a typical retentivity of 0·2 and molecular weight of 100, the equation (3.50) reduced to

$$t = 1·3 \times 10^4 W/Qc \quad \text{hours} \tag{3.51}$$

which should give an approximate value for the life of an active carbon filter. For odour control filters velocities of about 25–35 ft/min are used through the thin layers, compared with the higher velocities in solvent recovery filters. Temperatures should not exceed 125°F (52°C), as above this temperature the gases are not so easily adsorbed. Also relative humidities greater than 50 per cent should be avoided, because the retentivity is somewhat reduced at higher humidities.

TABLE 3.9. RETENTIVITY OF VAPOURS BY ACTIVE CARBONS[497]
ALSO SOME ODOUR THRESHOLD CONCENTRATIONS

	Formula	Molecular weight	Odour threshold concentration, ppm by volume	Retentivity* S
Acetaldehyde	C_2H_4O	44·1	—	0·07
Acrolein (heated fat odour)	C_3H_4O	56	1·8–17	0·15
Amyl acetate	$C_7H_{14}O_2$	130·2	—	0·34
Butyric acid	$C_4H_8O_2$	88·1	0·00083 –2·4	0·35
Carbon tetrachloride	CCl_4	153·8	—	0·45
Ethylacetate	$C_4H_8O_2$	88·1	190	0·19
Ethyl mercaptan	C_2H_6S	62·1	—	0·23
Eucalyptole	$C_{10}H_{18}O$	154.2	—	0·20
Formaldehyde	CH_2O	30·0	—	0·03
Hexane	C_6H_{12}	86	—	0·16
Methyl chloride	CH_3Cl	50·5	—	0·05
Phenol (carbolic acid)	C_6H_6O	94	0·29–1	0·30
Putrescine	$C_4H_{12}N_2$	88·2	—	0·25
Skatole	C_9H_9N	131·2	$3·34 \times 10^{-7}$ –0·22	0·25
Sulphur dioxide	SO_2	64·1	3·0	0·10
Toluene	C_7H_8	92·1	—	0·29
Valeric acid (body odour)	$C_5H_{10}O_2$	102	7	0·35

* Fractional retentivity S at 20°C and 760 mm pressure.

Polar adsorbents are oxides, either silica or metallic oxides. The siliceous materials are silica gel, Fuller's earth, diatomaceous earths such as kieselguhr and synthetic zeolites. These materials have an affinity for polar as well as non-polar molecules and will adsorb polar molecules in preference to non-polar ones. Metallic oxides, aluminium oxide in the form of activated alumina or activated bauxite have an even higher attraction for polar molecules. These materials are therefore commonly used for removal of water vapour from gas streams rather than organic molecules. The synthetic zeolites, sometimes called "molecular sieves", are sodium or calcium aluminosilicates, activated by heating which drives off water of crystallization. The chief advantage of the molecular sieves is that they can be used

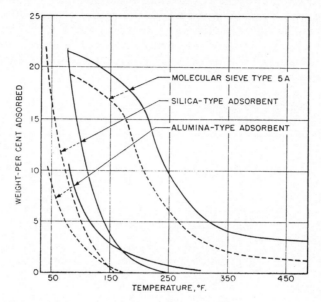

FIG. 3.31. Water vapour adsorption isobars at 10 mm partial pressure[501] for silica, alumina and artificial zeolite (molecular sieve) type adsorbents.

This isobar shows that at 250°F molecular sieves have over four times the drying power of alumina and silica type adsorbents, assuming complete regeneration. The dotted line shows the effect of 2 per cent residual water at the start of adsorption.

for drying at elevated temperatures, where silica gel and alumina lose their effectiveness (Fig. 3.31). The other application is the use of these adsorbents for the selective adsorption of polar molecules such as water, carbon dioxide, ammonia, acetylene, hydrogen sulphide and sulphur dioxide (Fig. 3.32). They are, therefore, used for the purification of inert gases, the removal of carbon dioxide and water from ethylene before subjecting this to polymerization for polyethylene, and the purification of natural gas.

The plant used in these cases is nearly always similar to the one shown in Fig. 3.33 for drying natural gas and consists of two or more vessels with the dessicant. Of these one is on stream while the others are being regenerated by the passing of the regeneration gas, either air heated by steam

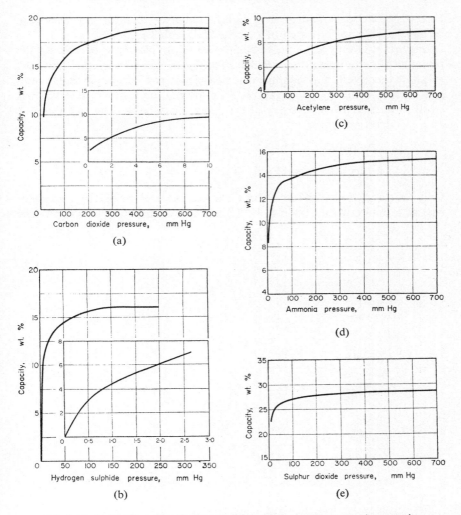

FIG. 3.32. Artificial zeolites ("molecular sieves"), Type 5.A. adsorptive capacity with polar molecules.[501]

(a) Carbon dioxide.   (b) Hydrogen sulphide.   (c) Acetylene.
(d) Ammonia.   (e) Sulphur dioxide.

or combustion gases, or directly heated by combustion gases at about 200 °C, through the bed.

Adsorbent surfaces which react chemically with the gas molecules, changing these to more useful or desirable ones before release, open the whole field of surface reactions and catalysis. Only a few examples of particular interest in air pollution control and gas purification can be given here. As in the case of adsorption without chemical reaction, it is necessary to have a large surface area of reagent accessible to the gas.

Important among these processes are the dry oxidation processes for the removal of sulphur compounds from coal gas. Chemically the hydrogen sulphide is converted to sulphur, using oxygen in carriers which react readily with it at ordinary temperatures. The most important of these is ferric oxide, and the basic chemistry of the process can be written as a reaction and regeneration stage:

Reaction: $6H_2S + 2Fe_2O_3 = 2Fe_2S_3 + 6H_2O$

Regeneration: $2Fe_2S_3 + 3O_2 = 6S + 2Fe_2O_3$.

Only the α and γ forms of ferric oxide are reactive, and the reaction proceeds best at a temperature 100 °F (37·8 °C) and in an alkaline environment. The

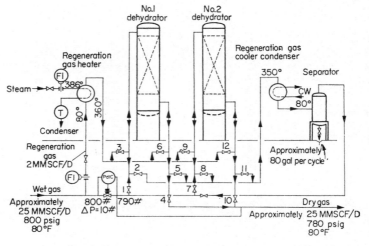

FIG. 3.33. Flow diagram of a typical natural gas dehydration plant.[267]

iron oxide is used in a finely divided form either mixed with peat or fibrous matter, containing 40 per cent water and with a porosity of about 60 per cent. Alternatively the iron oxide can be supported on a large surface area such as wood shavings or crushed slags, and the pH is carefully controlled to pH 8–8·5.

The pellets, or iron oxide on shavings, are distributed in large containers called "dry boxes" or on trays in towers (Figs. 3.34a and 3.34b). The process is a two stage one, the first stage removing the hydrogen sulphide, while the second stage re-oxidizes the iron sulphide to the oxide. In some countries the sulphur deposited on the oxide is recovered either by combustion or by solvent extraction using solvents such as perchlor-ethylene.

Another process uses hot iron oxide pellets in static or preferably fluidized beds (Fig. 3.35) at 340–360 °C.[393] The iron oxide in this case is recovered by roasting at 600–800 °C to give sulphur dioxide which can be used for acid making.

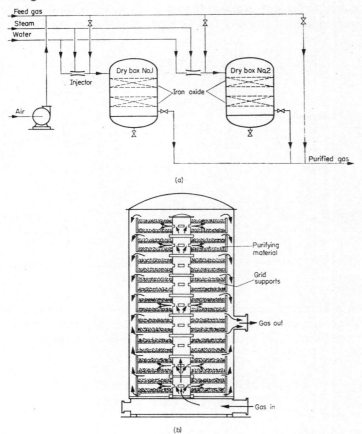

(a)

(b)

FIG. 3.34. Iron oxide purification process.

(a) Basic flow diagram.[267]

(b) Thyssen–Lenze tower.[180]

The soda iron process uses iron oxide mixed with sodium carbonate as a catalyst and oxidizes the hydrogen sulphide to sulphur trioxide which can be directly dissolved to give sulphuric acid.

Such compounds as peroxides, ozonides and similar compounds with $-O-O-$ linkages are readily converted to simpler compounds on catalyst surfaces. Untreated active carbon is sometimes suitable but other compounds are only decomposed when a metal catalyst has been deposited on the carbon. Typical catalysts are metallic copper, silver, platinum and palladium, which are put into the catalyst by deposition from solutions of complex salts.

There are numerous other examples, such as the oxidation of carbon monoxide on copper oxide or iodine pentoxide to give the dioxide which

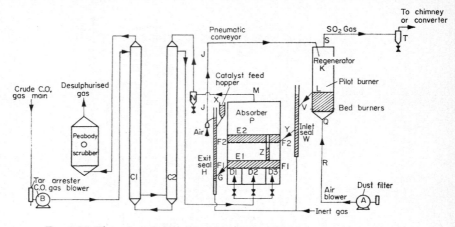

FIG. 3.35. Flow sheet fluidized bed hydrogen sulphide removal process (Appleby–Frodingham process).[393]

can then be adsorbed on soda lime; the bromination of an olefin by passing the gas through carbon impregnated with bromine; iodine for mercury vapour; lead acetate for hydrogen sulphide or sodium silicate for hydrogen fluoride.

3.9. COMBUSTION PROCESSES — FLAME COMBUSTION

When atmospheric pollutants are oxidizable, such as hydrocarbon vapours from industrial solvents or paint, then their control can be achieved by combustion of the gases to give carbon dioxide and water in the case of organic material or sulphur dioxide and water from organic sulphides. If the concentration of the gas is sufficiently high to be in the flammable range, the oxidation process can be self-supporting after the mixture is ignited. The lowest vapour concentration at which this occurs is the lower flammable limit, while the maximum concentration is the upper flammable limit. Within this range controlled combustion can be achieved, but under certain circumstances explosions also occur.

The temperature above which combustion of the vapour and gases is sustained is the *autogenous combustion temperature* and this depends on the type of hydrocarbon and the *fume energy concentration* which is the available net heat of combustion per standard cubic foot of gas (B.t.u./ft^3 at 70 °F). The lower flammable limit is approximately 52 B.t.u./ft^3 (70 °F) and fume energy concentrations higher than this are necessary for self-supporting flames, while for a flame with good combustion characteristics a fume energy concentration of about 100 B.t.u./ft^3 (70 °F) is desirable.

All combustion processes require adequate oxygen for oxidizing all the combustible material. Conventional combustion methods need about 15 to 20 per cent more than the stoichiometric amount, while catalytic combustion techniques need only the stoichiometric quantity. In addition, the temperature in the combustion chamber or in the flame must be sufficiently high, there must be adequate turbulent mixing of oxygen and the combustible gases, and sufficient time for combustion has to be available. The design of the burner and combustion chamber and the degree of premixing of gases determines these factors. A pre-mixed flame tends to be shorter and hotter, and blue in colour, while a non-pre-mixed flame tends to be luminous because of the cracking of hydrocarbon vapours which produces luminous carbon particles.

Where waste gases contain hydrocarbons in a quantity to give fume energy concentrations above the minimum of 52 B.t.u./ft^3, and these hydrocarbons contain toxic gases such as hydrogen cyanide, they are usually burned in a flare stack. A problem which occurs in these cases, particularly in the petroleum industry, is the wide variation of gas flow rates which occur. Certain hydrocarbons, particularly aromatics and others with a low carbon–hydrogen ratio tend to burn with a smoky flame, but this can be overcome by adding water vapour in the form of steam. This sets up a water gas reaction giving hydrogen and carbon monoxide which helps to give smokeless flames. A typical design of a steam injection flare is shown in Fig. 3.36. The steam jets surrounding the flame induce air together with the steam to assist in rapid combustion. Steam requirements vary from $\frac{1}{20}$ to $\frac{1}{3}$ lb steam/lb gas, depending on the quantity of aromatic constituents. A pilot flame is also provided. If the combustible gases are diluted so that the minimum fume energy concentration is not reached, then preheating of the gases may in some cases achieve an energy concentration able to support combustion. A ring burner is then used for preheating. When oil mists are found in the flare gases these must be removed at the base of the stack for safe flare operation. Flash-back precautions are also necessary when oxygen is present in the gases.

An alternative to an open flare is to burn the gases in an enclosed combustion chamber. A typical design which uses a circular flow pattern to give a high degree of turbulence and an adequate residence time (0·2–0·7 sec) in a small space is shown in Fig. 3.37.[401] The temperature in the chamber is maintained between 900° and 1400 °F (482 and 760 °C) and the waste gases can be exhausted to atmosphere or passed through a heat exchanger to recover much of the sensible heat in the gases. In these designs a supplementary gas or oil fired burner is generally used to heat the gases above their autogenous combustion temperature.[409] The lower temperatures are suitable for naphtha vapour while methane and aromatic hydrocarbons require the higher temperature.

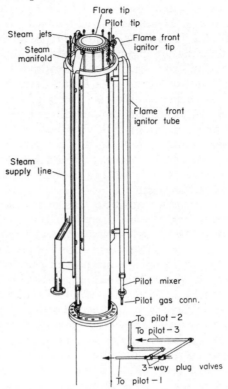

FIG. 3.36. Steam injection flare.[410]

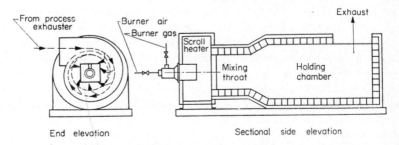

FIG. 3.37. Combustion chamber for combustible gases,
with supplementary flame.[410]

Great care must be taken in the design of these combustion chambers to avoid overheating the refractory lining and to build the unit in such a way as to avoid explosions by including burner controls which protect the unit.

These combustion chambers can be applied where the variation in the gas stream is not too great, and where additional fuels, when required, are fairly cheap, because the gases, and the air required, (which is in excess of the stoichiometric quantity) have to be heated to the combustion temperature. Well designed systems, however, are more than 98 per cent efficient, and can be used when there is considerable inorganic and particulate material present which precludes catalytic combustion.

3.10. CATALYTIC COMBUSTION

Catalytic combustion is an extension of the technique of using a combustion chamber with the advantage that oxidation on the catalyst surface will occur well below the autogenous combustion temperature, and also in gas concentrations below the fume concentration energy required for self-supporting combustion processes. An additional advantage is that only the stoichiometric quantity of oxygen (as air) has to be provided, minimizing the preheat requirements.

Normally any gas-borne organic material can be treated by catalytic combustion provided the combustion products are gaseous. Therefore organic sulphur and nitrogen compounds can generally be treated, but organic silicones and phosphates must be excluded because of the nature of the combustion products. If dusts of inorganic materials are present in an appreciable quantity they should be removed, but small quantities such as are normally found in the air will pass through the catalytic combustion unit or occasionally be caught in it. These residues can be removed by occasional (annual or semi-annual) washing of the elements.

The central feature in catalytic combustion is the nature of the oxidizing element. This may be:

(1) palladium supported on activated alumina which is used to remove oxygen from a gas stream containing hydrogen as well as oxygen (Deoxo process) in stoichiometric or greater amounts;

(2) a combination, platinum and other metals of the precious metals group, together with promoters, supported on high nickel alloy ribbon media. One particular mixture is used for the normal range of organic compounds, while specific catalysts for selective reactions have also been developed (Catalytic Combustion Corporation Process); or

(3) platinum and alumina combined as a catalyst supported on a high grade spark plug type porcelain, which has a similar coefficient of thermal expansion (Oxycat Process).

The temperature which is necessary to initiate the reaction on the catalyst depends on the hydrocarbons present. Thus hydrogen oxidizes at ambient temperatures, benzene at 440°F (227°C) while methane only oxidizes at 760°F (404°C). For normal paint baking ovens for example, it is usual to provide a catalyst inlet temperature of 625°F (330°C) under starting conditions, allowing a reduction to 400°F (204°C) when running and the concentrations approach a quarter of the lower flammable limit. A more detailed list of catalyst entry temperatures is given in Table 3.10.

TABLE 3.10. CATALYST INLET TEMPERATURES FOR CATALYTIC COMBUSTION[358]

Industrial process	Contaminating agents in waste gases	Approximate temperature required for catalytic oxidation
Asphalt oxidizing	Aldehydes, anthracenes, oil vapors, hydrocarbons	600–700°F
Carbon black Mfg.	Hydrogen, carbon monoxide, methane, carbon	*1200–1800°F
Catalytic cracking units	Carbon monoxide, hydrocarbons	650–800°F
Core ovens	Wax, oil vapors	600–700°F
Formaldehyde Mfg.	Hydrogen, methane, carbon monoxide, formaldehyde	650°F
Nitric acid Mfg.	Nitric oxide, nitrogen dioxide	†500–1200°F
Metal lithography ovens	Solvents, resins.	500–750°F
Octyl-phenol Mfg.	Phenol	600–800°F
Phthalic anhydride Mfg.	Maleic acid, phthalic acid, naphthaquinones, carbon monoxide, formaldehyde	600–650°F
Polyethylene Mfg.	Hydrocarbons	500–1200°F
Printing presses	Solvents	600°F
Varnish cooking	Hydrocarbon vapors	600–700°F
Wire coating and enamelling ovens	Solvents, varnish	600–700°F

* Temperatures in excess of 1200°F required to oxidize carbon.
† Reducing atmosphere required.

The catalyst temperature is only just above that of the gases being discharged and the temperature rise for the gases is approximately that calculated from the heat release of the reaction.

The arrangement of the catalyst in the gas stream can be with or without recirculation and with use of the waste gases as the preheating source or to produce steam (Fig. 3.38). For ribbon type catalyst a face velocity of 500 ft/min gives a satisfactory residence time with a 2½ in. deep bed. The pressure drop is about 0.4 in. W.G. for this design.

The heat recovery which is possible in some cases with a catalytic oxidation unit makes this a source of heating in industries where hydrocarbon vapours are produced as an effluent.[409]

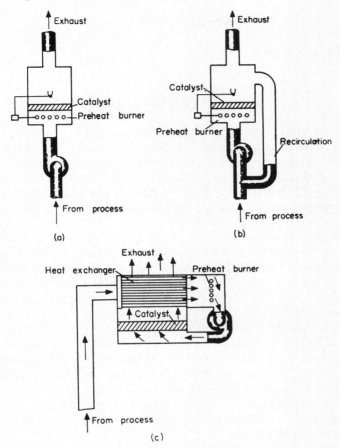

FIG. 3.38. Arrangement catalytic combustion units in gas stream.[358]

(a) Basic installation, using preheat burner
(b) Installation with preheat burner, obtaining some preheat by direct recirculation
(c) Installation with preheat burner, obtaining some preheat from the use of a heat exchanger.

CHAPTER 4

FLUID RESISTANCE TO PARTICLE MOTION

4.1. INTRODUCTION

The removal of molecules from gas streams, which was discussed in the previous chapter, depends solely on diffusion. On the other hand, the removal of particles relies only partly on their diffusion from the gas stream to a collecting surface or space, and other mechanisms such as gravitational or centrifugal separation, interception and inertial impaction, or the action of electrostatic, thermal or magnetic forces play a more important role.

Essentially, the plant for the removal of particles is a system through which the gas stream passes while the particles are acted on by forces enabling them to leave the gas stream. To be effective, these forces must be sufficiently large to take the particle out of the gas stream during its residence time in the cleaning system. The forces acting give the particles a component of velocity in a direction other than that of the gas stream, and in their movement across the streamlines the particles encounter the resistance of the gas to their movement. The motion of particles in moving fluids has not been studied extensively, although it is certain that particles spin and so have components of lift and sideways shift similar to those experienced by an airfoil. Because of the limited knowledge of fluid resistance under these conditions, it is assumed that the resistance of the moving fluid is the same as that which the particle would experience in moving through a stationary fluid.

The calculation of the fluid resistance to the cross-stream movement of the particle is essential to determining the effectiveness of a particular mechanism in removing the particle from the gas stream. For example, in a gravitational settling chamber, which is the simplest type of plant, being merely an enclosed space through which the gas stream moves, the Earth's gravitational field acting on the particles is opposed by the resistance of the gas to the falling particles. Large particles, which move more quickly, are collected, while smaller ones, which do not settle out during the residence time of the gas stream in the chamber, may escape.

This chapter discusses the calculation of the resistance of a fluid to the movement of particles when these are acted on by forces outside the fluid. Subsequent chapters are concerned with the interaction of the applied

122

external forces with the fluid resistance, and the method of using these calculations to assess the effectiveness of gas cleaning plant for particle removal.

The simplest calculations concerning gas–particle systems are those for a sphere in steady state motion in a continuous fluid of infinite extent. This will therefore be discussed first, because other types of particles, and other factors can be related to this system. The modifications that have to be considered are:

    (i) When the fluid is not continuous.
    (ii) When the particles are accelerating.
    (iii) When there are walls near to the particle.
    (iv) When there are numbers of particles which affect one another.
    (v) When particles are not spherical in shape.

A survey of many of these factors has been recently published by Torobin and Gauvin[493] which should be referred to for a comprehensive discussion. The following sections will however give a brief review of the most important working equations required.

4.2. FLUID RESISTANCE TO SPHERES IN STEADY STATE MOTION

Even for the simplified model of a sphere in steady state motion through a laminar fluid, the relation between fluid resistance and particle speed is very complex. However, the data relating these functions can be presented by a single curve[390] (Fig. 4.1). The abscissa is the logarithm of a dimensionless function of the relative velocity in the form of the particle Reynolds number

$$\mathrm{Re} = u d \varrho / \mu \qquad (4.1)$$

which is the relative velocity u multiplied by a linear dimension for the particle, which is the diameter d, in the case of a sphere, the fluid density ϱ, and the reciprocal of the fluid viscosity, μ.

The ordinate is the logarithm of a function called the drag coefficient, C_D, and is given by

$$C_D = \frac{F}{A \cdot \tfrac{1}{2} \varrho u^2} \qquad (4.2)$$

where F is a function of the fluid resistance, A is the surface area perpendicular to the direction of motion and $\tfrac{1}{2} \varrho u^2$ is the kinetic energy of one square unit of area of fluid moving past the particle.

In the case of a spherical particle, A is $\pi d^2 / 4$, and equation (4.2) becomes

$$C_D = \frac{8F}{\pi \varrho u^2 d^2} \qquad (4.3)$$

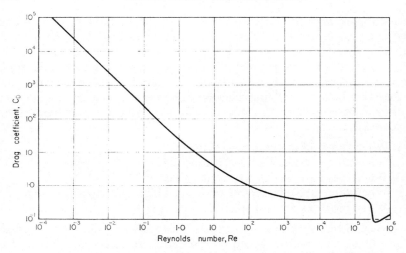

FIG. 4.1. Relation between the drag coefficient ($\log_{10} C_D$) and the Reynolds number ($\log_{10} Re$) for spheres.[298]

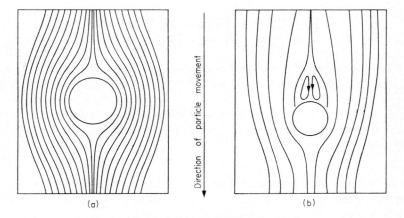

FIG. 4.2. Streamlines around a sphere in steady state motion in a laminar fluid.[118]

(a) Viscous flow region.
(b) Transition region ($Re \approx 2$).

The curve shown in Fig. 4.1 can be divided into 4 sections, each of which has certain phenomena associated with it as regards flow pattern of the fluid around the particle, and specific formulae can be used to calculate the drag coefficient in each section.

At very low velocities, associated with particle Reynolds numbers up to about 0·1, the flow around the sphere has an up and down stream symmetry (Fig. 4.2a). Elements of fluid meeting in front of the particle are slowly accelerated sideways, and the inertia effects are too small to cause a time lag in the closing up of the flow behind it. This is the viscous, streamline or Stokes' law region. For these conditions Stokes[471] deduced that the fluid resistance can be calculated from:

$$F = 3\pi\mu du \qquad (4.4)$$

This equation was obtained by neglecting the inertia terms in the Navier-Stokes equation for a rigid sphere in an unbounded fluid. From equation (4.4) the drag coefficient for the viscous flow region becomes

$$C_D = \frac{24}{Re} \qquad (4.5)$$

At $Re = 0.05$, the fluid resistance calculated from equation (4.4) agrees to within one per cent with the experimental value, but at $Re = 1$, the calculated fluid resistance underestimates the experimentally determined fluid resistance by about 13 per cent.

At Reynolds numbers somewhat greater than 0.1, the time lag of the elements of fluid closing up behind the particle increases, and the formation of a wake commences. To allow for this, Oseen[284] introduced a modification which partially takes into account the inertia terms in the equations of motion. This gave the equation.

$$C_D = \frac{24}{Re} \left(1 + \frac{3}{16} Re\right) \qquad (4.6)$$

The drag coefficient given by this equation is 3 per cent greater than the experimental value at $Re = 1$.

Initially in forming a wake the fluid curls up to form stationary vortex rings (Fig. 4.2b), which grow in size as the velocity of the particle increases. This is the transition region and is often called the *Allen* region after H. S. Allen, who was one of its first investigators. Allen[11] found experimentally that in the range $30 < Re < 300$

$$C_D \approx 10/\sqrt{Re} \qquad (4.7)$$

It is sometimes convenient to use this approximate relation in equations involving integrations since more precise relations can only be integrated by numerical methods.

More precise values of the drag coefficient for this transition range, which, for practical purposes stops at $Re = 1000$ are based on extensive experimental data. Two of the most useful are those by Schiller and Naumann[419] for the range $0.5 < Re < 800$ and by Langmuir and Blodgett[297] for the narrower range $1 < Re < 100$. These are:

$$C_D = \frac{24}{Re} (1 + 0.150 Re^{0.687}) \quad \text{(Schiller and Naumann)} \qquad (4.7a)$$

and

$$C_D = \frac{24}{Re}(1 + 0.197Re^{0.63} + 0.0026Re^{1.38})$$

(Langmuir and Blodgett)   (4.7b)

The latter equation contains more terms than (4.7a) and can therefore be expected to give more exact drag coefficient values within the more limited range. At somewhat greater values than Re = 500, which is at the upper end of the transition region, the vortex rings break away from the body and form an extended wake. This wake is stable above Re = 1000, and the drag coefficient remains approximately constant in the range 0.38–0.5. The fluid resistance is therefore also approximately constant, according to the equation:

$$F = [C_D]_{constant} \, A \cdot \tfrac{1}{2}\varrho u^2 \tag{4.8}$$

This relation was first deduced by Newton, who assumed that the drag coefficient was unity, and this region is usually referred to by his name.

At much greater velocities in the vicinity of Re = 2×10^5 the boundary layer of fluid at the front of the sphere becomes unstable, and at a still higher velocity the separation circle moves to the rear of the particle, resulting in a sharp decrease in the drag coefficient from 0.4 to 0.1.[541]

The terminal velocity reached by a particle is the velocity it attains when the fluid resistance is equal to the external force applied to the particle. If this force is G, then from equation (4.2), the terminal velocity u_t is

$$u_t = \sqrt{\left(\frac{2G}{A\varrho C_D}\right)} \tag{4.9}$$

If the particle is a sphere moving in the viscous flow region, then equation (4.9) becomes

$$u_t = \frac{G}{3\pi d\mu} \tag{4.10}$$

If the force on the particle is gravity, then

$$u_t = \frac{d^2(\varrho_p - \varrho)g}{18\mu} \tag{4.11}$$

where ϱ_p = density of particle.

In the general case, outside the viscous flow region, if the force on the particle is gravity, then

$$u_t = \sqrt{\left(\frac{4d(\varrho_p - \varrho)g}{3\varrho C_D}\right)} \tag{4.12}$$

In the transition region, where C_D is a function of the Reynolds number, this equation is difficult to solve except by successive approximation. This problem has been overcome by expressing the Reynolds number in the transition region as a function of $C_D \text{Re}^2$, which does not contain the velocity.[117] If the force is gravity:

$$C_D \text{Re}^2 = 4\varrho(\varrho_p - \varrho) \, d^3 g / 3\mu^2 \qquad (4.13)$$

otherwise

$$C_D \text{Re}^2 = 8G\varrho / \pi\mu^2 \qquad (4.14)$$

Davies[117] statistically analysed reliable experimental data[21, 305, 319, 341, 423, 541] and obtained two equations:

For moderate values: Re < 4 and $C_D \text{Re}^2$ < 134

$$\text{Re} = \frac{C_D \text{Re}^2}{24} - 2{\cdot}3363 \times 10^{-4} (C_D \text{Re}^2)^2 + 2{\cdot}0154 \times 10^{-6} (C_D \text{Re}^2)^3$$
$$- 6{\cdot}9105 \times 10^{-9} (C_D \text{Re}^2)^4 \qquad (4.15)$$

For the range of Re: 3 < Re < 10,000 and 100 < $C_D \text{Re}^2$ < 4·5 × 10⁷,

$$\log_{10} \text{Re} = 1{\cdot}29536 + 0{\cdot}986 \log_{10} (C_D \text{Re}^2) - 0{\cdot}046677 \log_{10} (C_D \text{Re}^2)^2$$
$$+ 0{\cdot}0011235 \log_{10} (C_D \text{Re}^2)^3 \qquad (4.16)$$

Table 4.1 lists maximum sizes of spheres falling through air in the Earth's gravitational field for which the terminal velocities can be calculated using equation (4.15) and Stokes' law.

TABLE 4.1.[118] THE MAXIMUM SIZES OF SPHERES (IN MICRONS) FOR WHICH TERMINAL FALLING
VELOCITIES CAN BE CALCULATED BY STOKES' LAW (EQUATION 4.11)
AND EQUATION (4.15)[117]

The spheres are falling through air at 20°C and 760 mm pressure ($\mu = 0{\cdot}01816$ centipoise, $\varrho = 0{\cdot}001205$ g/cm³)

Density of sphere g/cm³	Maximum diameter for Stokes' law			Max. dia. with eqn. (4.15)
	within 10%	within 5%	within 1%	
	microns	microns	microns	microns
0·2	132	100	57	240
0·4	105	79	45	191
0·8	83	63	36	152
1·0	77	59	34	141
2·0	61	46	27	112
4·0	48	37	21	89
6·0	42	32	18	78
8·0	38	29	17	70
10·0	36	27	15	65
12·0	34	25	15	62
Re	0·82	0·38	0·074	4
$C_D \text{Re}^2$	21·9	9·60	1·80	133·6

4.3. FLUID RESISTANCE
TO ACCELERATING PARTICLES

The two previous sections have discussed the resistance to a particle in steady state motion in a laminar fluid, and the terminal velocity achieved when a particle is acted on by a specific force such as gravity. However, when a particle at rest is acted on by a force it accelerates until it reaches its terminal velocity. If a particle is acted on by a constant force, it has its maximum acceleration at the start, and the acceleration decreases the more closely the particle velocity approaches its terminal value. For a particle to move with constant acceleration, the force on the particle must increase as the speed of the particle increases.

The drag force on an accelerating particle is larger than that on a particle moving with the same velocity in the steady state. Early experimenters accounted for this by assuming an increase in the mass of the particle to an effective value greater than its actual mass. However, the drag force is a function of the acceleration, and so the "added mass" concept is unsatisfactory because it assumes a constant effect. It is more satisfactory to use a modified drag coefficient C_{DA} which is defined by[493]

$$G - ma = R_A = C_{DA} \cdot \tfrac{1}{2}\varrho u^2 \cdot A \qquad (4.17)$$

where G = force on the particle
m = mass of the particle
a = particle acceleration relative to fluid
R_A = drag on the accelerating particle.

The modified drag coefficient can be found from the extensive data of Lunnon[318] which has been re-plotted by Torobin and Gauvin[493]. The curves are shown in Fig. 4.3. Other, more recent data, which cover other ranges have also been reviewed by these workers,[493] but these do not cover the lower Reynolds number which are of importance in gas cleaning plant.

Integrating equation 4.17, assuming the particle is a sphere and C_{DA} is a constant at an average value, gives

$$t = \frac{d^2(\varrho_p - \varrho)}{3C_{DA}^{1/2}\,\varrho^{1/2}} \bigg/ \left(\frac{\pi}{2G}\right) \ln \frac{\dfrac{2}{d}\sqrt{\left(\dfrac{2G}{\pi\varrho C_{DA}}\right)} + u}{\dfrac{2}{d}\sqrt{\left(\dfrac{2G}{\pi\varrho C_{DA}}\right)} - u} \qquad (4.18)$$

and substituting the terminal velocity (equation 4.9) to give the time taken to reach this is

$$t_t = \frac{d^2(\varrho_p - \varrho)}{3C_{DA}^{1/2}\,\varrho^{1/2}} \bigg/ \left(\frac{\pi}{2G}\right) \ln \frac{\sqrt{C_D} + \sqrt{C_{DA}}}{\sqrt{C_{DA}} - \sqrt{C_D}} \qquad (4.19)$$

Integrating again yields the distance travelled in time t:

$$x = \frac{4d(\varrho_p - \varrho)}{3C_{DA}\varrho} \ln \cosh \left\{ \frac{3\sqrt{(2C_{DA}\varrho G)}}{2d^2(\varrho_p - \varrho)\pi^{1/2}} \cdot t \right\} \tag{4.20}$$

Since terminal velocity is an assymptotic value and cannot be reached in practice a value such as 99 per cent of the terminal velocity has to be used. Thus, in the solution of equation (4.19) the value of C_{DA} must be based on such an approximation, and an average value from experimental data is used.

The distance travelled during the time to reach 99 per cent of the terminal velocity can then be calculated by substituting the time given by equation (4.19) in (4.20).

In practice, the calculation is required to yield the cross stream distance travelled by a particle during the gas stream residence time in the collection

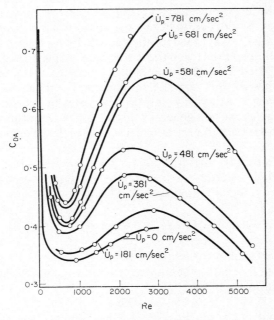

FIG. 4.3. Modified drag coefficient C_{DA} for accelerating spheres falling in air. Redrawn by Torobin and Gauvin,[493] based on experiments by Lunnon.[319]

system. Assuming that the force applied to the particle is known, as well as the physical properties of the particle and the gas stream, the time and distance travelled by the particle to reach 99 per cent of the terminal velocity can be found. If the time taken to reach 99 per cent of the terminal velocity is greater than the gas stream residence time, then the cross stream distance travelled by the particle can be found by integration of equation (4.18) between the time limits set by the gas stream residence time. If this time to reach 99 per cent of the terminal velocity is less than the gas stream residence time, the distance travelled to reach this velocity must be subtracted from the total cross stream distance, and it can then be assumed that the remaining distance is travelled by the particle at its terminal velocity.

For particles smaller than 10 microns a velocity approaching the terminal value is attained in a very short distance with the forces that are used in normal gas cleaning plant (centrifugal, electrostatic, thermal, etc.) and the effects during acceleration can generally be neglected.

4.4. FLUID RESISTANCE IN A NON-CONTINUOUS MEDIUM

When particles are very small, that is of the order of the mean free path of gas molecules, or smaller, then the assumption that a gas behaves as a continuous medium with respect to the particles is no longer valid. Under these circumstances particles tend to move more quickly than is predicted by the classical theories of Stokes and others which assume a continuous medium. To allow for this "slip", Cunningham[108] calculated a correction based on the kinetic theory of gases, the form of which has been retained in the empirical equations generally used. Other important theoretical studies of the movement of particles much smaller than the mean free path were made by Epstein.[140]

The most precise slip correction factor for particles in the viscous flow region can be obtained from the equation by Davies[117] based on weighted averages of experimental falling speeds. This is:

$$C = 1 + \frac{2\lambda}{d}\left\{1\cdot257 + 0\cdot400 \exp\left(-1\cdot10d/2\lambda\right)\right\} \qquad (4.21)$$

where C = Cunningham Correction Factor

λ = mean free path of gas molecules based on the Chapman–Enskog equation

$$\lambda = \mu/0\cdot499\varrho\bar{u} \qquad (4.21a)$$

$\bar{u}$ = mean molecular velocity – equation (3.3).

The modified Stokes law equation, which is usually referred to as the Stokes Cunningham equation, is

$$F = 3\pi\mu du/C. \qquad (4.22)$$

The slip correction is less than 1 per cent for 20 micron particles (density 1) in ambient air, about 5 per cent for 5 micron particles, $16\frac{2}{3}$ per cent for 1 micron particles and almost 300 per cent for 0·1 micron particles.

Outside the viscous flow region, no accurate experimental data are available, but approximate measurements by Benarie[42] indicate that Cunningham corrections calculated from equation (4.21) overestimate the slip correction by at least 0·2 per cent.

4.5. FLUID RESISTANCE TO PARTICLE MOTION IN A BOUNDED FLUID

In some types of particle collection equipment, such as settling chambers, cyclones or electrostatic precipitators, the particles are negligibly small compared with the dimensions of the plant. In other types, however, such as compressed felt filters or pebble beds with fine granules, the inter-fibre or pebble distances are sufficiently small to make the fluid passing through the filter behave as one which has one or more effective boundaries. These can increase the fluid drag on a particle moving through the filter. It should however be noted that the present theories of filtration (Chapter 7) do not include this factor.

A finite boundary to the fluid in which the particle is moving will have two effects. When the outward movement of fluid thrust aside by the particles is stopped by the boundary, a return flow of fluid is produced, and as the streamlines around the particle are distorted by the boundary this also acts on the particle.

The boundary effects depend on the type of boundary. Theoretical considerations or experimental work have established factors for modifying the Stokes law equation (4.4) for the following cases:

  (i) Particle near a single wall.
 (ii) Particle between two parallel walls.
(iii) Particle moving along the axis of an infinitely long cylinder.

The fluid resistance near a boundary, F_W, can be calculated by dividing the Stokes law fluid resistance, F, by the boundary correction factor K

$$F_W = F/K \tag{4.23}$$

In the three cases, the correction factor is given by the following:
  (i) Sphere moving parallel to an infinite plane wall of infinite extent, at a distance $l/2$ from the wall[315]

$$K = 1 - \frac{9}{16}\frac{d}{l} \tag{4.24}$$

 (ii) Sphere moving between and parallel to, two equidistant walls, separated by a distance l[147]

$$K = 1 - 1\cdot004d/l + 0\cdot418(d/l)^3 - 0\cdot169(d/l)^5 \tag{4.25}$$

This equation can be used when the ratio d/l is less than 1/20, but for larger d/l ratios, the correction equation (4.25) gives an underestimate of the fluid resistance. For example, when d/l is 1/2, then the fluid resistance is about twice that calculated from equations (4.23) and (4.25).

While the sphere remains fairly close to the centre line between the walls, the correction does not vary very much. When the sphere moves towards one wall, and its effect increases, the effect of the other wall is reduced by a similar amount. However, when a particle approaches fairly closely to one

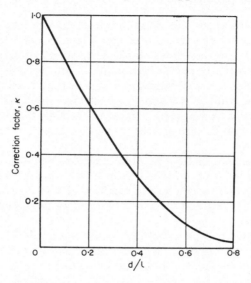

FIG. 4.4. Experimental correction factor for fluid resistance for spheres moving along the axis of a cylinder (after A. W. Francis).[160]

wall, the fluid resistance does increase to an appreciable extent. For example,[147] it has been calculated that when a sphere is only $\frac{1}{8} l$ from one of the walls, the correction factor is:

$$K = 1 - 1 \cdot 305 d/l \qquad (4.26)$$

which gives an increase in the fluid resistance of about 30 per cent compared with the sphere moving at the centre between the walls.

(iii) Sphere moving along the axis of an infinitely long cylinder with diameter l[148]

$$K = 1 - 2 \cdot 104 d/l + 2 \cdot 09(d/l)^3 - 0 \cdot 95(d/l)^5 \qquad (4.27)$$

This equation has been confirmed experimentally for small values of d/l, where the correction is not very large.[305]

For d/l values up to 0·25, the correction factor[321]

$$K = [1 + 2·25d/l + 5·06_2(d/l)^2]^{-1} \qquad (4.28)$$

agrees with experimental evidence, while for larger d/l ratios, experimental curves such as those shown in Fig. 4.4 can be used.[160]

When particles are not spherical,[370] the correction factor to be used is the same as for spheres with equivalent diameters (section 4.7).

At velocities greater than those which occur in the streamline region, Faxén[147, 148] the author of some of the major theoretical developments (equations 4.25, 4.26 and 4.27), has obtained a very complex relation, discussed by Liebster,[305] which is applicable to particles for which d/l is less than 0·05. At very high velocities (Re about 10^4) the available experimental evidence indicates that wall effects are negligible.[318]

4.6. FLUID RESISTANCE WHEN A NUMBER OF PARTICLES ARE PRESENT

Almost invariably in the removal of particles from gas streams, there are large numbers of particles, so the equations for the fluid resistance to the movement of single particles have to be modified to allow for the influence of particles on one another. Particle interactions become appreciable at quite low concentrations, so that a particle volume concentration (the ratio of particle volume to total volume) of 0·002 will increase the fluid resistance to particle movement by about one per cent.

The movement of a group of particles in an unbounded fluid results in movement of fluid around the group. When the particles are sufficiently close together, the fluid between the particles moves with the particles, and the group can be considered to be a cloud. When there are walls enclosing the particle group or the particles are sufficiently far apart, then the fluid will also move between the particles. In a practical case there is likely to be some movement of particles as cloud groups and other intermediate cases of temporary groups and also individual particles.

The problem is so complex that so far only partial solutions have been obtained for the prediction of cloud movement and hindered movement effects. In general, clouds tend to move more quickly than individual particles, while groups bounded by walls tend to move more slowly than single particles.

It has been suggested[82] that clouds in an unbounded fluid behave similarly to droplets of one fluid moving through another. For this case, in the viscous flow region, a correction factor has been calculated which allows for internal circulation because of the viscous drag, but neglects surface energy effects.[283] The resistance to a drop or bubble is given by:

$$F = 3\pi\mu du \left(\frac{2\mu + 3\mu_d}{3\mu + 3\mu_d}\right) \tag{4.29}$$

where μ_d is the viscosity of the droplet fluid.

In the case where the viscosity of the droplet fluid is the same as the surrounding fluid, the correction factor is $\frac{5}{6}$; where the droplet viscosity is much lower than the surrounding fluid (i.e. a gas bubble in a liquid) the correction factor is $\frac{2}{3}$; while for a droplet with very high viscosity compared with the fluid, the extreme case for which is a rigid sphere, the correction factor becomes unity, and equation (4.29) reduces to the simple Stokes' form.

Therefore, if it is assumed that the particle cloud is spherical and that the viscosity within the cloud is the same as in the surrounding fluid, then the fluid resistance to the cloud, F_c is:

$$F_c = \tfrac{5}{2} \pi\mu d_c u \tag{4.30}$$

where d_c is the diameter of the cloud.

The assumption of equal viscosities cannot be justified, particularly when there are ranges of sizes of particles present, and the smaller ones effectively constitute part of the fluid surrounding the larger ones in the cloud. The viscosity of a suspension μ_c is given by[72, 400]

$$\mu_c = \mu(1 - c)^{-k} \tag{4.31}$$

where c = volume concentration

volume of particles/total volume of suspension

k = constant = $2 \cdot 5$ for spheres.[132]

At low volume concentrations, equation (4.31) simplifies to

$$\mu_c = \mu(1 + kc) \tag{4.32}$$

A model for clouds of large and small particles together does not appear so far to have been used for the calculation of fluid resistance for particle groups.

When fluid flows between the particles in a bounded system, the resistance to movement of the particles depends on whether the particles retain their original orientation due to certain inter-particle forces or whether there is a tendency for the particles to align themselves. Considerable experimental work, particularly in connection with fluidization[304, 395] has shown that the equation

$$F_c = F(1 - c)^{-4 \cdot 65} \tag{4.33}$$

can be used to calculate the resistance to the movement of a particle group in a bounded fluid when there are no particle interactions. At low volume concentrations this simplifies to

$$F_c = F(1 + 4{\cdot}65c) \qquad (4.34)$$

a relation which had been suggested earlier by Hawksley.[203]

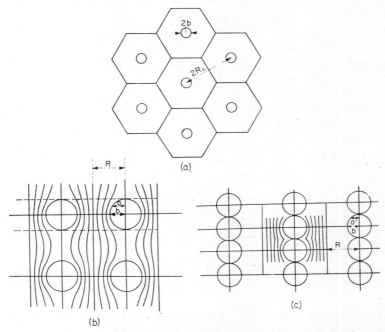

Fig. 4.5. Models for particle orientation with respect to one another for hindered settling.[394]

(a) Hexagonal pattern (horizontal section).
(b) Particle configuration I at 10 per cent volumetric concentration
(c) Particle configuration II at 10 per cent volumetric concentration.

In cases where there are particle interactions, as in the case of flocculated suspensions, the relation

$$F_c = F(1 - c)^{-6{\cdot}875} \qquad (4.35)$$

may be expected to apply, in analogy with equation (4.33). The form of this equation for low concentrations has been derived elsewhere as [82,203]

$$F_c = F(1 + 6{\cdot}875c) \qquad (4.36)$$

The constant, 6·875 is based on the arrangement the particles take up relative to one another and assumes that surrounding particles may take all positions around a particle with equal probability.

The most satisfactory theoretical approach to the calculation of hindered motion velocities in a suspension is that of Richardson and Zaki[394] who suggest two models for the settling of equal sized spheres. In both, the particles are arranged as centres of hexagons of fluid (Fig. 4.5a) and in one[321] the vertical distances between the particles are the same as the horizontal distances (Fig. 4.5b) while the other[203] arranges the particles in

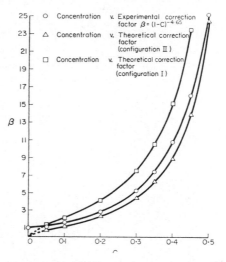

FIG. 4.6. Experimental and calculated correction factors for hindered settling, "β". The calculated corrections are based on configurations I and II. (Fig. 4.5.)[395]

adjacent horizontal layers (Fig. 4.5c) so as to offer the minimum resistance to the fluid.

The volumetric concentration for both configurations can be calculated from the geometry of the systems. In configuration I,

$$c = \frac{\pi}{3\sqrt{(3)}} \left(\frac{b}{R_h} \right)^3$$

and in configuration II

$$c = 2\pi b^2 / 3\sqrt{(3)} R_h^2,$$

where b is the radius of the spheres and R_h is half the distance between centres. Boundary conditions were simplified by assuming that each sphere was surrounded by a cylinder and not a hexagonal prism of fluid, and the resultant shearing force at the surface of the sphere was calculated. The resultant equation gave a correction factor, β, for the drag on a particle surrounded by others, compared with a single sphere, in terms of the sphere radius, the radius of the cylinder of equal cross-sectional area to the hexagonal section, and an elementary ring on the sphere surface. The correction factor equation was evaluated for both configurations I and II, and the solution, together with experimental data and equation (4.36) is plotted in Fig. 4.6.

The curves indicate that configuration II, which implies alignment of the particles in rows agrees fairly well with experimental work at high concentrations (greater than $c = 0.2$). At very low concentrations the assumption of an average pressure gradient made in the derivation of the correction factor is not entirely valid, as it tends to zero, and gives the trend to $\beta = 0$ rather than $\beta = 1$. At higher concentrations this pressure gradient is finite and the result follows closely on the experimental curve.

4.7. FLUID RESISTANCE TO NON-SPHERICAL PARTICLES

While small droplets and fume particles formed from condensing vapours tend to be spherical, those particles formed by crystallization or by milling tend to have other shapes. The equations in the previous sections apply only to spheres and have to be modified when they are to be used for non-spherical particles. Furthermore, not only do shape factors have to be considered, but also the orientation of the particle and whether this orientation changes during particle translation.

Because gas cleaning plant calculations are concerned with the aerodynamic behaviour of the particles, the most useful particle size data is obtained in the same flow region as is used in the plant by methods based on aerodynamics, such as sedimentation or elutriation. The particle "size" is based on the fluid resistance equations and is expressed as the diameter of a sphere with the same fluid resistance characteristics as the particle and the same density. This is the *drag diameter*, and can be substituted for the diameter of the sphere in the fluid resistance equations for spheres in the earlier sections.

If the drag diameter is not known for the flow region required by the calculations, or if particle sizes have been measured by some other means, such as those depending on particle geometry (screening, microscopic sizing), then the calculation of the fluid resistance becomes difficult, and requires a detailed knowledge of the behaviour of nonspherical particles.

Particle orientation depends on the flow region. For viscous flow it has been theoretically predicted[168] that particles with three mutually perpendicular planes of symmetry will retain their initial orientation, while those with only two planes of symmetry will take up a preferred orientation with the lines of the intersection of the planes in the direction of flow. In agreement with these predictions it has been observed that isometric particles (cubes, tetrahedra, octahedra) and some non-isometric particles (cylinders, parallel pipeds) do retain their initial orientation,[213, 370] while round disks[423] and triangular laminae[515] take up the preferred orientation. It has also been observed however that *Bacilli Subtilis* spores, which are prolate spheroids 1·38 microns long and 0·74 microns diameter tend to move with their longest axis in the direction of motion.[187]

Outside the viscous flow range (Re > 0·05) there is a tendency for particles to take up a preferred orientation with the largest projected area perpendicular to the direction of movement. The preferred orientation has been definitely established for tetrahedra and cubes by Re = 10, and for other shapes by Re = 20. At higher Re values, between 70 and 300, particle instability sets in. Some particles wobble from side to side while others spin; rods spin about their axis while cubes and disks sideslip; tetrahedra tend to follow a spiral path.[202] The side to side oscillation of disks such as falling leaves is a common observation.

TABLE 4.2. EQUIVALENT DIAMETERS AND SHAPE FACTORS

Name	Symbol	Definition
Surface diameter	d_s	Diameter of sphere with the same external surface area as the particle
Volume diameter	d_v	Diameter of sphere with same volume as the volume of the particle
Area diameter	d_A	Diameter of circle with same area as projected area of particle
Drag diameter	d_e	Diameter of sphere with same resistance to motion as the particle in a fluid of same viscosity and at the same velocity
Sphericity	Ψ	Ratio of surface area of sphere with same volume as the particle to the actual surface area of the particle
Circularity	χ	Ratio of the circumference of a circle having same cross-sectional area as the irregular particle to the actual perimeter of the irregular particles cross-section

Besides particle orientation two other factors must be introduced in the fluid resistance equations for spheres if equations of the same form are to be used for non-spherical particles. These are a linear dimension equivalent to the diameter of the sphere, and a correction factor based on the surface area of the particle to adjust the surface area term in equation (4.2). Incorporating both these factors and dependent on the aerodynamic behaviour of the particles is the *drag diameter* which was introduced previously. When fluid resistance is to be deduced from the geometry of the particles, then the two factors must be considered separately. The equivalent diameter is defined in terms of either the particle surface area, volume or projected area, while the area correction terms are dimensionless ratios called "shape" factors. The most useful of these were introduced by Wadell[509] and are the sphericity Ψ, which is excellent as a correlation factor for non-spherical particles, and the circularity χ.

The definitions of the equivalent diameters and shape factors are summarized in Table 4.2.

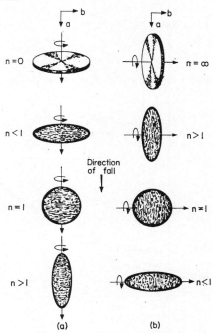

FIG. 4.7. Ellipsoids of revolution.[118]
(a) Moving along axis of revolution.
(b) Moving in a direction perpendicular to axis of revolution.

In the *viscous flow region*, the drag diameter can be deduced theoretically[118] for ellipsoidal particles. The drag diameter in each case depends on the orientation, which may be the ellipsoidal particle moving in line, or at right angles to its axis of revolution, as shown in Fig. 4.7. In the first case ellipsoidal particles have a major axis, a, and two equal minor axes, b and c, which can be expressed as fractions, the major axis by using a multiplier, n. The other cases are variants of this. The results are graphed for four cases, these being shown in Fig. 4.8.

Case (i) Ellipsoid of revolution moving along its axis of revolution

$$a = \text{axis of revolution}$$

$$a = nb, \quad b = c$$

Case (ii) Ellipsoid of revolution moving in a direction at right angles to its axis of revolution

$$b = \text{axis of revolution}$$
$$a = nb$$
$$a = c$$

Case (iii) Elliptical plate moving edgeways

$$a = nb$$
$$c = 0$$

Case (iv) Elliptical plate moving in a direction perpendicular to its own plane

$$a = 0$$
$$b = \text{major axis}$$
$$c = nb$$

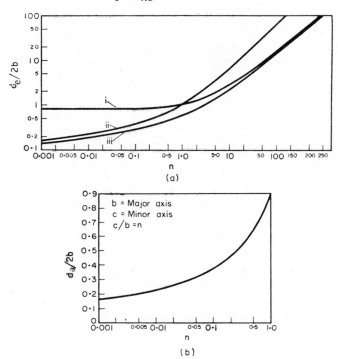

FIG. 4.8. Equivalent diameters d_e for ellipsoids of revolution.[118]

(a) Moving in direction of a axis:

    (i) $a = $ axis of rotation. $a = nb$, $b = c$.

    (ii) $b = $ axis of rotation. $a = c = nb$.

    (iii) Elliptical plate moving sideways. $a = nb$, $c = 0$.

(b) Elliptical plate moving in direction perpendicular to its own plane.

The equivalent diameter required, d_e, can be found by equating $d_e/2b$ to the value read off the curves in Fig. 4.8 for the value of n for the appropriate case.

For isometric particles[94,370] — cubes, octahedra, cube octahedra and tetrahedra — the particle velocity can be obtained by multiplying the velocity

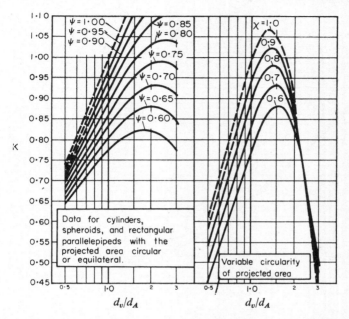

FIG. 4.9. Correlation of settling factor K as a function of the sphericity Ψ and circularity χ for various ratios d_v/d_A for non-isometric particles in the viscous flow region.[213]

for a sphere with equivalent volume diameter, d_v, by an empirical correction factor K, given by:

$$K = 0.843 \log_{10} \Psi/0.065 \qquad (4.37)$$

where Ψ = sphericity = d_v^2/d_s^2.

For non-isometric particles[213] — cylinders, parallel pipeds and spheroids — the particle velocity can be found by using a series of correlation curves (Fig. 4.9), which also yield a correction factor K. This is a function of the ratio of volume diameter to area diameter, d_v/d_A, and the particle sphericity as a parameter. These curves are probably also applicable to irregular particles. Outside the viscous flow region, experimental results are more limited, but a number of empirical correlations have been suggested.[32,41,322,370,377] The simplest method is to employ the empirical correlations using the sphericity of the particles as graphed in Fig. 4.10 for isometric particles. For more irregular particles it has been suggested that the drag coefficient can be calculated from[202]

$$C_D = \frac{4(\varrho_p - \varrho)\ g d_v^3}{3\varrho u^2 d_s^2} = \frac{\Psi\ 4(\varrho_p - \varrho)\ g d_v}{3\varrho u^2} \tag{4.38}$$

for

$$\mathrm{Re} = \frac{\varrho u d_s}{\mu} = \frac{1}{\sqrt{(\Psi)}} \cdot \frac{\varrho u d_v}{\mu} \tag{4.39}$$

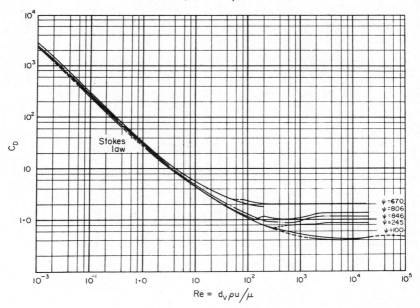

FIG. 4.10. Correlation of drag coefficient C_D for isometric particles with different sphericity Ψ.[370]

In the fully turbulent region (Re > 2000) the relation

$$C_D = 5.31 - 4.88\Psi \tag{4.40}$$

has been fitted to experimental values.[370]

4.8. PARTICLE ROUGHNESS

At present no measure of roughness of particles exists similar to that which has been introduced for pipe flows, although the effect of roughness on particle behaviour has been observed. For example, while smooth spheres will not spin in fluids at high Reynolds numbers, rough ones have been observed to do so.

It is suggested that at low speeds rough particles carry an envelope of fluid in the indentations and the particle dimension to be considered is the external diameter of the particle.[204] At higher velocities, the critical value of C_D will occur much lower with rough particles than with smooth ones.

4.9. PARTICLE DENSITY

Even particles which appear to be homogeneous often consist of agglomerates and non-homogeneous mixtures. This has been demonstrated for smokes and other particle systems from vapour phase processes by Whytlaw-Grey and Patterson,[540] who measured particle density by a method identical with that employed by Milliken in his "oil drop" experiment for measuring the electronic charge.

TABLE 4.3. OBSERVED DENSITIES OF PARTICLES (WHYTLAW-GREY AND PATTERSON)[540]

Material	Normal density	Maximum value		Average of low values	
		density	diameter microns	density	diameter microns
Cadmium oxide	6·5	2·70	2·42	0·51	5·96
Silver	10·5	4·22	1·79	0·94	4·30
Gold	19·3	8·00	2·35	1·24	5·54
Mercuric chloride	5·4	4·32	4·53	1·27	3·63
Mercury	13·6	10·8	2·05	1·7	3·08
Magnesium oxide	3·6	3·48	3·26	0·35	7·29

Table 4.3 lists some of the experimental densities measured, together with the normal densities of the material, the average of the lower group of values and the corresponding particle sizes. The data indicates that some of the particles are virtually homogeneous, for example mercuric chloride and magnesium oxide fume, consisting of tightly packed units. Other particles appear to be loosely grouped agglomerates and have much lower masses than would be expected with the diameters measured microscopically. Therefore, in many cases of agglomerate particles, a knowledge of particle size and shape factor from physical examination may not be adequate for determination of fluid resistance.

CHAPTER 5

GRAVITY AND MOMENTUM
SEPARATION EQUIPMENT

5.1. INTRODUCTION

The simplest method of removing particles from a moving gas stream is to allow them to settle out under the force of gravity. Large particles will often do so on the floor of a horizontal duct, which acts in this instance as a simple settling chamber, while specially designed chambers will act as efficient collectors of coarse particles. Coarse particles, frequently designated as grit, are usually defined as those unable to pass through a 200 mesh screen, or larger than 76 microns. For these particles, particularly if they are abrasive, simple settling chambers are a preferred means of collection because of the low pressure loss through the plant as well as the long maintenance free periods obtained with this type of plant.[79]

Momentum separators rely essentially on producing a sudden change of direction in the gas stream. The particles, because of their inertia, will continue to move in the same direction as the initial gas flow, and move into a collecting hopper, while the gas stream, freed of its larger particles, leaves the collector. Momentum separators are slightly more complex in construction than settling chambers, but have the advantage that they take up less room, and in their more sophisticated form, are able to collect particles down to about twenty microns with reasonable efficiency.

5.2. THEORY OF SETTLING CHAMBER DESIGN

In settling chambers the gas stream is slowed down sufficiently to allow particles to settle out. In theory, a very large settling chamber would give sufficient time for even very small particles to be collected, but practical size limitations restrict the applicability of these chambers to the collection of coarse particles.[22] In the horizontal type chamber (Fig. 5.1), an average gas velocity U (ft/sec) can be assumed to represent piston flow through the chamber. This can be simply derived from the gas flow rate Q (ft^3/sec) and the height (H ft) and breadth (B ft) of the chamber:

$$U = Q/B \cdot H \quad \text{ft/sec} \tag{5.1}$$

From the length (L ft) of the chamber, the *residence time* (t secs) of the gas can be calculated:

$$t = \frac{L}{U} = \frac{L.B.H}{Q} = \frac{V}{Q} \text{ sec} \qquad (5.2)$$

where V = volume of the chamber.

If a particle of size d of a particular material will settle a distance h ft in t secs, then h/H represents the fraction of particles of this size that will be collected. If h is equal to or greater than H, all particles of that size (or larger) will be collected in the settling chamber. A curve of h/H ratios for

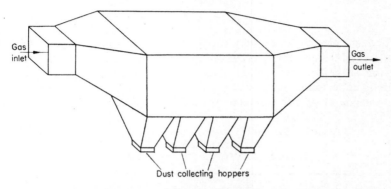

Gas inlet

Gas outlet

Dust collecting hoppers

FIG. 5.1. Horizontal flow settling chamber with square cross-section.

the different sizes of a material is the *fractional* or *grade* efficiency curve for the settling chamber.

The value of h can be found from the product of the mean falling speed u_m of the particle, and the residence time t

$$h = u_m t \qquad (5.3)$$

If the particles are sufficiently small to reach their terminal velocity u_t in a negligibly small fraction of the residence time, this can be taken as equal to the mean velocity u_m. If the particles are of such a size that this assumption cannot be made, then the distance settled by the particles must be calculated in two stages. First the distance fallen, and time taken to reach 99 per cent of the terminal velocity are found (equations 4.18 and 4.20) and then the distance fallen during the remaining residence time is calculated. If the terminal velocity is not reached during the gas stream residence time, equation (4.17) has to be used in the integrated form with the residence time (0 to t) as boundary conditions. When the particles are smaller than 76 microns Stokes' law gives a reasonable approximation to the terminal falling speed. For larger particles, the general equation (4.12) must be used, with the correct drag coefficient C_D, calculated from equation (4.7). Settling velocities for spherical particles of unit density, both experimental and calculated from Stokes' law, are listed in Table 5.1.

When Stokes' law can be used for the terminal velocity, and this is a reasonable approximation for the average settling velocity, the particle size that will be wholly retained within the chamber can be found from:

$$d_{min} = \sqrt{\left(\frac{18HU\mu}{(\varrho_p - \varrho)\,gL}\right)} \qquad (5.4a)$$

$$= \sqrt{\left(\frac{18Q\mu}{(\varrho_p - \varrho)\,gBL}\right)} \qquad (5.4b)$$

These simple equations should only be used as a guide to the collection efficiency of the chamber, as the complicating factors of falling speeds outside the Stokes' law range are nearly always of some importance for the particles collected by settling chambers. Other factors which must be taken into consideration are hindered settling effects which will occur at high

TABLE 5.1. SETTLING VELOCITIES OF SPHERICAL PARTICLES OF
UNIT DENSITY IN AIR
Temperature: 20°C (68°F): Pressure 760 mm Hg.

Particle diameter microns	Experimental cm/sec	Calculated from Stokes' law cm/sec
0·1	$8·7 \times 10^{-5}$	$8·71 \times 10^{-5}$
0·2	$2·3 \times 10^{-4}$	$2·27 \times 10^{-4}$
0·4	$6·8 \times 10^{-4}$	$6·85 \times 10^{-4}$
1·0	$3·5 \times 10^{-3}$	$3·49 \times 10^{-3}$
2	$1·19 \times 10^{-2}$	$1·19 \times 10^{-2}$
4	$5·0 \times 10^{-2}$	$5·00 \times 10^{-2}$
10	$3·06 \times 10^{-1}$	$3·06 \times 10^{-1}$
20	1·2	1·2
40	4·8	5
100	24·6	25
400	157	483
1000 = 1 mm	382	3050

particle concentrations (section 4.6). All these tend to reduce the collection efficiency.

The other major design factor in specifying settling chamber dimensions is that gas flow velocities must be kept below the re-entrainment or "pick up" velocity of the deposited dust. As a general rule[298] velocities below 10 ft/sec are satisfactory for most materials. Some materials, such as starch powder and carbon black, however, are re-entrained at lower velocities, while for heavy particles which have agglomerated into larger lumps, much higher velocities could be used. Some experimental re-entrainment velocities are given in Table 5.2. Because of these factors, and the problem of obtaining an even gas flow through the chamber, the actual efficiency of the chamber is not likely to be as predicted by the simple relations given above.

TABLE 5.2. PICK UP VELOCITIES OF VARIOUS MATERIALS[30]

Material	Density g/cm³	Median size microns	Pick up Velocity ft/sec
Aluminium chips	2·72	335	14·2
Asbestos	2·20	261	17·0
Non-ferrous foundry dust	3·02	117	18·8
Lead oxide	8·26	14·7	25·0
Limestone	2·78	71	21·0
Starch	1·27	64	5·8
Steel shot	6·85	96	15·2
Wood chips	1·18	1370	13·0
Wood sawdust	—	1400	22·3

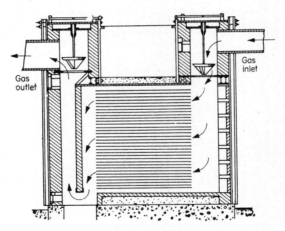

FIG. 5.2. Howard multi-tray settling chamber.[298]

Improved settling chamber efficiencies in the horizontal flow type chamber can be achieved by decreasing the height a particle has to fall before being collected. This has been applied in the Howard settling chamber (Fig. 5.2) where a number of collecting trays have been inserted in the chamber. The main objection to the wide use of the Howard chamber is

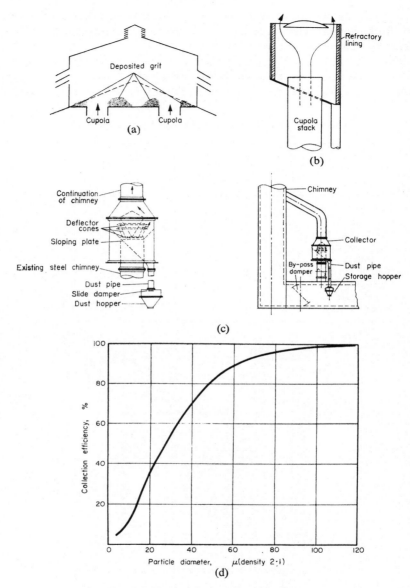

FIG. 5.3. Vertical flow settling chambers.

(a) Simple penthouse grit arrestor.[437]

(b) Simple grit arrestor for cupolas.[437]

(c) Deflector-type grit arrestor.[376]

(d) Fractional efficiency curve for arrestor shown in Fig. 5.3(c).[376]

that the spaces between the trays are difficult to clean, although this could be overcome by installing a self-cleaning system, such as a spray washer.

If a chamber, height H, contains N trays, then the height in each section is approximately $H/(N + 1)$, and the fractional efficiency $h(N + 1)/H$.

The vertical flow settling chamber is essentially an elutriator, removing those particles whose settling speed is greater than the gas velocity. Units of this type are used as grit arrestors on small cupolas and in small boiler plant. In its simplest form as in the penthouse type for several cupolas (Fig. 5.3a) the dust moves to heaps at the side of the arrestor entry, and some material falls back into the cupola. The penthouse is cleaned manually when the plant is not operating. More sophisticated are the deflector type units, where the gas stream is deflected outwards, so that the particles fall into the collecting annulus around the stack (Figs. 5.3b and 5.3c).

In a unit of type Fig. 5.3b, where the arrestor diameter is about two and a half times the stack diameter, the velocity in the arrestor is only $1/(2\frac{1}{2})^2$, i.e. $1/6\frac{1}{4}$, of the stack velocity, and so very coarse particles of the order of 200–400 microns, which are carried away in a stack with a gas velocity of 5–7 ft/sec will be collected in an arrestor of this type.

5.3. APPLICATION OF SIMPLE SETTLING CHAMBERS

For the collection of coarse grit the simple settling chambers have a number of advantages and disadvantages. The advantages are:

(i) Simple construction.
(ii) Low initial cost and maintenance.
(iii) Low pressure losses and no temperature and pressure limitations except those of materials of construction.
(iv) Dry disposal of collected materials.
(v) No problems with abrasive materials.

The major disadvantage, for the horizontal flow unit, is the very large space requirement of the chamber.

In one typical installation on a sinter plant,[79] the volume handled is 81 million ft³/hr (ambient temperatures). With an inlet concentration of 0·4 gr./ft³ (1 g/Nm³), this is equivalent to 50 tons/day of solids. The settling chamber (Fig. 5.4) reduces this to 10 tons/day or 0·16 gr./ft³. With such large volumes, the low power consumption with the low pressure loss in the unit is of great economic importance.

Jennings[237] has calculated fractional efficiency curves for the two most important dust constituents from a sinter plant, quartz (sp. gr. 2.6) and iron oxide (sp. gr. 4.5). The chamber in this example is 10 ft high and wide, and 20 ft long. The volume flow is 2 million ft³/hr. The curves (Fig. 5.5) show that all particles with a density of 4·5 larger than 80 microns are likely to be collected but only 70 per cent of the lighter particles when these are 100 microns in diameter.

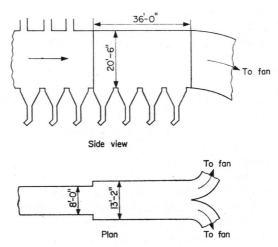

FIG. 5.4. Settling chamber in a sinter plant.[79]

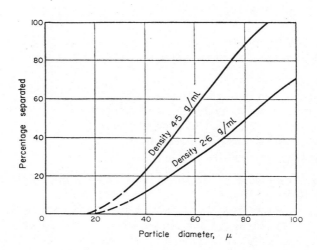

FIG. 5.5. Predicted fractional efficiency curves for dusts from a sinter plant.[237]

The efficiency for a vertical flow stack collector is not very high. For a typical shell boiler plant, 75 per cent overall collection efficiency was obtained with a stack arrestor (type Fig. 5.3c).[229] For small plants this may, however, be satisfactory.

5.4. MOMENTUM SEPARATORS

The efficiency of a simple settling chamber can be improved, and space requirements reduced, by giving particles a downward momentum in addition to the gravity settling effect. The number of possible designs incorporating this principle is very great, varying from a simple baffle in the chamber to specially designed jets which give accelerated settling.

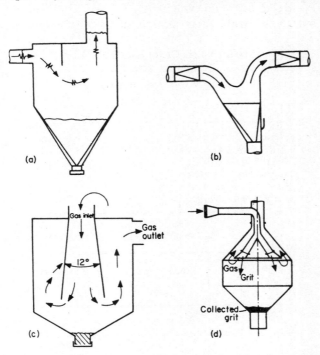

FIG. 5.6. Baffle-type collectors where particles are slightly accelerated towards the hopper.
(a) Simple baffle type.[6]
(b) Rounded inertial trap.[6]
(c) Downward facing entry.[237]
(d) Accelerated settling chamber with deepened hopper.[380]

Simple baffle chambers (Fig. 5.6a) are sometimes placed in series. Although their efficiency is of the same order as the horizontal chamber, the pressure loss is greater. This can be lowered by using a pattern which has rounded baffles (Fig. 5.6b).

Other momentum collectors use a downwards facing tube to give additional downwards movement to the particles, which is of the order of $g/3$

in addition to the normal gravitational force g. One worker (Fig. 5.6c)[237] has suggested that a cone with gradually increasing diameter gives a slower moving gas at the base of the chamber and reduces re-entrainment. Similar ideas were probably responsible for features of Prockat's accelerated settling chamber such as the hopper following a deep cylindrical section (Fig. 5.6d).[381] Test results for both coal and fly ash samples are available for this model, and are shown in Table 5.3, together with the dust gradings used. The data shows that increased gas velocity reduces the chamber efficiency. The depth of the turbulent zone in the cylindrical portion of the chamber must be critical in determining the re-entrainment of particles.

TABLE 5.3. SIZE GRADING OF TEST DUST[381]

	Pulverized coal %	Boiler fly ash %
Greater than 200 micron	0	2·08
120 microns–200 microns	1·84	7·08
90 microns–120 microns	2·92	14·88
75 microns– 90 microns	6·48	5·28
60 microns– 75 microns	13·52	10·08
Smaller than 60 microns	75·24	60·60

Efficiency of the Prockat model momentum collector

Gas velocity at inlet ft/sec	Dust content g/m³	Efficiency %
Pulverized coal		
24·2	34·9	74·3
32·4	91·0	63·0
39·8	23·4	47·0
Boiler fly ash		
17·6	19·8	79·7
28·6	21·1	70·5
44·4	10·3	55·5

More elaborate, and also more efficient, is the collector where the gas is allowed to impinge on a surface which is shaped in such a way as to retain the particles while allowing the gas to escape. In one type, the venturi momentum collector (Fig. 5.7),[483] the gas passes horizontally through a

series of venturi shaped passages (a) formed by the diamond shaped ducts
(b) extending from within a short distance of the top to the bottom of the
main duct. The velocity of the gas increases as it approaches the throat of
the venturi passages, and the momentum of the particles causes them to
concentrate along the conveying walls. The concentrate passes through the
slots (f) in the vertical ducts and is trapped in the V of the vertical duct. The

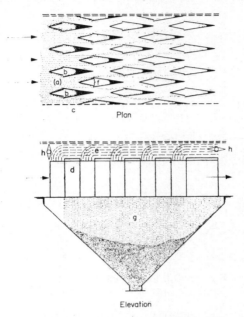

FIG. 5.7. Venturi baffle collector.[483]

dust drops into the hopper, while the gas leaves the top of the ducts. The
traps are arranged in series of 6, 9 or 12 rows, and dampers (h) control the
flow and act as by-pass valves.

Another device, which also has a very low pressure drop, is the D.E.P.
curtain type collector.[320] (Fig. 5.8). The basic element is a U profile where
the jets of dust laden gases, formed by the spaces in a row of these profiles,
impinge on the base of the U, and the gas rebounds or moves in a circular
motion in the curved portion. The impingement and circular movement
throw the dust out of the gas stream, and it falls into the hopper below.
Rapping or vibration is applied in some cases to assist the dust to fall off
the U channels. Liquid sprays can also be used for this, and these prevent
re-entrainment.

The system is very robust and can be used at high temperatures and in
corrosive conditions. For example, in acid conditions the collector cells can
be made of acid resistant stainless steels, and the chamber walls lined with

acid resistant tiles. The pressure drop through installations varies from 0·1 to 0·4 in. W.G., and may be lower in certain plants. Data on actual plants show the following results:

(a) Cement plant, limestone rotary dryer.

      Inlet concentration: 8·8–30 gr./ft³, 38 per cent less than 10 microns

Temperature:	260°F
Flow rate:	28,000 (ft)³/min
Pressure loss:	0·063 in. W.G.
Efficiency:	80–91 per cent

(b) Steam generator fed with pulverized coal.

Pressure loss:	0·13 in. W.G.
Efficiency (12 rows):	80 per cent.

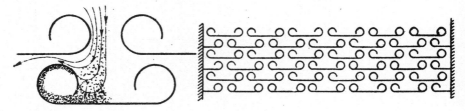

FIG. 5.8. D.E.P. curtain collector.[320]

Incomplete data on a number of other plants show generally the same results.

A collector which combines some features of both the ones just described is the reverse nozzle impingement separator (Fig. 5.9) where the dust laden gases impinge on a curved slotted surface which reverses the gas flow but allows the dust particles to pass through the slots to an enclosed channel where they can fall into the hopper.

Also in the category of momentum collectors is the Calder–Fox scrubber,[145] which is used for the recovery of acid mists. (Fig. 5.10). The gas carrying the acid mist droplets is forced through orifices where agglomeration takes place and then impinges on baffles, where the agglomerated droplets are deposited. The construction of the plant uses either lead sheets with holes or alternatively, for operation at higher temperatures, strips of glass which are more fragile, but better able to withstand high temperature. In the case of lead sheets, ⅛ in. thick sheets are used, with ⅛ in. dia. holes machined on a ⅜ or ½ in. square pitch, followed by the impact plate, with holes on the same centres, but ¼ in. dia. This is followed by a collector plate

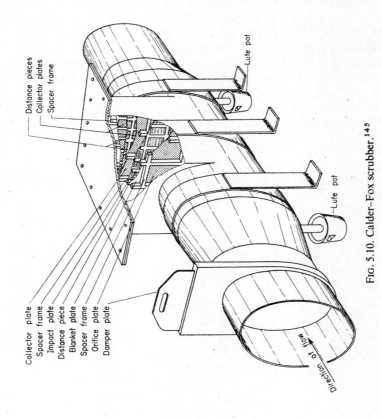

Fig. 5.10. Calder–Fox scrubber.[145]

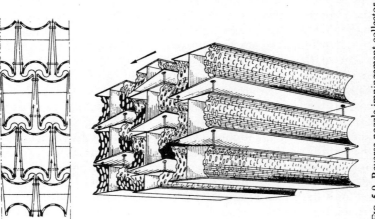

Fig. 5.9. Reverse nozzle impingement collector.[298]

with $\frac{1}{12}$ in. dia. holes, $\frac{1}{8}$ in. apart. In the glass unit the orifice slots are $\frac{1}{16}$ in. wide and the impact slots $\frac{1}{8}$ in. wide, spaced on $\frac{5}{16}$ in. centre lines. The published literature shows how difficult it is to get straight edged glass without curvature for the glass strips. Velocities in the "scrubber" are about 95–115 ft/sec, with a pressure drop of 3·5–5·5 in. W. G. Higher velocities lead to re-entrainment, while at lower velocities, less efficient collection takes place. The efficiency of the Calder–Fox type collector is 90–97 per cent, and droplets as small as 2–2·5 microns are collected.

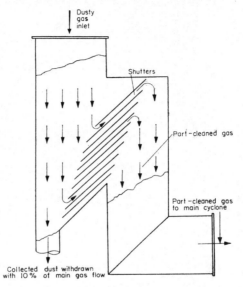

FIG. 5.11. Shutter-type collector.[462]

The principle that a sudden change in direction of the gas stream will leave the coarser particles to continue to move directly ahead is also applied in the shutter type of collector (Fig. 5.11), which is sometimes used as a low resistance pre-cleaner before cyclones or bag houses. Here about 80 per cent of the gas stream, partially cleaned, is drawn through the shutters while the rest of the dusty gas is passed to a cyclone.

Much more efficient are the louvred collectors where the dust laden gas stream enters the larger end of a truncated cone (Fig. 5.12), having almost its entire surface perforated with louvred slots. The gas stream changes direction to pass through the cone, while the dust is not deflected but passes on to the end of the cone, together with a small fraction of the gas stream, where it is drawn off to a secondary collector. The developers of this equipment also claim that the flow pattern near the louvres tends to send the particles towards the central gas stream in the cone. This type of equipment is very useful for the collection of fly ash in small installations with a varying

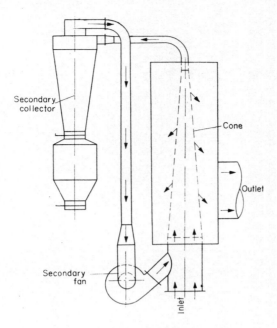

FIG. 5.12. Louvre-type collector.[239]

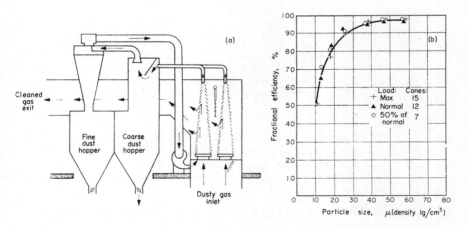

FIG. 5.13. Louvred cone collector for power stations.

(a) Diagrammatic representations for louvre-type collector followed by baffled chamber and cyclone in series.[193]

(b) Fractional efficiency curves.[193]

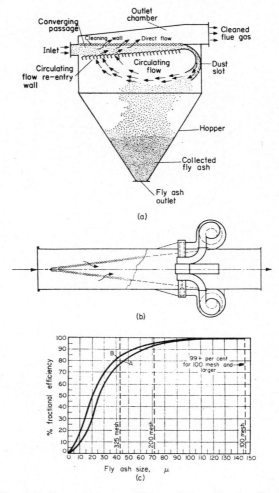

Fig. 5.14. Two other types of low-resistance fly ash collectors:
(a) Using gravity settling for dust separation.[230]
(b) Using cyclones for dust separation.[230]
(c) Fractional efficiency graphs for these two types.[230]

load, as the efficiency of the collector seems to be relatively constant under these conditions.[193]

For larger throughput of gases, several of these collectors can be arranged in parallel. A typical arrangement is shown in Fig. 5.13a, where the louvred collector is followed by a baffled settling chamber and cyclone in series. The efficiency of this combination has been measured[193] and the fractional efficiency curve is shown in Fig. 5.13b. for fly ash collection. It is seen that the efficiency is similar to a high throughput medium efficiency cyclone, but the pressure drop is of the order of $1-1\frac{1}{2}$ in. W.G., which is somewhat lower than that of the cyclone. Other examples of louvred collectors are shown in Figs. 5.14a. and 5.14b. The resistance in these collectors is lower, and so is the efficiency, as may be seen from the fractional efficiency curves (Fig. 5.14c.). These units are widely used as grit arrestors in small boiler plants.

CHAPTER 6

CENTRIFUGAL SEPARATORS

6.1. INTRODUCTION

Cyclones, the generic name for collection systems where particles are removed from spinning gases by centrifugal forces, are probably the most common dust removal systems used in industry. They are simple to construct and the conventional types have no moving parts. Because they can be made from a variety of materials, including those with refractory and corrosion resistant properties for special applications, there are no temperature limits to the use of cyclones and maintenance can be reduced to a minimum.

The centrifugal force on particles in a spinning gas stream is much greater than gravity, therefore cyclones are effective in the removal of much smaller particles than gravitational settling chambers, and require much less space to handle the same gas volumes. On the other hand, the pressure drop in a cyclone is greater, and power consumption is much higher. Cyclones are distinguished from momentum separators, which were discussed in Chapter 5, in that in the latter there is simply a diversion of the gas stream from its original path, while in cyclones there are a number of revolutions of the gas stream. Gravity settling chambers and momentum separators are used, with few special exceptions, for the collection of coarse grit — particles greater than 75 microns — while commercial cyclones are effective in collecting particles down to 10 microns (when their density is unity) and can be used for smaller particles in certain designs.

When large grit particles are present in appreciable quantities, particularly if these are very hard, the cyclone walls may suffer from erosion and it is often desirable to introduce a collector of the momentum separator or gravity settling chamber type as a precursor to the cyclone.

The spinning motion can be applied to the gas stream in several ways, and cyclone types can be classified accordingly. The gases can be drawn through curved vanes in a duct, in a unit called the *straight through cyclone*[307] or *vortex air cleaner*,[113] or they can be spun in a special turbine.[545] In the conventional or *reverse flow cyclone* the gases are admitted tangentially to a cylindrical upper section which contains a centrally placed exhaust pipe penetrating below the tangential inlet, while a conical lower section is connected to the dust hopper. The gases in this case spiral down

160

towards the apex of the cone and then are reversed up again through the exit.

This chapter discusses the theory of particle separation in a spinning gas, and the application of this to the design of the various types of cyclone. Commercial types are described, and, as far as possible, experimental fractional efficiency data is presented for these. Methods of calculating cyclone efficiency and pressure drop are reviewed in detail.

6.2. PARTICLE SEPARATION IN A SPINNING GAS

The simplest system that can be studied in the case of cyclone separators is the motion of a particle in a spiralling gas stream. If a gas stream enclosing a particle moves round the arc of a circle (Fig. 6.1), and it is assumed that the particle has the same tangential velocity as the gas stream, then the centrifugal force on the particle, F, that is the force normal to the tangent of the arc, is given by

$$F = m \frac{u_T^2}{R} \qquad (6.1)$$

where m = mass of the particle

R = radius of the circle

u_T = tangential component of the gas velocity.

When the path of the gas is a spiral along the walls of a cylinder (the system used commercially in the straight-through cyclone), the particles will move outwards as they are carried along by the gas stream, and their path will be an expanding helix. The particle velocity can be resolved into three velocity components: the tangential velocity u_T, tangential to the gas spiral and normal to the axis; the radial drift velocity u_R, normal to the tangential component and normal to the axis; and the axial velocity u_H, along the axis of the gas spiral. The magnitude of the centrifugal force is frequently described in terms of the number of times **n** this exceeds the force of gravity, mg. This number is therefore found by dividing the centrifugal force (equation 6.1) by mg:

$$\mathbf{n} = \frac{u_T^2}{Rg} \qquad (6.2)$$

It is often assumed that the free vortex formula can be applied to the system.[35, 113, 120, 149, 472, 500]. Then the tangential velocity u_T and the radius are related by the equation:

$$u_T R^n = \xi \qquad (6.3)$$

where ξ = constant

and $n = 1$.

It should be noted however that experimentally for gas cyclones the value of the exponent n is found to be 0·5–0·7 and not unity. The following analysis however, has not yet been completed[472] with the experimental exponent.

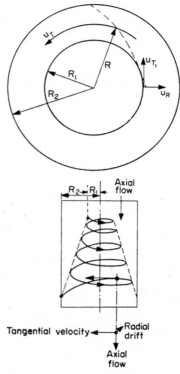

Fig. 6.1. Resolution of velocity of a particle in a spiralling gas stream.

If at a time t, the position of the particle in cylindrical co-ordinates is given by (R, θ), then the radial drift velocity component of the particle is

$$u_R = \frac{\mathrm{d}R}{\mathrm{d}t} \tag{6.4}$$

and the tangential velocity component is

$$u_T = R\frac{\mathrm{d}\theta}{\mathrm{d}t} \tag{6.5}$$

(assuming that the tangential particle and gas velocities are the same).

The radial acceleration is then equal to

$$\frac{du_R}{dt} = \frac{d^2R}{dt^2} - R\left(\frac{d\theta}{dt}\right)^2 \tag{6.6}$$

and the tangential acceleration is given by

$$\frac{du_T}{dt} = R\frac{d^2\theta}{dt^2} + 2\frac{d\theta}{dt}\cdot\frac{dR}{dt} \tag{6.7}$$

Multiplying the accelerations on the particles by the particle mass gives the forces on the particles (Newton's second law), and these forces will be opposed by the resistance of the gas to any relative movement of the particles. If it is assumed that the particles encounter the same resistance as in steady state motion through a laminar gas, and their relative velocity is in the viscous flow region, then Stokes' law (equation 4.4) may be applied, and the equations of motion of the particle (assumed to be a sphere) relative to the gas stream are:

(a) Radially:

$$\frac{m}{3\pi d\mu}\left\{\frac{d^2R}{dt^2} - R\left(\frac{d\theta}{dt}\right)^2\right\} = -u_R = -\frac{dR}{dt} \tag{6.8}$$

(b) Tangentially:

$$\frac{m}{3\pi\mu d}\left\{R\frac{d^2\theta}{dt^2} + 2\frac{dR}{dt}\cdot\frac{d\theta}{dt}\right\} = 0. \tag{6.9}$$

(The tangential component is zero because it is assumed that the particle and gas tangential velocities are the same).

To integrate these equations (6.8) and (6.9) they are put into dimensionless form by:

(i) Expressing the radii in terms of the external radius R_2:

$$R = rR_2 \tag{6.10}$$

(ii) Expressing the velocities in terms of the velocity at the external radius u_{T_2}:

$$u_R = u\cdot u_{T_2} \tag{6.11}$$

(iii) Expressing the times in terms of the ratio R_2/u_{T_2}:

$$t = \tau R_2/u_{T_2} \tag{6.12}$$

where r, u and τ are dimensionless variables.

Equations (6.8) and (6.9) now reduce to:

(a) Radially:

$$T \left\{ \frac{d^2 r}{d\tau^2} - r \left(\frac{d\theta}{d\tau} \right)^2 \right\} = -\frac{dr}{d\tau} \tag{6.13}$$

(b) Tangentially:

$$T \left\{ r \frac{d^2\theta}{d\tau^2} + 2 \cdot \frac{dr}{d\tau} \cdot \frac{d\theta}{d\tau} \right\} = 0 \tag{6.14}$$

where

$$T = \frac{mu_{T_2}}{3\pi\mu d R_2}$$

substituting $\pi d^3(\varrho_p - \varrho)/6$ for m, assuming that the particles are spherical, with diameter d, then

$$T = \frac{d^2(\varrho_p - \varrho)u_{T_2}}{18\mu R_2} \tag{6.15}$$

Equation (6.14) reduces to:

$$\frac{T}{r} \frac{d}{d\tau} \left(r^2 \frac{d\theta}{d\tau} \right) = 0 \tag{6.16}$$

which gives:

$$r^2 \frac{d\theta}{d\tau} = \text{constant} \tag{6.17}$$

By multiplying equation (6.5) by R on both sides:

$$R^2 \frac{d\theta}{dt} = u_T R = u_{T_2} R_2 \tag{6.18}$$

and substituting for u_{T_2} and R_2 it can be shown that the constant in equation (6.17) is unity.

Substituting (6.17) in equation (6.13) gives:

$$\frac{d^2 r}{d\tau^2} + \frac{1}{T} \frac{dr}{d\tau} - \frac{1}{r^3} = 0 \tag{6.19}$$

Equation (6.19) is a non-linear differential equation which cannot be solved directly. A similar equation has however been solved with a differential analyser[500] and the results of this calculation for a specific case[113] are given in Table 6.1.

If the second order differential is neglected, equation (6.19) reduces to

$$\frac{dr}{d\tau} = \frac{T}{r^3} \tag{6.20}$$

and this, on integration gives:

$$\tau_2 - \tau_1 = \frac{1}{4T} (r_2^4 - r_1^4). \tag{6.21}$$

Substituting the original dimensions, the time taken for a spherical particle to drift from radius R_1 to radius R_2, using this solution, is:

$$t = \frac{9}{2} \left(\frac{\mu}{\varrho_p - \varrho} \right) \left(\frac{R_2}{u_{T_2} d} \right)^2 \left\{ 1 - \left(\frac{R_1}{R_2} \right)^4 \right\} \qquad (6.22)$$

This equation has been used for a solution in the same case as used in the numerical solution of equation (6.19). The results are also given in Table 6.1. and it is seen that this simplification gives an estimated separating

TABLE 6.1. SEPARATING DISTANCES FOR SPHERICAL PARTICLES IN A SPIRALLING GAS STREAM[113]

Data: *Air:*		
	kinematic viscosity (60°F)	= 1·56 × 10⁻⁴ ft²/sec
	density (1 Atm, 60°F)	= 0·00237 slugs/ft³
	volume flow	= 2500 ft³/hr
	mean axial velocity	= 40 ft/sec
Dimensions:	R_1 = 7/16 in.	
	R_2 = 1 in.	
	R_2/R_1 = 2·3	
	uR = constant	= 500 in²/sec
Density of dust:	= 2·7	

Particle dia. microns	Optimum separating length (in.) (eqn. 6.19)	Optimum separating length (in.) (eqn. 6.21)
3	35·6	26·8
5	11·5	8·8
10	3·5	2·4

distance about 26 per cent less than the numerical solution of the complete equation. Cyclone efficiency calculations based on this simplified equation[120] will therefore tend to over-estimate the effectiveness of the unit.

6.3. STRAIGHT THROUGH CYCLONES WITH FIXED IMPELLERS

Straight through cyclones or "vortex" gas cleaners are able to handle very large quantities of gases in a small plant. However, because of the high gas velocities used, a large amount of re-entrainment occurs: eddies formed at the walls help to "bounce" particles back into the main gas stream. In practice this is reduced by introducing a water spray at the dirty gas inlet.

In a fixed impeller straight through cyclone (Fig. 6.2) it is usual to have the suction fan on the clean air side, to reduce erosion damage to the fan blades. The separation chamber, following the fixed impeller where most of the pressure drop occurs, is therefore at a lower pressure than the gases entering the impeller. It is therefore necessary to provide additional suction on the dirty gas (concentrated dust) exit line to prevent sucking back of the collected particles.

Because of the simple flow pattern in the straight through cyclone it is possible to calculate theoretically[472] the smallest particle which should be

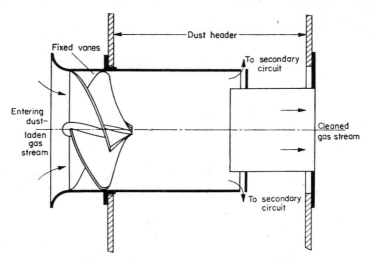

FIG. 6.2. Fixed impeller straight through cyclone.[116]

completely removed from the gas stream. Four assumptions have to be made:

    (i) There are no heat gains to the cyclone from the surroundings due to the cooling effect of the adiabatic expansion through the impeller.

  (ii) The pressure losses occur in the impeller only.

 (iii) The free vortex equation holds for the motion of the particle in the separation chamber.

 (iv) The particles leave the blades of the impeller at the blade angle.

Assuming adiabatic expansion through the impeller blades, the pressure p, temperature T and volume Q of the gas in the separation chamber (denoted by subscript c) can be calculated from the initial conditions (denoted by subscript i) before the impeller:

$$Q_c = Q_i \left(\frac{p_i}{p_c}\right)^{1/\gamma} \tag{6.23}$$

and

$$T_c = T_i \left(\frac{p_i}{p_c}\right)^{\gamma-1} \tag{6.24}$$

where γ = specific heat ratio C_p/C_v

  = 1·67 for monatomic gases
   1·40 for diatomic gases (including air)
   1·30 for triatomic gases (including superheated steam)
   1·135 for wet steam.

The pressure drop for a straight through cyclone, which occurs largely in the impeller, can be calculated from the surface area of the impeller and walls exposed to the gases.[485] Experimentally it is found to be about 5 in. water gauge (0·18 psi), and this may be taken as an approximate value over the impeller section.

If the diameter of the cyclone is D and the diameter of the core D_c, then the *average* velocity of the gases leaving the curved impeller blades u_c in terms of the initial velocity u_i is given by

$$u_c = u_i \left(\frac{D^2}{D^2 - D_c^2} \right) \frac{Q_c}{Q_i} \tag{6.25}$$

$$= u_i \left(\frac{D^2}{D^2 - D_c^2} \right) \left(\frac{p_i}{p_c} \right)^{1/\gamma} \tag{6.26}$$

The velocity u_c can be resolved into three components—tangential, axial and radial (Fig. 6.3). If the angle at which the gases leave the blades

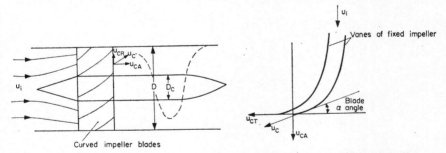

FIG. 6.3. Resolution of velocity and path of particle leaving impeller in a straight-through cyclone.
(a) Path of particle.
(b) Velocity resolution.

of the impeller is the same as the blade angle, α and the central core is extended through the separation chamber, the *average* velocity tangentially u_{CT} is:

$$u_{CT} = u_c \cos \alpha$$

$$= u_i \left(\frac{D^2}{D^2 - D_c^2} \right) \left(\frac{p_i}{p_c} \right)^{1/\gamma} \cos \alpha \tag{6.27a}$$

while the average velocity in the axial direction, u_{CA} is

$$u_{CA} = u_c \sin \alpha$$

$$= u_i \left(\frac{D^2}{D^2 - D_c^2} \right) \left(\frac{p_i}{p_c} \right)^{1/\gamma} \sin \alpha. \qquad (6.27b)$$

The residence time in the separation chamber can now be found from the length of the chamber L and the axial velocity:

$$t = \frac{L}{u_{CA}} = \frac{L}{u_i \sin \alpha} \left\{ 1 - \left(\frac{D_c}{D} \right)^2 \right\} \left(\frac{p_c}{p_i} \right)^{1/\gamma} \qquad (6.28)$$

In the general theory of cyclone separators (section 6.2) an expression (equation 6.22) was obtained for the time taken for a particle of diameter

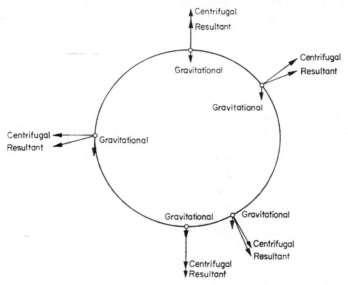

FIG. 6.4. Forces on particle moving in circular motion in a vertical plane. The force parallelograms are based approximately on particles with a tangential velocity of 2 ft/sec moving on a 1 ft radius.

d to drift from an inner to an outer radius. Then, for given chamber dimensions, it is possible to calculate the smallest particle (diameter $d_{\min}$) that could theoretically be collected in the straight through cyclone.

$$d_{\min} = \frac{3}{4} \frac{D}{\cos \alpha} \left\{ 1 - \left(\frac{D_c}{D} \right)^2 \right\} \sqrt{\left(\frac{\mu \sin \alpha}{(\varrho_p - \varrho) u_i} \left\{ \frac{p_c}{p_i} \right\}^{1/\gamma} \right)} \qquad (6.29)$$

If the further assumption is made that the particles in the gas stream are evenly distributed on leaving the impeller, then the fractions of particles smaller than d_{min} can also be calculated. Such a calculation would tend to be conservative as separation will have started in the impeller blades.

If the tangential gas velocity in a horizontal straight through cyclone is low (less than 50 ft/sec for a 2 ft dia. cyclone) then the net normal force on the particle varies appreciably according to the particle position. Thus in the bottom position (Fig. 6.4) the gravity acceleration may be added on to the centrifugal acceleration:

$$\frac{u_{CT}^2}{\sqrt{\left(\dfrac{D_c^2 + D^2}{8}\right)}} + g \tag{6.30}$$

In the top position the gravity acceleration must be subtracted from the centrifugal acceleration:

$$\frac{u_{CT}^2}{\sqrt{\left(\dfrac{D_c^2 + D^2}{8}\right)}} - g \tag{6.31}$$

while generally, in the intermediate positions the net resolved force can be obtained by adding "$g \cos \theta$"

$$\frac{u_{CT}^2}{\sqrt{\left(\dfrac{D_c^2 + D^2}{8}\right)}} + g \cos \theta \tag{6.32}$$

where θ is the angle which the radius makes with the vertical.

For tangential velocities greater than 50 ft/sec when D is not too large (less than 2 ft) the maximum correction becomes less than 0·1 per cent and can be neglected.

6.4. STRAIGHT THROUGH CYCLONES WITH MOVING IMPELLERS

An alternative to giving gases a rotational motion by sucking them through a fixed impeller has been achieved by using a specially designed turbo-compressor (Fig. 6.5).[545] A very complex design was employed to give a large tangential velocity component to the gases with a very low pressure increase.

The mean velocity u_C of the gases (and, as a first approximation, of the particles) can be calculated from:

$$u_C = N\pi \left(\frac{D + D_c}{2}\right) e \tag{6.33}$$

where N = number of turbine revolutions/unit time

e = turbine efficiency (usually about 85 per cent).

From the mean turbine velocity and each blade angle, the tangential and axial velocity components can be calculated. A procedure similar to that used with the fixed impeller unit can then be adopted for calculating fractional efficiencies for each row of turbine blades.

Three pairs of rows of turbine blades in series were used, the blade angles were 75 and 60° in the first pair, 63 and 38½° in the second, and 43° and

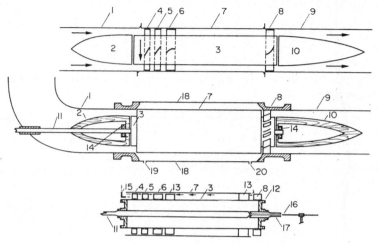

FIG. 6.5. Turbo-compressor air cleaner.[545]

1 is a fixed cylindrical inlet duct, 2 a streamlined fairing, 3 the rotating cylindrical inner sleeve of the centrifuge, and 7 the rotating outer sleeve. The compressor turbine blades 4, 5 and 6 are attached to the inner casing 3 and are separated from the outer casing 7 by small clearances. The reaction turbine blades 8 are also attached to the inner sleeve but are not included in the outer casing 7. 9 represents a cylindrical outlet duct and 10 a streamlined fairing fixed in this duct. Two clearances, left between the outer casing of the centrifuge 7 and the fixed inlet and outlet ducts, permit free rotation of the centrifuge and discharge of the liquid film.

The inlet and outlet ducts are connected by a fixed outer sleeve 18, which seals the centrifuge for operation on gases above or below atmospheric pressure. Two small outlets 19 and 20 are provided. The inlet duct 1 has been connected to a bend to permit the mounting of an electric motor for driving the centrifuge. Power is transmitted by shaft 11, which passes through fairing 2 and is supported on two sets of self-aligning ball races 14. For a large installation the motor would be mounted inside one of the fairings.

−8½° in the final pair. Rotor speeds of 5000 rev/min were used and the chamber was 6 in. dia., with a 4 in. hub, giving a tangential gas velocity of 110 ft/sec with a radial velocity of 30 ft/sec. A detailed theoretical analysis of a unit of this type is extremely difficult, and will not be attempted here.

6.5. CENTRIFUGAL FAN CYCLONE SEPARATORS

Cyclone separators based on conventional fan design are similar to the axial flow turbo-blower (section 6.4). These will act as induced draft fans in addition to acting as dust cleaning devices. Their aerodynamic characteristics are those of a forward curved centrifugal fan, for which the relations between volume flow, pressure difference and power consumption follow the standard pattern.

The dirty gas entering the fan is turned through 180° into the volute chamber, while the dust particles are accelerated by the impeller fan blades through an angle of 90°. The maximum velocity given to the particles can be calculated from the fan speed (number of revolutions per unit time N and diameter D), and the angle of the blades (α).

$$u_c = N\pi D \cos \alpha \qquad (6.34)$$

The gas flow pattern, and the particle trajectory in these units, is complex and no detailed study is available at the present time. It is therefore not possible to calculate the size of particle for which 100 per cent collection is to be expected. In general, it can however be stated, that while the centrifugal forces developed in these units is high, the gas stream residence time is comparatively small.

6.6. CONVENTIONAL (REVERSE FLOW) CYCLONES

The conventional cyclone (Fig. 6.6) has a much more complex flow pattern than the fixed impeller straight-through cyclone. Essentially the flow consists of a double spiral, the outer spiral moving down towards the hopper while the inner one moves up towards the exit pipe. Superimposed on this is a secondary gas flow from the outer towards the inner spiral. These patterns have been extensively investigated experimentally by a number of workers[151, 257, 307, 345a, 438, 462] and have recently been the subject of a detailed review.[230] The methods used have included extensive pitot tube measurements with a globe pitot tube,[345a] smoke visualization[438] in gas cyclones, dye tracers,[65, 462] and aluminium powder combined with an elegant optical technique in liquid cyclones.[257]

The most detailed measurements in gas cyclones have been carried out by ter Linden at Delft,[307] in a cyclone of normal dimensions with a scroll entry. Ter Linden's diagrams, showing tangential, radial and axial velocities as well as total and static pressures, are given in Fig. 6.7. Similar patterns, but more sharply defined, were also obtained by Kelsall[257] for a hydraulic cyclone (Fig. 6.8). From the tangential and axial velocity curves, it can be seen that there is a zone near the walls where the gases spiral downwards with increasing tangential velocity, while towards the centre the gases move towards the exit with greater tangential velocity than at the same height near the wall. The tangential velocities rise to a maximum at a ring about $\frac{1}{2}-\frac{2}{3}$ of the exit tube diameter. Within this ring is a central core with decreasing tangential velocity although the axial velocity tends to a maximum.

The radial velocity which is very much lower than the tangential velocity tends to be almost constant over much of the cyclone cross-section. The positive value indicates drift towards the axis, except at the central core where the drift is outwards. Near the core ring the radial velocity tends to have a zero value, giving some experimental confirmation to the assumptions made in calculating the cyclone "cut" particle diameter.

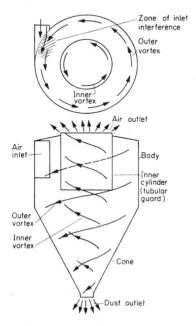

FIG. 6.6. Flow pattern in a conventional, reverse flow cyclone.[6]

The pressures at various radii show positive pressure near the wall, not very different from the pressure at the gas entry and a zone of negative pressure at the core, which is found to extend right into the hopper. Any air leaks into the hopper tend to cause an upward current right through the cyclone and out the exit pipe, re-entraining the collected dust. Conversely when the hopper is placed under suction a marked improvement in efficiency can be obtained.[130]

There is some disagreement whether the secondary flow pattern due to the axial and radial velocity components consists of a single vortex over the whole length of the cyclone (Fig. 6.9a) or a double vortex (Fig. 6.9b), one near the top next to the exit pipe and one in the conical section. The concentration of dust near the top, and the marked improvement in cyclone performance when this is removed by a special duct (van Tongeren or Ambuco types) tends to favour the double vortex, as do some ink tracer

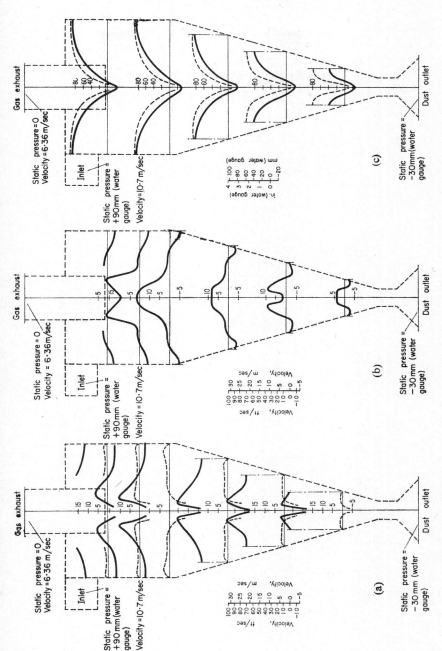

Fig. 6.7. Variation of tangential, radial and vertical components of velocity in a gas cyclone.[307]

(a) Variation of tangential velocity and radial velocity.   (b) Variation of vertical velocity.   (c) Total and static pressures.

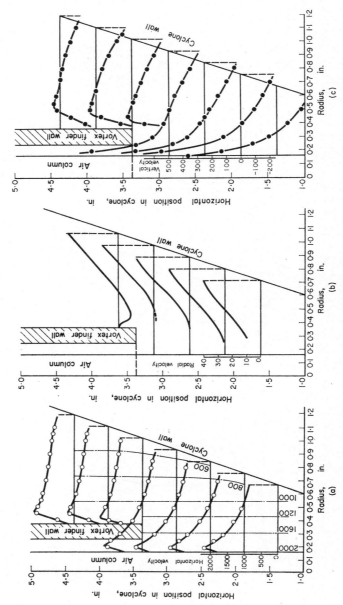

FIG. 6.8. Variation of tangential, radial and vertical components of velocity in a liquid cyclone.[257]

(a) Tangential velocities.　(b) Radial velocities.　(c) Vertical velocities.

studies in hydraulic cyclones.[156] The actual secondary flow pattern is probably an intermediate pattern of the type plotted by ter Linden.[308] (Fig. 6.9c).

The variation of tangential velocity with radius outside the central core of a conventional gas cyclone follows the vortex equation (6.3) with the exponent n equal to 0·5 in all cases measured experimentally with the exception of the early work by Prockat,[381] and the more recent studies by

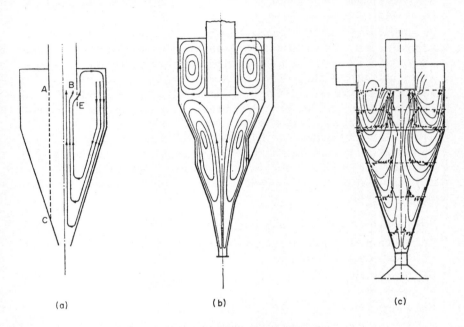

(a)   (b)   (c)

FIG. 6.9. Secondary flow patterns in cyclones.

(a) Single vortex.[158]
(b) Double vortex.[522]
(c) Intermediate pattern.[308]

First[151] and Alexander[7] which give 0·88 and 0·7 respectively for the exponent n. For liquid cyclones the exponent tends to vary between about 0·7 and 1,[230] the unit values being typical of work with cylindrical vessels. Present experimental evidence therefore tends to favour 0·5 as the value most applicable to the relation between tangential velocity and radius for gas cyclones, and for the calculation of tangential velocity the equation

$$u_T R^{0·5} = \text{constant} \qquad (6.35)$$

will be used in the next sections.

6.7. PREDICTION OF CYCLONE PERFORMANCE

A number of attempts have been made to predict the effectiveness of conventional reverse flow cyclones. Theoretical models make a number of assumptions which are not confirmed experimentally, and the predictions are only very approximate. Other methods of predicting efficiency use experimental factors which enable the whole fractional efficiency curve to be forecast with considerable precision.

A satisfactory theoretical model which makes realistic assumptions regarding the path of a particle in a cyclone of conventional design still remains to be developed, and no decision as to the most promising approach can be made at this stage. The assumptions used for several attempts to calculate the *critical particle diameter*, the particle size, which it is calculated will be collected with 100 per cent efficiency, are presented together with modifications that may lead to a more realistic estimate.

The first attempt to estimate the critical particle size was made by Rosin, Rammler and Intelmann in 1932.[406] The major assumption made was that the particle has to reach a wall by moving across a gas stream, which retains its shape after leaving the cyclone entry, in order to be collected. Other assumptions were:

(i) Particles do not influence one another.

(ii) When particles reach the cyclone wall there is negligible chance of their being re-entrained.

(iii) Stokes law can be applied to the movement of the particles relative to the gas stream.

(iv) Buoyancy effects can be neglected.

(v) Cyclones are assumed to be cylindrical in shape, with diameter D, with entrance cross-section a by b.

(vi) The tangential velocity of the particles is constant and independent of position.

The critical particle size d_{crit} was then given by :

$$d_{crit} = 3 \sqrt{\left\{ \frac{\mu g}{\pi \varrho_p u_i} \cdot \frac{R}{\mathcal{N}} \left(1 - \frac{R}{D} \right) \right\}} \tag{6.36}$$

where $R = D/2 - b/2$ (average distance of particle in inlet from cyclone axis)

$\mathcal{N}$ = number of gas stream revolutions in cyclone

u_i = velocity in inlet.

The number of revolutions, $\mathcal{N}$, are to be found from:

$$\mathcal{N} = \frac{tu_i}{\pi D} \tag{6.37}$$

where t = residence time of the gas stream

$\quad = V/Q$

Q = gas throughput per unit time

V = volume of cyclone

The effective volume of a cyclone with dimensions as shown in Fig. 6.10 is:

$$V = \frac{\pi}{4} \left\{ \left(\frac{H-h}{D-B} \right) \left(\frac{D^3 - B^3}{3} \right) + D^2 h - D_e^2 S \right\} \tag{6.38}$$

Dalla Valla[111] however has suggested that an experimental value for $\mathcal{N}$ varying between 0·5 and 3 should be used.

The importance of the gas stream configuration as it enters the cyclone has also been stressed by Rietema.[396] He suggests that all collection takes place in the layer of gas around the cyclone wall which has the thickness of the width of the cyclone entrance. The critical particle diameter is found from:

$$d_{crit} = \sqrt{\left\{ \frac{9u_H}{u_i} \cdot \frac{D}{aH} \frac{Q\mu}{\Delta p} \left(\frac{\varrho}{\varrho_p - \varrho} \right) \right\}} \tag{6.39}$$

where u_H = axial velocity.

Rietema states that above an unspecified Reynolds number, the ratio u_H/u_i can be considered approximately constant, and then for a cyclone with known dimensions D, a and H, the critical diameter becomes a function of the volume throughput and pressure drop.

These calculations of critical diameter which depend on the width of the wall layer can yield a complete fractional efficiency curve by considering the distance through which a particular particle will move in the allotted time. Thus, the d_{50} particle size (50 per cent collected) can be obtained by using the half distance across the entry. Those particles which can move this distance will be collected, while the other half will escape.

Using assumptions similar to those of Rosin, Rammler and Intelmann, except for assuming that the particle has to move across an annular ring in free vortex motion instead of the gas stream of the same shape as in the entry, Davies[120] calculated that

$$d_{crit} = \frac{3}{2} \sqrt{\left(\frac{D^2 \mu}{2H(\varrho_p - \varrho)u_t} \left\{ 1 - \left(\frac{D_e}{D} \right)^4 \right\} \right)} \tag{6.40}$$

The other major assumption here was that the residence time was given by H/u_i, which is very approximate, ignoring all other cyclone dimensions except overall height. A more practical residence time can be obtained from cyclone volume (equation. 6.38) and gas throughput Q, which gives a modified form of equation (6.40):

$$d_{\text{crit}} = 3 \sqrt{\left(\frac{Q\mu}{2\pi u_i^2(\varrho_p - \varrho)} \left\{ \frac{1 - (2D_e/3D)^4}{\dfrac{H - h}{D - B} \cdot \dfrac{D^3 - B^3}{D^2} + h - S\left(\dfrac{D_e}{D}\right)^2} \right\} \right)}$$

(6.40a)

Results similar to Davies were obtained by Feifel[149] who also assumed a free vortex particle path in a cylindrical cyclone.

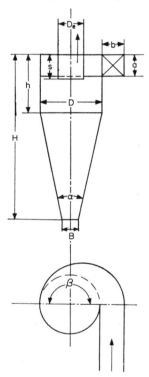

FIG. 6.10. Conventional cyclone, showing dimensions used in calculations.

The assumptions made in the theoretical derivations for critical particle diameter are not confirmed in practice, and methods for calculating cyclone efficiency based on experiment tend to be more reliable. These usually calculate the *cut* of a cyclone, which is the particle size for which 50 per cent collection efficiency is achieved.

Particles spinning in a ring at the point of maximum tangential velocity have a 50 per cent chance of being collected or passing into the exit pipe. To continue spinning in this ring the outward movement of the particles towards the wall must be balanced by the inward (radial) drift of the gases.

Stairmand[462] has suggested that the maximum tangential velocity $u_{T\max}$ is reached at a radius one half of that of the exit pipe (diameter D_e). The

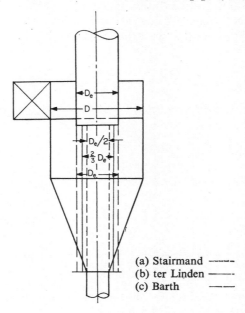

(a) Stairmand ------

(b) ter Linden ------

(c) Barth ------

FIG. 6.11. Central cores assumed by various workers.

average radial drift in to the central core is given by dividing the gas flow by the surface area of the central core (Fig. 6.11a):

$$u_{R\text{av.}} = \frac{2Q}{\pi D_e(H - S)} \tag{6.41}$$

If the fluid resistance encountered by the particle is given by Stokes' law (equation 4.4), using $u_{R\text{av.}}$ as the velocity, and this is balanced by the centrifugal force on the particle, then

$$d_{50} = \frac{3}{u_i\varphi} \sqrt{\left(\frac{Q\mu D_e}{2\pi(\varrho_p - \varrho)(H - S)D}\right)} \tag{6.42}$$

where $d_{50} = cut$ diameter for the cyclone

φ = friction factor (section 6.8 equation 6.50)

An additional modification used in deriving (6.42) has been that

$$u_{T\max}^2 D_e/4 = u_i^2 D/2 = \text{constant} \qquad (6.35a)$$

which was the experimental relation found by Stairmand.

Similar ideas to those introduced by Stairmand have been used by Barth,[35] except that the maximum tangential velocity is reached in a ring in line with the exit tube, and not within this (Fig. 6.11c). The drift velocity through the cylinder in line with the exit tube is:

$$u_{R\text{av.}} = \frac{Q}{\pi D_e(H - S)}. \qquad (6.43)$$

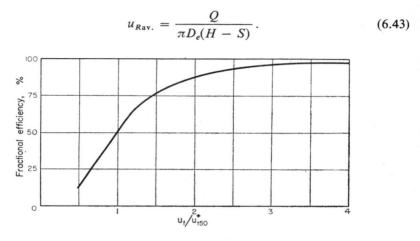

FIG. 6.12. Curve for fractional efficiency calculation (Barth).[35]

A particle with cut diameter d_{50} will have a velocity outwards equal to this, and in terms of a gravitational terminal settling velocity $u_{t_{50}}^*$ this diameter can be found by using equation (4.11) assuming viscous flow resistance, while

$$u_{t_{50}}^* = \frac{u_{R\text{av.}}}{\mathbf{n}} = \frac{Qg}{2\pi(H - S)u_T^2} \qquad (6.44)$$

The efficiency of collection of particles of other diameters, can be found by calculating their terminal gravitational settling velocities u_t, and then referring to Barth's experimental determinations (Fig. 6.12) where the ratio $u_t/u_{t_{50}}^*$ is graphed against efficiency of collection.

Ter Linden, on the basis of extensive experimental investigations has suggested that the critical particle diameter is a function of the tangential velocity u_T and cyclone exit pipe diameter only, while the general shape of the fractional efficiency curve is dependent on the other dimensions as well, such as H, S, D, the included cone angle α and the inlet angle β, and this shape remains unchanged as long as the relative dimensions are kept constant. The critical particle size is given by:

$$d_{\text{crit}} = 3\sqrt{\left(\frac{2D_e g \mu u_R}{3u_T^2(\varrho_p - \varrho)}\right)} \tag{6.45}$$

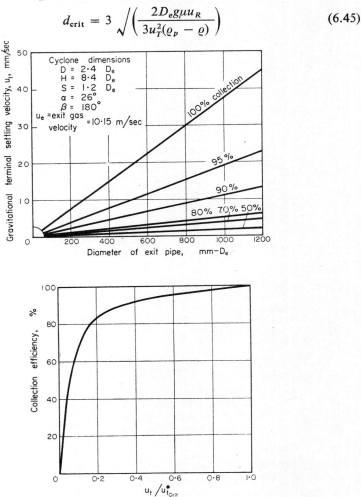

FIG. 6.13. Curves for fractional efficiency calculation for specific cyclone (ter Linden).[308]

This equation assumes that the maximum tangential velocity is reached at two thirds of the radius of the exit pipe (Fig. 6.11b) and that those particles which have a drift velocity outwards because of the centrifugal force equal to the radial inward drift of the gases u_R will be collected. The method of finding the fractional efficiency curve for the cyclone is then identical with the gravitational settling speed ratio method by Barth, except that

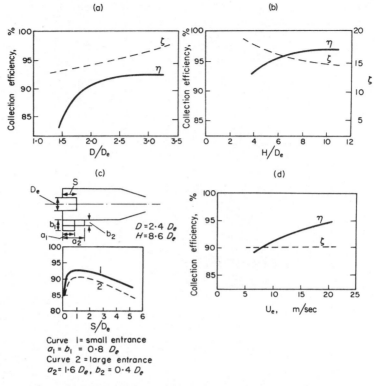

Curve I = small entrance
$a_1 = b_1 = 0.8\ D_e$
Curve 2 = large entrance
$a_2 = 1.6\ D_e,\ b_2 = 0.4\ D_e$

FIG. 6.14. Effect of variation of cyclone dimensions on efficiency
and pressure loss factor ζ.[308] [Cyclone dimensions as in Fig. 6.13.]

(a) Cyclone diameter.
(b) Cyclone height.
(c) Depth of exit pipe.
(d) Entrance velocity.

only a graph for cyclones with one set of the same relative dimensions has
been published[308] (Fig. 6.13).

The effect of changing cyclone dimensions on overall efficiency, using
standard test dusts, has been investigated by both ter Linden[307] and Stairmand.[462] The specifications of the standard dusts used are given in
Table 6.2.

Ter Linden studied the efficiency (and also pressure drop characteristics)
of a cyclone where he was able to vary one dimension at a time, such as the
cyclone diameter, D, length H, or distance of penetration of exit pipe S, as
well as the inlet velocity u_t. The results obtained are shown in Fig. 6.14. He
was able to show that increasing the relative dimension of diameter D to
the exit pipe diameter D_e gave an increase in efficiency until a $3:1$ ratio

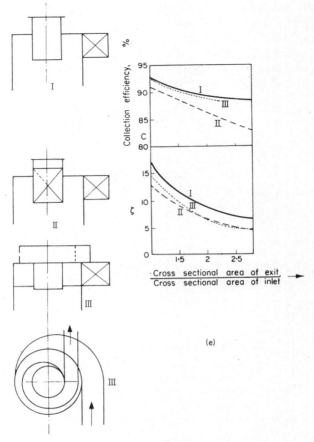

FIG. 6.14 *(continued)*

(e) Exit area as ratio of inlet area.

TABLE 6.2. Standard Test Dusts

Size range microns	% by weight		
	Pulverized clay (ter Linden)	Fine sand (Stairmand)	Fly ash (U.S. Standard)
0–5	30	20	35·8
5–10	12	10	22·3
10–20	18	15	21.4
20–50	28	27	14·1
Over 50	12	28	6·5

was achieved, after which further diameter increases have little effect on efficiency (Fig. 6.14a). Increased length H also tends to improve efficiency (Fig. 6.14b), while for the particular cyclone investigated, when the exit pipe penetrated one pipe diameter into the cyclone, and ended just below the entrance, maximum collection efficiency was attained (Fig. 6.14c). Increased inlet velocity was found to improve efficiency and the ratio of the

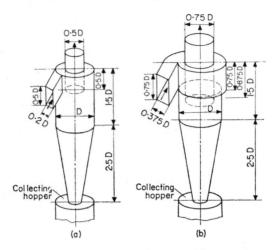

FIG. 6.15. Standard cyclone designs (Stairmand).[462]

(a) High efficiency, medium throughput pattern.
Normal flow rate $= 300D^2$ ft^3/min.
(b) Medium efficiency, high throughput pattern.
Normal flow rate $= 900D^2$ ft^3/min.

Entrance velocity at these flows is approx. 50 ft/sec in both types.

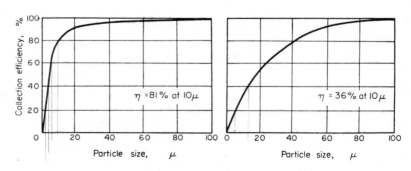

FIG. 6.16. Fractional efficiency curves.[462]

(a) High efficiency cyclone, Fig. 6.15a.
(b) High throughput cyclone, Fig. 6.15b.
(Density of dust was 2·7 g/cm^3.)

cross-sectional area of outlet and inlet pipes was also found to play a part, smaller ratios giving higher efficiency (Fig. 6.14e).

Stairmand[462] obtained fractional efficiency curves for two cyclone types, one being a high efficiency, low throughput type (Fig. 6.15a) and the other a medium efficiency, high throughput model (Fig. 6.15b). The fractional efficiency curves are shown in Fig. 6.16. These curves were obtained for 8-in. dia. cyclones, with dust of a specific gravity of 2 and air at 20°C, operating with an entrance velocity of 50 ft/sec. These curves tend to confirm ter Linden's investigations, as the relatively longer cyclone with small diameter exit pipe is more efficient than the cyclone with the larger exit pipe and relatively shorter trunk. The performance of a cyclone for conditions other than those for which experimental fractional efficiency data are available can be predicted from these by transposition of the experimental curves as follows:[462]

(i) If there is a change in the density of the dust then the particle size of the new dust, which will be collected with the same efficiency as a particular size of the test dust, can be obtained by multiplying the test dust size by:

$$\sqrt{\left(\frac{\text{density of test dust}}{\text{density of new dust}}\right)}$$

(ii) If there is a change in the volume flow through the cyclone, the particle size at the new flow, which will be collected with the same efficiency as a particle at the test flow rate, can be calculated by multiplying the test dust size by:

$$\sqrt{\left(\frac{\text{test flow}}{\text{new flow}}\right)}$$

(iii) If there is a change in gas velocity, such as would associate a temperature change of the gases, the particle size for equal efficiency can be calculated by multiplying the test dust size by:

$$\sqrt{\left(\frac{\text{new viscosity}}{\text{test viscosity}}\right)}$$

(iv) If there is a change in the diameter of the cyclone, but retaining geometrical similarity to the test cyclone, the particle size for equal efficiency can be calculated by multiplying the original cyclone particle size by:

$$\sqrt{\left(\frac{\text{diameter of new model}}{\text{diameter of test model}}\right)}$$

An independent factor that is known to affect cyclone performance is dust concentration. It is found experimentally that, in general, cyclone efficiency improves with high dust loads. The explanation offered for this is that large particles moving towards the wall entrain smaller particles or alternatively collide with them.[268] Quantitative prediction of the effect is however not possible at this stage.

6.8. PREDICTION OF CYCLONE PRESSURE DROP

A knowledge of cyclone pressure drop and the factors which affect it is required so that power consumption can be predicted, and if possible minimized by better choice of cyclone parameters, and also so that correct fans can be selected.

Pressure losses or gains occur at the following places for the reasons given:

(i) Friction losses in the entrance pipe.
(ii) Losses due to gas expansion or compression at the entry.
(iii) Losses due to wall friction in the cyclone.
(iv) Kinetic energy losses in the cyclone.
(v) Losses at the entrance to the exit pipe.
(vi) Static head losses between inlet and exit pipe.
(vii) Recovery of energy in the exit pipe.

While Stairmand[459] and Barth[35] present detailed theories which include a number of the sources of pressure losses, Shepherd and Lapple[438] and ter Linden[308] both consider that the kinetic energy loss by the gases in the cyclone is so large compared to the other sources of pressure loss, that this is the only one that has to be considered. Ter Linden gives the pressure loss in terms of the entrance velocity and a dimensionless pressure loss factor ζ:

$$\Delta p = \zeta \, \frac{u_i^2(\varrho + \varrho_p')}{2g}. \qquad (6.46)$$

where $\varrho_p' = c(\varrho_p - \varrho)$ allows for the particle concentration c.

For the cyclones investigated by ter Linden the experimental pressure loss factor has been plotted as broken lines in Fig. 6.14.

Barth[35] presents an elaborate method of calculating the pressure loss factor from two components which are:

(i) Pressure loss at entry and friction loss at the walls (denoted by subscript i).
(ii) Pressure loss at the central core and exit pipe entry (denoted by subscript e).

The pressure loss factor ζ is expressed in terms of the inlet gas velocity, which equals $u_{T\max}$, and is given by Barth as a function of a *loss number* ε, defined by:

$$\varepsilon = \zeta \Big/ \left(\frac{ab}{\pi D_e^2/4}\right)^2 \left(\frac{u_{T\max}}{u_e}\right)^2 \qquad (6.47)$$

where ab = cross-sectional area of entrance pipe

$\quad u_e$ = velocity at entry to exit pipe

$\qquad = 4Q/\pi D_e^2$.

The loss number consists of the *sum* of two components ε_i and ε_e

$$\varepsilon = \varepsilon_i + \varepsilon_e \qquad (6.48)$$

and these components can be found from

$$\varepsilon_i = \frac{\Delta p_i}{u_{Tmax}^2(\varrho + \varrho'_p)/2g} = \frac{D_e}{D}\left\{\frac{1}{\left[1 - \dfrac{2u_{Tmax}(H - S)\,\mu'}{u_e D_e}\right]^2} - 1\right\} \qquad (6.48a)$$

where $\mu' = $ coefficient of friction (gas and wall)
(frequently assumed to be 0·02 in m.k.s. units)

$$\varepsilon_e = \frac{\Delta p_e}{u_{Tmax}^2(\varrho + \varrho'_p)/2g} = \frac{K}{(u_{Tmax}/u_e)^{2/3}} + 1 \qquad (6.48b)$$

The velocity ratio u_{Tmax}/u_e has been expressed by Barth in terms of the dimensions of the cyclone, the coefficient of gas–wall friction μ' and an entrance design loss factor α:

$$\frac{u_{Tmax}}{u_e} = \frac{\pi D_e(D - b)}{2ab\alpha + \pi(H - S)(D - b)\,\mu'}. \qquad (6.49)$$

The entrance design loss factor depends on the type of entry used. Three types are shown in Fig. 6.17a. For the wrap around inlet, α is unity, while for the other types shown α is either less than or greater than one. The third inlet type is not recommended practice, while the entrance correction factor for the second inlet type can be obtained from Fig. 6.17b.

Weidner[521] measured $\zeta/\{ab/(\pi D_e^2/4)\}^2$ for a series of values of the velocity ratio u_{Tmax}/u_e, and these are plotted in Fig. 6.17c. Curve "*a*" applies to sharp edged exit pipes: curve "*b*" to round edged ones. Values of K and the pressure loss factor are listed in Table 6.3.

TABLE 6.3. VALUES OF K AND ζ FOR BARTH PRESSURE
LOSS CALCULATIONS

			Sharp edged exit pipe	Round edged exit pipe
	K		4·40	3·41
$\zeta\big/\left(\dfrac{ab}{\pi D_e^2/4}\right)^2$		$\dfrac{u_{Tmax}}{u_e} > 1$	Curve a Fig. 6.17c	Curve b Fig. 6.17c
		$\dfrac{u_{Tmax}}{u_e} < 1$	2·0	1·1

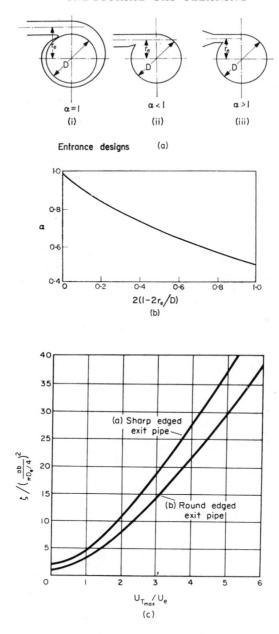

FIG. 6.17. (a) Alternative cyclone entry designs for loss factor calculations.[35]

(b) Values of loss factor α for pattern (ii) when $\alpha < 1$.[35]

(c) Weidner's experimental curves for pressure loss function.[521]

To calculate the pressure loss factor ζ it is therefore necessary to find ε_i and ε_e from equations (6.48a) and (6.48b), and the velocity ratio $u_{T\max}/u_e$ from equation (6.49), and then apply equation (6.47).

An alternative method for calculating the pressure loss in cyclones is by Stairmand[459] which is based on the losses measured at various points in terms of velocity heads, given by $u^2(\varrho + \varrho'_p)/2g$.

(i) At the entry—1 velocity head $u_i^2(\varrho + \varrho'_p)/2g$.
(ii) At the exit—2 velocity heads $u_e^2(\varrho + \varrho'_p)/g$.
(iii) Losses within the cyclone.

In addition the losses actually within the entrance and exit ducts must be found from the normal equations for pressure losses in ducts (Fanning equation).

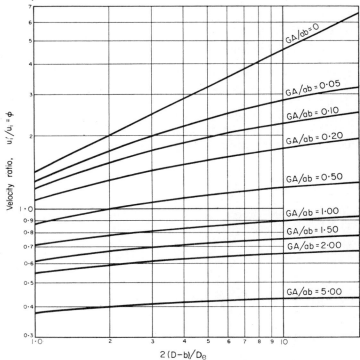

FIG. 6.18. Curves for friction loss factor φ against entrance radius ratio for different cyclones.[459]

a = depth of entrance pipe.
b = width of entrance pipe.
D = cyclone diameter.
D_e = cyclone exit pipe diameter.
A = internal surface area of cyclone.
G = friction factor = 0·005 (assumed constant).
φ = friction loss factor.

Stairmand finds that the losses within the cyclone are friction losses at the wall and a kinetic energy loss. The latter was found to be twice the difference between the velocity head at the entrance and at the periphery of the inner core, i.e.

$$(\varrho + \varrho_p')\,(u_i^2 - u_{T\max}^2)/g$$

while the wall friction factor φ is found as the ratio of the spinning speed u_i' at the inlet radius $(D/2 - b/2)$ and the linear velocity in the inlet duct u_i i.e.

$$\varphi = u_i'/u \tag{6.50}$$

where

$$\varphi = \frac{-\sqrt{\left(\dfrac{D_e}{D - b}\right)} + \sqrt{\left(\dfrac{D_e}{2(D - b)} + \dfrac{2GA}{ab}\right)}}{2GA/ab} \tag{6.51}$$

where G = friction constant

$\qquad$ = 0·005 for gas cyclones

$\quad A$ = surface area of cyclone exposed to gases

ab = cross sectional area of inlet duct.

The value of the friction factor φ can be obtained from the curves of φ vs. $2(D - b)/D_e$ for various GA/ab (Fig. 6.18). The total pressure loss can then be calculated from combining the loss factors:

$$\Delta p = \frac{\varrho + \varrho_p'}{2g}\left[u_i^2\left\{1 + 2\varphi^2\left(\frac{2(D - b)}{D_e}\right)\right\} + 2u_e^2\right]. \tag{6.52}$$

Stairmand found that the pressure loss calculated from this equation agreed to within 10 per cent of the values obtained experimentally.

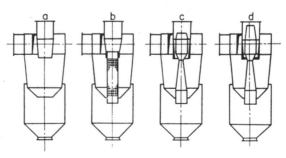

FIG. 6.19. Methods of reducing cyclone pressure drop by internal modification.[418]

$\qquad$ (a) Plain cyclone $\qquad\qquad\qquad\quad \zeta = 17\text{·}4.$
$\qquad$ (b) Sieve tube insert $\qquad\qquad\quad\; \zeta = 13\text{·}9.$
$\qquad$ (c) Double cone insert $\qquad\qquad\; \zeta = 16\text{·}4.$
$\qquad$ (d) Double cone insert and vanes $\;\; \zeta = 10\text{·}0.$
$\qquad \zeta$ = friction loss factor (Barth and ter Linden).

There is some disagreement as to whether some of the rotational energy given to the gases can be recovered and so reduce the pressure loss.

Ter Linden has been able to reduce the pressure loss by 20–25 per cent by introducing a spiral at the entrance to the exit pipe, while Schiele,[418] using a solid central core shaped like a venturi, with vanes at the exit pipe entrance (Fig. 6.19), reduced the friction loss factor ζ from 17·4 to 10, an effective reduction of 42 per cent in the pressure loss. Stairmand[459] has however not been able to find a reduction in pressure loss by introducing internal modifications.

6.9. COMMERCIAL CYCLONES

Many commercial cyclone types are available. These range from comparatively crude designs for the collection of wood chips and sawdust to carefully designed and tested units able to collect fine particles as small as 5 microns. These designs have been arrived at after extensive developmental work by the manufacturer. This has shown the smallest particle sizes effectively collected, and the optimum gas flow rate with the minimum pressure loss for the particular system.

In many cases the manufacturer publishes a fractional efficiency curve based on tests carried out with standard dusts as a guide for those selecting cyclones. These may be somewhat misleading with certain types of dust and so most manufacturers will only give guarantees based on tests carried out with some of the material to be collected. In this section typical examples of commercial cyclones will be presented together with fractional efficiency curves where these are available.

6.9.1. Straight through cyclones with fixed impellers

Straight through cyclones act as dust concentrators, where the concentrated dust, together with some gas is drawn off at the periphery, and led to a secondary collector, while the clean gas is passed out axially. The secondary collector may be another cyclone of conventional pattern or a settling chamber. Multi-cellular straight through cyclones are frequently applied as preliminary cleaners for flue gases with very high fly ash concentrations, such as would come from burning high ash content pulverized coal, before passing the partially cleaned gases to electrostatic precipitators. A typical design for a multicell unit is shown in Fig. 6.20 a. The concentrated dust is drawn to a settling chamber, then through cyclones, after which the cleaned gas joins the gas from the straight through cyclone cells. A single straight through cyclone cell is shown in Fig. 6.2, and a fractional efficiency curve is shown in Fig. 6.20 b. A slightly different arrangement (Fig. 6.21 a) allows the heavy dust concentrate particles to settle into a gravitational settling chamber,

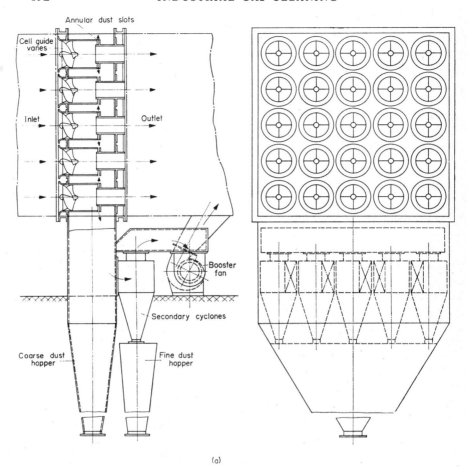

(a)

FIG. 6.20. Multicellular straight through cyclones, drawing down concentrated
dust through settling chamber and cyclones in series.

(a) Diagram of installation.[116]

while the lighter ones are drawn off overhead to cyclones, the clean
exhaust from which is also passed into the clean gas stream from the
cells. The fractional efficiency curve for this arrangement is shown in
Fig. 6.21 b.

Large single cell units are used for applications on comparatively small
boiler plant (gas volumes to 50,000 ft³/min) where low pressure losses are
essential, and the degree of particle removal required is not very critical,
as in marine boilers. The upflow collectors (Figs. 6.22 a and 6.22 b) are par-

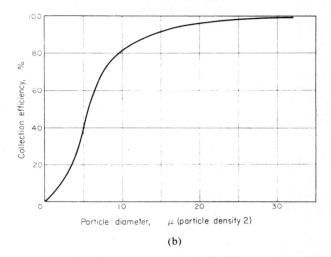

(b)

FIG. 6.20 *(continued)*
(b) Fractional efficiency curve for installation.[116]

ticularly useful for installation in a chimney using natural draught. In one type (a) a settling chamber is provided, while a cyclone is shown in the second type (b). Where the unit cannot be installed in a chimney, a down-flow collector with tangential entry (Fig. 6.22c) may be installed. Typical efficiency data is shown in Fig. 6.22d. As would be expected, the unit with cyclone secondary collector is more effective than the type with only a settling chamber, while the downflow unit is better than the upflow type (Chapter 5).

Very elegant designs using extended impellers have been described elsewhere[113] but are not manufactured commercially. These designs have demonstrated that the smallest particle, with a density of 1, that can be removed is about 3 – 5 microns dia., using entrance velocities as high as 700 ft/sec. Turbulence seems to re-entrain smaller particles, while larger ones tend to bounce off the walls and back into the main gas stream.

This can be overcome by irrigating the cyclone by introducing a water spray at the entry. A commercial design of this type is shown in Fig. 23a, together with a fractional efficiency curve. (Fig. 6.23b). This curve, which is for coal dust, shows that efficiencies of 80 per cent for 1 micron particles are achieved with this unit.

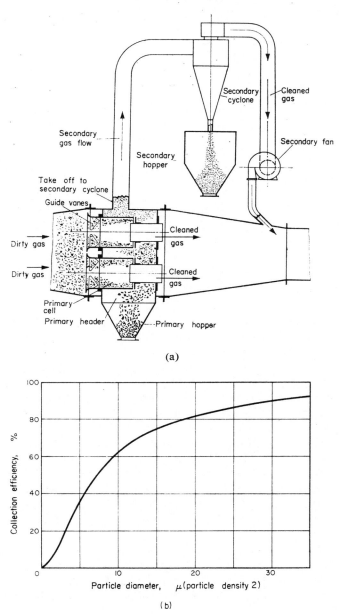

(a)

(b)

FIG. 6.21. Multicellular straight through cyclone with settling chamber (primary hopper) and cyclones in parallel.

(a) Arrangement of installation.[478]

(b) Fractional efficiency curve.[478]

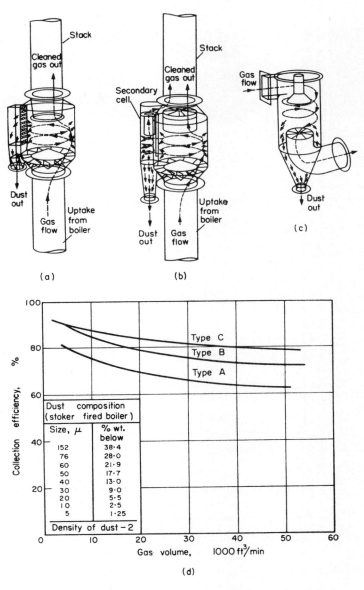

FIG. 6.22. Upflow and downflow centrifugal collector.[222]

(a) Upflow collector with settling chamber separator.

(b) Upflow collector with cyclone separator.

(c) Vortex downflow collector.

(d) Efficiency/volume flow correlation for types shown.

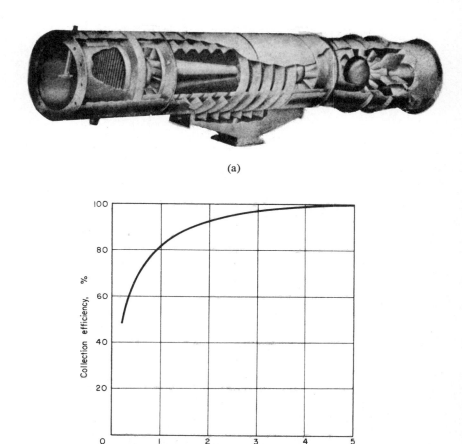

(a)

(b)

FIG. 6.23. Straight through irrigated dust collector.[249]

(a) Installation of unit.
(b) Fractional efficiency curve.

6.9.2. Straight through cyclones with moving impellers

A diagram of this unit has been shown in Fig. 6.5, and a fractional efficiency curve is given in Fig. 6.24.[545] This equipment may be expected to give efficiencies of about 90 per cent with 5 micron sized particles (sp. gr. 2·6) which is somewhat better than for conventional cyclones of the high efficiency type.

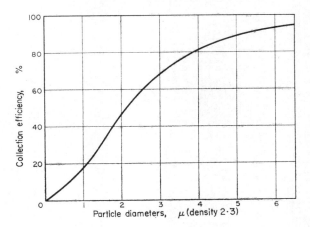

FIG. 6.24. Fractional efficiency curve for straight through cyclone with moving impeller.[545]

6.9.3. Scroll collectors

Several fixed scroll type collectors are manufactured. In these units the scroll imparts a centrifugal motion to the gas stream, concentrating the dust in the peripheral layer, which is passed to a secondary collector, while the clean gas is passed on to the exhaust. The secondary collector is almost invariably a conventional cyclone. Figure 6.25 a shows one pattern for which a fractional efficiency curve has been obtained by Stairmand[463] using a 7 ft diameter unit passing 14,000 ft³/min. Another collector, similar in principle but with tangential entry and scroll exit is shown in Fig. 6.25 b. Fractional efficiency curves for both types plotted on the same scale indicate that the second pattern has somewhat greater efficiencies at particle sizes about 30 microns (Fig. 6.25 c).

6.9.4. Collectors combined with induced draught fans

Instead of using a fixed scroll to impart rotation to the gas stream, this can be accomplished by an induced draught fan. Figure 6.26 shows two typical arrangements, a fractional efficiency curve being shown for the first type (Fig. 6.26 d). A modification of type b, shown in Fig. 6.26 c uses a water spray to improve performance.

6.9.5. Conventional (reverse flow) cyclones

The design of these cyclones has been discussed in some detail in the earlier sections on cyclone theory, performance and pressure loss. The

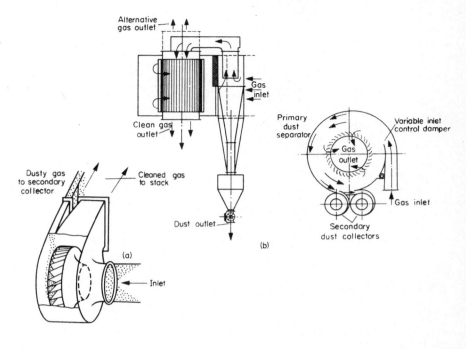

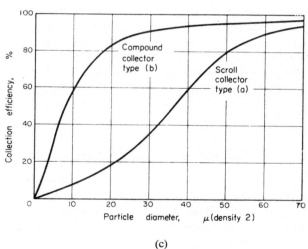

FIG. 6.25. Scroll collectors.

(a) Simple scroll collector.[463]

(b) Buell–van Tongeren scroll collector.[81]

(c) Fractional efficiency curves for both types.[81,463]

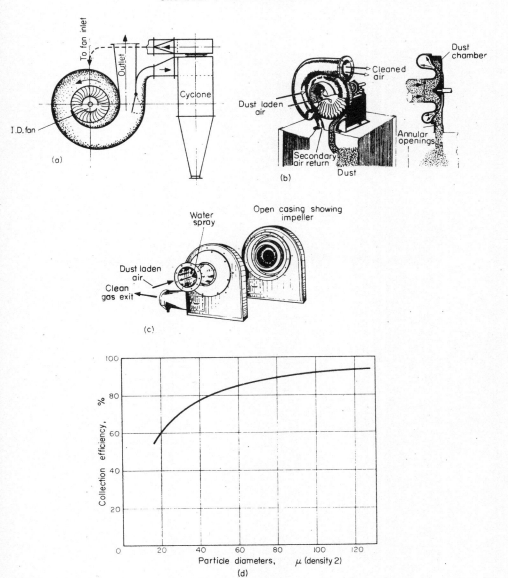

FIG. 6.26. Collectors combining induced draught fans.

(a) Induced draught fan followed by conventional cyclone for concentrated dust.[376]

(b) Induced draught fan followed by gravity settling hopper for concentrated dust.[12]

(c) Irrigated induced fan type unit.[12]

(d) Fractional efficiency curve for unit shown in Fig. 6.26a.[376]

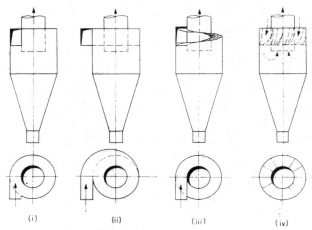

FIG. 6.27. Basic types of cyclone entry.
(i) Tangential entry. (ii) Wrap around entry. (iii) Curved entry. (iv) Axial entry.

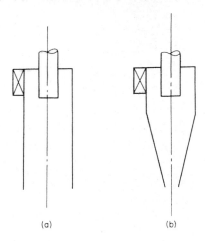

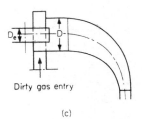

FIG. 6.28. Basic cyclone trunk patterns.
(a) Straight cylinder.   (b) Cylinder and cone (straight).   (c) Bent cone.[306]

various types produced commercially differ as to means of dust entry, exit, and in relative proportions. Four types of entry are common (Fig. 6.27).

 (i) Tangential entry, without spiral.

 (ii) Wrap around inlet without spiral.

 (iii) Wrap around inlet with spiral.

 (iv) Axial gas inlet with vanes.

The trunk may be cylindrical or cone shaped, and in some cases, where head room is limited, can be bent through a 90° angle (Fig. 6.28). The exit

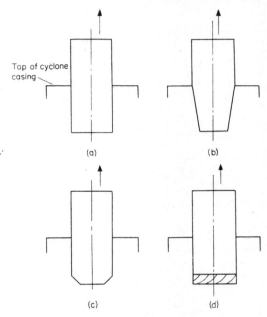

FIG. 6.29. Basic cyclone exit patterns.

 (a) Straight exit pipe.
 (b) Sloping exit pipe.
 (c) Sloping exit pipe.
 (d) Straight exit pipe with vanes to reduce pressure drop.

pipe can be either straight, inclined, with vanes (Fig. 6.29) or fitted with an internal structure of the type discussed previously as reducing the pressure loss (Fig. 6.19).

 The efficiency of these types in various combinations has been extensively studied by a number of workers.

 The fractional efficiency curves of two typical designs (Fig. 6.15) have been given (Fig. 6.16). The efficiency of other models can be obtained by using the methods outlined in section 6.6.

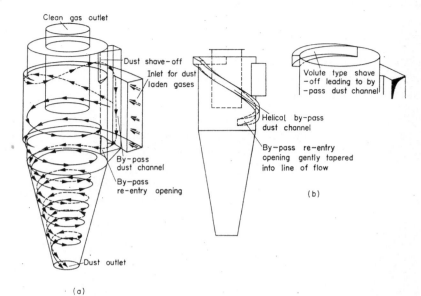

Clean gas outlet

Dust shave-off
Inlet for dust
laden gases

By-pass
dust channel
By-pass
re-entry opening

Dust outlet

(a)

Helical by-pass
dust channel

By-pass re-entry
opening gently tapered
into line of flow

(b)

Volute type shave
-off leading to by
-pass dust channel

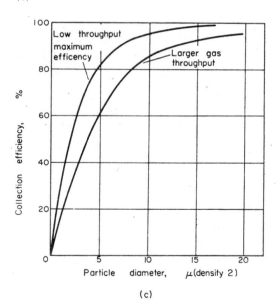

(c)

FIG. 6.30. Cyclones with dust shave-off.[81]

(a) Flow pattern.

(b) C—by-pass design (van Tongeren).

(c) Fractional efficiency curves for cyclones with shave-off.

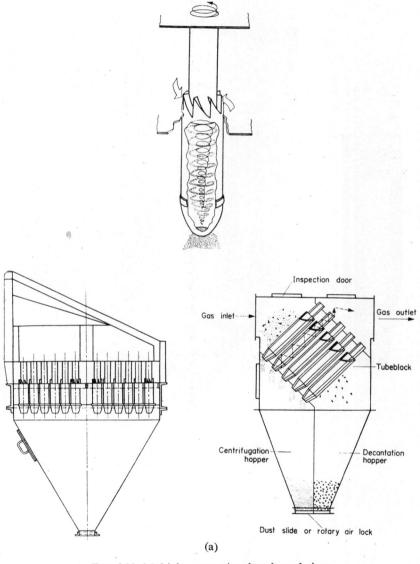

(a)

FIG. 6.31. Multiple conventional cyclone designs
(a) Axial entry type with preliminary settling chamber.[376]

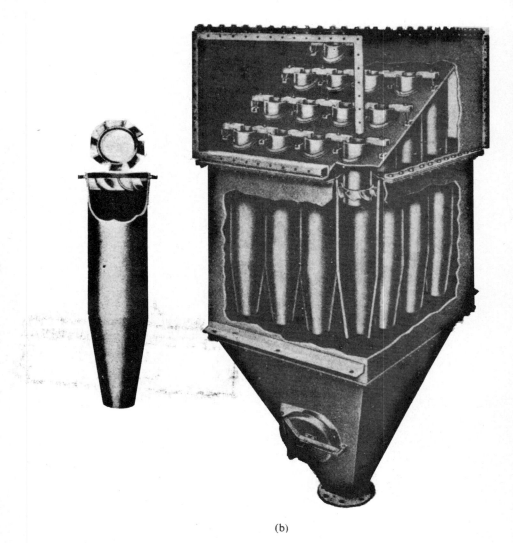

(b)

FIG. 6.31 (*continued*)

(b) Axial entry with mechanism for rapid dismantling of cyclones.[524]

Improvements in performance have been achieved by providing a dust shave off channel which moves the dust which collects near the cyclone roof, where it is likely to find its way into the exit tube by short circuiting into the exit pipe if it is not removed into the conical section (Fig. 6.30a). Typical fractional efficiency curves for commercial installations are shown

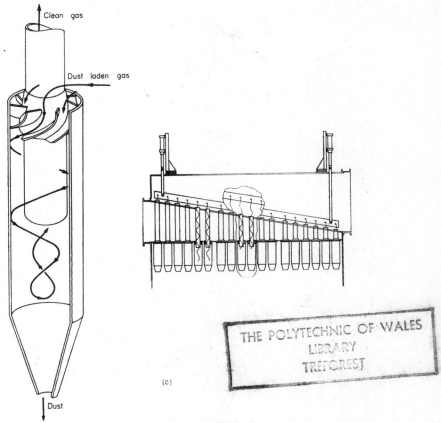

FIG. 6.31 (*continued*)
(c) Axial entry cyclones fitted with dust scraper.[222]

in Fig. 6.30b. Maximum performance was obtained when a low through-put was used with a cyclone about 3 ft diam. Modified designs with in-creased gas throughput had somewhat lower efficiencies.

6.9.6. Multiple cyclones

The formulae for critical particle size show that, in theory, smaller cy-clones, using the same gas velocities, are more effective collectors of small particles than larger cyclones. In practice this improved efficiency is re-duced because of the increased short circuiting that takes place in small cyclones. One worker, in comparing high efficiency cyclones with multiple small cyclone designs has shown that the multiple cyclone arrangement is only marginally better than the large cyclone, although much more ex-

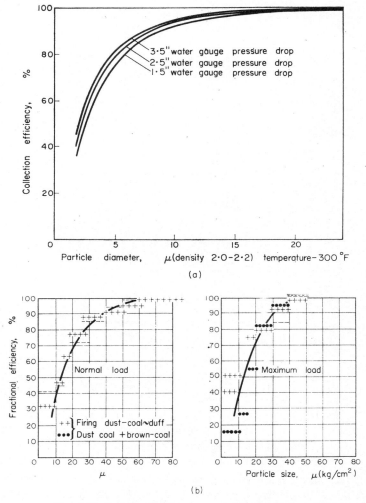

FIG. 6.32. Fractional efficiency curves for multiple cyclones.

(a) Cyclones of type Fig. 6.31a (test dust).[376]

(b) Cyclones of type Fig. 6.31c (power station operating on high ash coal).[193]

pensive to manufacture.[463] Other problems, such as blocking up of the cone and hopper, occur with certain dust types and high dust loads, and special modifications for easy cleaning have to be included. One important advantage of sets of multiple cyclones is that a single high efficiency cyclone with a capacity of 2700 ft³/min, 3 ft dia., requires 25 ft headroom, (cyclone, hopper and exhaust), while a multiple cyclone set of similar capacity only require 8 ft headroom.

Typical multiple cyclone types with axial and tangential entry are shown in Fig. 6.31.

The first type (a) is made of heavy duty cast iron for erosion resistance, type (b) shows a simplified rapid dismantling design, while type (c) is a

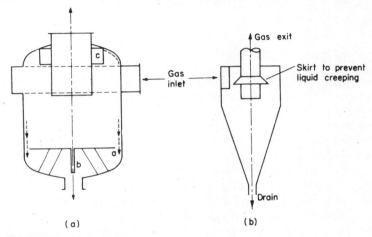

(a)   (b)

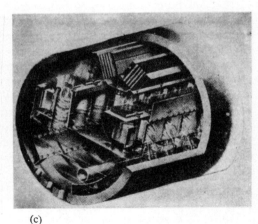

(c)

FIG. 6.33. Droplet collecting cyclones.

(a) Cylindrical model with baffle (*b*) over exit drain (*c* = skirt to prevent liquid creep).[310]

(b) Tangential entry conventional cyclone fitted with skirt to prevent liquid creep.[462]

(c) Mist eliminator fitted into boiler drums.[25]

design incorporating a wire scraper which is actuated externally and enables the cyclone to be cleaned intermittently, either manually or automatically, without dismantling.

Typical fractional efficiency curves are shown in Fig. 6.32 a for standard dusts, while Fig. 6.32 b shows fractional efficiency curves obtained for a type (c) unit for fly ash collection under difficult operating conditions.[193]

6.9.7. Cyclones for liquid droplets

When droplets, formed from condensing vapours or entrained in gases, have to be collected, the design of an appropriate cyclone has to make provision for the additional problem of creeping layers of liquid. These layers, formed from agglomerated droplets, are whipped into the exit pipe by the fast moving gas stream. The layers creep to the edge of the exit pipe where they are easily re-entrained. The extent of the creeping depends on the liquid properties — surface tension and viscosity — and an oil tends to be more readily entrained than water. Entrainment will also occur in the low pressure zone at the axis of the cyclone, and liquid droplets moving towards the apex in a conical cyclone may be sucked into the exit gases. It has therefore been suggested[130] that a cylindrical cyclone design is more suitable for droplet collection than the more usual conical shape. One design of this type[310] (Fig. 6.33a) has a flat plate as a false base, b, surrounded by a slit a, which permits the liquid to run off to the drain chamber. A skirt c, on the cyclone roof prevents creep of liquid into the exit pipe, as the liquid is blown off the skirt and forced back against the wall. A conventional cyclone, with a skirt to prevent creep of liquid, is shown in Fig. 6.33 b.

Another design, for steam–water droplet separation in a boiler drum, also has wrap around entry for the steam–water droplet mixture, parallel walls and inclined vanes at the periphery of the base for the water, as well as corrugated plates in the vapour exit to prevent spray entrainment (Fig. 6.33 c). An alternative solution in a cyclone droplet separator is used in the cyclonic spray scrubber (Fig. 9.7), where the creeping liquid path is lengthened by having the gas–liquid entry at the base of the cyclone.

6.9.8. Design of hoppers

Hoppers fitted below the apex of a particle and gas separating cyclone are either the shape of an inverted cone or a pyramid. The hopper sides are usually sloped at an angle of 60° to the horizontal. Steeper sides may be used if the collected material does not flow easily, or a vibrator can be installed to help to empty the hopper. The size of the hopper should be such that only occasional opening of the hopper valve is required, because when the valve is open, the cyclone will not operate satisfactorily. The hopper

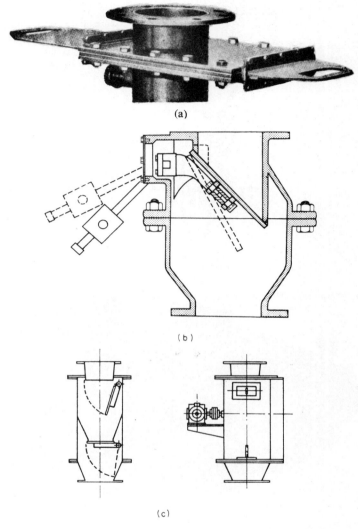

(a)

(b)

(c)

FIG. 6.34. Valve types fitted into base of cyclone hoppers.
(a) Push–pull valves (manual).
(b) Counterweighted flap valve (self-actuating).
(c) Double flap valve (mechanical).

may be used as a product storage, and there is no upper limitation on hopper size. The joints in the hoppers should be carefully made to ensure complete sealing against air infiltration. The valves also must seal easily, and may be either hand or mechanically operated.

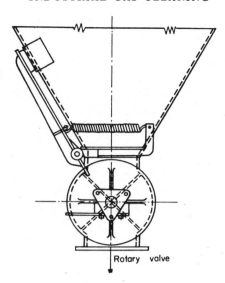

Rotary   valve

9-in. Motor-driven **Rotary** Air Lock

(d)

FIG. 6.34 (*continued*)

(d) Rotary valve (mechanical).

On small cyclones the hand operated valves may be of the gate valve pattern, with a push–pull opening (Fig. 6.34a) or of the spring loaded mushroom valve type. Another possibility is to have a counter-weighted flap valve (Fig. 6.34b) which opens automatically when there is a sufficient head of dust in the hopper. These cannot be used if the pressure in the cyclone is positive compared to the ancillary system (when the fan is located before the cyclone), and are generally restricted to heavy, free flowing dusts. Their application should also be limited because of the air leakages which can occur and remain undetected when the valve is not closed properly.

Two mechanical systems frequently used are the double flap valve (Fig. 6.34c) and the rotary airlock (Fig. 6.34d). The flap valves are alternately opened by a motor driven cam arrangement so that outside air can never be sucked through the cyclone hopper. This arrangement is recommended for heavy duty work, such as the handling of abrasive materials.

The rotary air lock is ideal for continuous discharge of material and consists of a slowly moving 4 or 6 bladed rotor with dust-tight glands and sealed-in shaft, driven by a geared down motor. This unit requires less headroom than the double flap arrangement.

The valve can discharge the product into bags, bins, dust conveyors, or some other means of disposing of the collected material.

6.10. CYCLONES IN SERIES

When the cyclone only acts as a dust concentrator the concentrated dust must be passed to a secondary collector, which will still have to collect the same quantity of dust, but deal with a far smaller quantity of carrier gas,

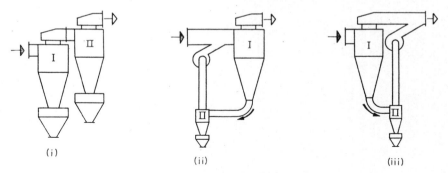

(i) (ii) (iii)

FIG. 6.35. Cyclone arrangements in series.[270]

(i) Arrangement for exit clean gases from one cyclone to be fed to second cyclone.

(ii) Concentrated dust and some gases bled off to secondary cyclone from base of primary cyclone, feeding clean gases to primary cyclone entry.

(iii) As for (b), but passing clean gases from secondary cyclone into clean gases from primary cyclone.

usually about 10 per cent of the initial gas volume. The efficiency of the combined system of course depends on the efficiency of the primary collector and cannot exceed this.

If the gas discharge from the secondary collector is returned to the gases entering the primary collector, the overall efficiency must be that of the primary collector. If, on the other hand, the secondary collector gas discharge is added to the clean gases from the primary collector, then the overall efficiency of the combined units is lower than that of the primary collector alone.

To amplify this, van der Kolk[270] has considered the overall performance of two cyclones in three possible combinations (Fig. 6.35):

(i) A second cyclone operates on the clean gas discharge of the first cyclone.

(ii) A second cyclone operates on the discharge of dust and some air at the cone tip of the first cyclone, and discharges into the entrance pipe of the primary cyclone.

(iii) A second cyclone operates, as in (ii) on the dust discharge, but in turn discharges into the clean gas discharge of the primary cyclone.

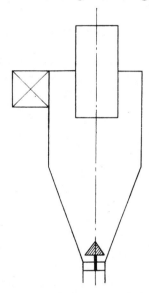

FIG. 6.36. Cyclone with adjustable conical stopper in cyclone cone to prevent vortex from reaching hopper.

In the first combination (i) the effect of the second cyclone is marginal, as it has to collect much finer particles than the primary cyclone. It should be emphasized that the pressure loss for this combination is twice that of a single cyclone, and only if the degree of cleaning achieved in this way is worth while can the power costs for the arrangement be justified. If two low efficiency cyclones are to be used in series, then the result will be no better than a single high efficiency cyclone, which accomplishes the same task with much lower pressure loss than the two cyclones, and the arrangement will not be the most economic.

It has been found experimentally[130] that the pressure in the hopper is a critical factor in cyclone performance. If air is permitted to leak into the hopper, efficiency is reduced, while bleeding air from the hopper improves efficiency. Continuous dust removal from the cyclone apex and hopper to a secondary collector (combinations (ii) and (iii)) will enhance performance in the same way, because the spiral of gas in the cyclone core penetrates into the hopper and stirs up the collected dust re-entraining the fine particles. This has been utilized in the liquid cyclone for rapid particle elutriation.[258] In gas cyclones a small disk is often placed in the centre of the hopper opening to eliminate the re-entrainment (Fig. 6.36).

The secondary cyclone in combinations (ii) and (iii) is only a very small unit compared to the primary cyclone, and its performance may be improved by the high dust concentrations present. Arrangement (ii) should give considerably better efficiencies than a single cyclone because of the continuous gas bleeding and particle removal, although some possibility of re-circulation of fine particle exists. Even when (combination (iii)) the secondary cyclone discharge passes into the clean gas discharge of the primary cyclone, improved performance will result. In both these combinations (ii) and (iii) the pressure loss is only a little greater than for a single unit.

Other systems in series with cyclones are sometimes suggested. One is the possibility of improving cyclone performance by establishing an electrostatic field which will tend to assist the particles to move towards the wall. Calculations[472] show that the effect is only of the order of 2 per cent using a standard small earthed cyclone, a discharge electrode at 60 kV and normal operating conditions with charged particles entering the cyclones. Experiments with such an arrangement did not achieve any measurable improvement in cyclone performance.[369]

CHAPTER 7

THE AERODYNAMIC CAPTURE
OF PARTICLES

7.1. INTRODUCTION

The collection of particles by fibrous filters and liquid scrubbers is essentially the capture of particles by collecting bodies. The gas stream passing through the filter or scrubber takes the particles close to these collecting bodies and then a number of short range mechanisms accomplish the actual collection.

In any particular case the relative importance of these short range mechanisms varies with the relative size and velocity of the particles, with the collecting body, and with the presence of electrostatic, gravitational or thermal attractive (or repulsive) forces.

The basic short range mechanisms are:

(i) Inertial impaction.
(ii) Interception.
(iii) Diffusion.

Mathematical models have been developed for each individual mechanism, and solutions are generally obtained by numerical methods. The combination of two or more of the short range mechanisms has not yet been attempted on a comprehensive basis, but numerical solutions have been found for some special cases. Fortunately, in most cases one mechanism predominates, enabling simplifying assumptions to be made. Thus, for particles in the micron size range and larger, inertial impaction and interception predominate, while diffusion is of much greater importance for sub-micron sized particles.

Electrostatic, thermal and gravitational forces modify the collection efficiencies of filters and scrubbers in special circumstances. For example, when the spray nozzles in a scrubber are insulated from the chamber and charged to a potential of 5 kV, greatly increased collection efficiencies are predicted[274] although the small charges acquired by droplets during normal atomization have been found to have a negligible effect.[242]

Under normal circumstances, thermal forces play a negligible part in filtration or scrubbing, because, to be effective, very large temperature differences between the particles and the collecting body are necessary. In practice, because of the small dimensions of the collecting fibre or droplet, these have a low heat capacity and rapidly reach the temperature of the gas stream and particles flowing through the filter or scrubber. Because of the short duration of any temperature difference, thermal forces generally do not have to be considered, and will be omitted from this chapter.

Two applications of filters have to be distinguished. In one, a relatively clean gas, such as atmospheric air, is filtered to give specially cleaned air for air conditioning, while in the other, industrial gases with a high dust concentration have to be cleaned. The collection of particles in the first case and initially in the second proceeds only rarely by a screening action because the particles are much smaller than the gaps between the fibres. Furthermore, collecting particles in the inter-fibre gaps rapidly blocks the filter and causes a rapid rise in pressure drop. Air conditioning filters are replaced when the particles penetrate through them, and the pressure drop exceeds a certain, low, value, and are not cleaned *in situ*. Filters for industrial dusts, on the other hand, after capturing a thin layer of particles on the fibres, build up a cake, which is removed at frequent intervals. The effect of cake formation on pressure drop, and the timing of cleaning cycles for industrial filters will be dealt with in the next chapter.

This chapter discusses the three basic mechanisms in aerodynamic capture: inertial impaction, interception and diffusion, first individually and then in combination. The effect of temperature, external forces (gravitational and electrostatic forces) and of series of collectors are also considered in detail.

7.2. INERTIAL IMPACTION

When a moving gas stream approaches an infinitely long cylinder placed normal to the gas stream or a sphere, the fluid streamlines spread around the body. The streamline configuration depends on the fluid velocity. At high velocities the streamlines diverge suddenly close to the body, while at low velocities the divergence commences a considerable distance upstream.

A Reynolds number can be defined as a function of the collecting body dimensions and the relative fluid velocity:

$$\mathrm{Re}_c = \frac{v_0 \varrho D}{\mu} \tag{7.1}$$

where v_0 = undisturbed upstream fluid velocity

D = diameter of collecting body

ϱ = density of fluid

μ = viscosity of fluid.

At Reynolds numbers of 0·2 a 3 per cent disturbance occurs at a distance of 100D upstream, while when Re$_c$ = 2000, there is practically no fluid disturbance at a distance of 2D upstream.

If an aerosol is introduced into a gas stream flowing past a collecting body, the aerosol particles will follow the gas streamlines until they diverge around the collector. The particles because of their mass will have sufficient momentum to continue to move towards the collector and break through

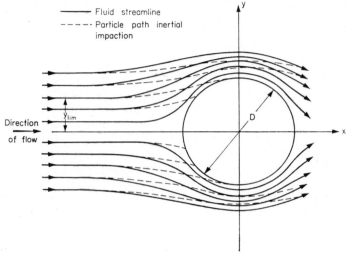

FIG. 7.1. Flow pattern around cylinder: the broken lines indicate path taken by particles being collected by inertial impaction.

the gas streamlines (Fig. 7.1). External forces such as gravity could assist in this.

In vector notation, the motion of the particle is described by the equation:

$$m \frac{d\vec{u}}{dt} = \vec{F_e} - \vec{F} \qquad (7.2)$$

where $\vec{u}$ = velocity of the particle

$\vec{F}$ = resistance of the fluid (Chapter 4, equation 4.22)

$\vec{F_e}$ = vector sum of external forces.

If the fluid resistance is considered to be in the viscous flow region, then Stokes' law (including the Cunningham correction factor C) can be applied to the fluid resistance $\vec{F}$:

$$\vec{F} = \frac{3\pi\mu d}{C} \left(\vec{u} - \vec{v} \right) \qquad (7.3)$$

where $\vec{u} - \vec{v}$ is the velocity of the particle relative to the fluid.

Neglecting the external forces $\vec{F_e}$ and assuming the particle to be spherical, then equation (7.2) can be written as:

$$\frac{C(\varrho_p - \varrho)d^2}{18\mu} \cdot \frac{d\vec{u}}{dt} = -(\vec{u} - \vec{v}) \tag{7.4}$$

It is convenient to convert this equation into a dimensionless form by writing the upstream and cross stream distances (x, y) in terms of the collector diameter D:

$$\tilde{x} = 2x/D, \quad \tilde{y} = 2y/D$$

and the velocities in terms of the reference velocity v_0

$$\tilde{v}_x = v_x/v_0, \quad \tilde{v}_y = v_y/v_0$$

the time in terms of both collector diameter and reference velocity:

$$\tilde{t} = 2v_0t/D$$

while the Stokes' law term can also be expressed using these terms as the *inertial impaction parameter*

$$\psi = \frac{C(\varrho_p - \varrho)d^2v_0}{18\mu D} \tag{7.5}$$

Then, in terms of rectangular co-ordinates $O\tilde{x}$ and $O\tilde{y}$, the equation (7.4) is:

$$2\psi \frac{d^2\tilde{x}}{d\tilde{t}^2} + \frac{d\tilde{x}}{d\tilde{t}} - \tilde{v}_x = 0 \tag{7.6a}$$

and

$$2\psi \frac{d^2\tilde{y}}{d\tilde{t}^2} + \frac{d\tilde{y}}{d\tilde{t}} - \tilde{v}_y = 0 \tag{7.6b}$$

Outside the Stokes' law region, when the drag coefficient, C_D is not given by 24/Re (where Re $= d\varrho(\vec{u} - \vec{v})/\mu$) these equations must be rewritten with a term including the drag coefficient:

$$\frac{48\psi}{C_D\text{Re}} \frac{d^2\tilde{x}}{d\tilde{t}^2} + \frac{d\tilde{x}}{d\tilde{t}} - \tilde{v}_x = 0 \tag{7.7a}$$

and

$$\frac{48\psi}{C_D\text{Re}} \frac{d^2\tilde{y}}{d\tilde{t}^2} + \frac{d\tilde{y}}{d\tilde{t}} - \tilde{v}_y = 0 \tag{7.7b}$$

Physically, the inertial impaction parameter ψ is the stopping distance, in still fluid, of a particle with an initial velocity of $2v_0/D$, assuming that the fluid resistance is in the viscous range. Many workers, particularly in the German literature, refer to the inertial impaction parameter as the stopping distance (Bremsstrecke).

The efficiency of capture by inertial impaction is defined by the fraction of particles (considered to be evenly distributed in the gas stream) which can be collected by the rod or sphere from a normal cross-sectional area of the gas stream equal to the frontal area of the collector. To find this it is therefore necessary to determine the trajectory of the particles in this section of the gas stream, and particularly, the trajectory of the particle which will just touch the collecting body. In the two dimensional case it is necessary to know the distance from the x co-ordinate at $x = -\infty$ at which a particle starts that will just touch the surface of the collector, i.e. the efficiency of collection by inertial impaction is:

$$\eta_I = \frac{y_{\text{lim}}}{D/2} = \tilde{y}_{\text{lim}} \tag{7.8}$$

This limiting trajectory can be shown to be a function of Re_c and ψ only.

As equations (7.6) or (7.7) cannot be solved directly, the limiting trajectory has been obtained by numerical methods involving step by step calculations. The various solutions obtained have been adequately reviewed elsewhere,[215, 548] and will therefore only be outlined here.

The first important investigation of inertial impaction was by W. Sell,[430] who determined the velocity profiles experimentally by studying streamlines in water moving past bodies of various shapes (sphere, cylinder and flat plate, all 10 cm dia.). Using the experimental streamlines, Sell calculated particle trajectories, assuming that the particles had mass, but no size, in finding the particle accelerations. Sell found that the efficiency of collection could be characterized by a dimensionless group mv_o^2/FD, which is identical with the inertial impaction parameter.

Using the potential flow equations for an ideal fluid, Albrecht[5] calculated the trajectory of the particle that would just touch the collector. Langmuir and Blodgett[296] and Bosanquet[58] similarly used the potential flow theory to determine particle trajectories. The dimensionless group derived by Bosanquet can be shown to be the reciprocal of the inertial impaction parameter. The potential flow theory gives the fluid at the surface of the collecting body a maximum velocity twice that of the upstream velocity v_0, while in fact, the boundary fluid layers make the surface velocity zero. The differences in the calculated trajectories for the various authors derive from the different starting points for the calculations, and the number of steps taken. For example, Albrecht[5] starts at $\tilde{x} = -3$ while Langmuir and Blodgett[296] start at $\tilde{x} = -4$, and use a differential analyser to compute a larger number of stages.

Measured inertial impaction efficiencies obtained by Landahl and Herrmann[289] for droplets on cylinders did not agree with Sell's predicted values; an efficiency curve was therefore derived from calculated and experimentally confirmed fluid velocities at Re_c values of 10 obtained by Thom.[486]

Davies[120] based his efficiencies for large Re_c (> 1000) on Sell,[430] Albrecht[5] and Glauert,[178] for $Re_c = 10$ on Thom's velocities,[486] while for Re_c values more applicable to flow past fibres in filters, which are of the order of $Re_c = 0.2$, he used his own viscous flow relations.[119]

The collection efficiency of droplets has also been calculated by Pearcey and Hill[365] and several other authors.[115, 155, 218, 219, 367, 371, 516]

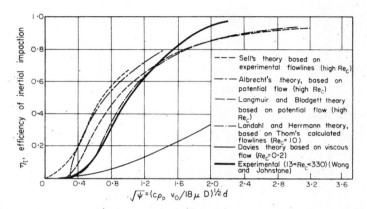

FIG. 7.2. Efficiency of inertial impaction by spheres on cylinders based on various theories and the experiments by Ranz, Wong and Johnstone.[387]

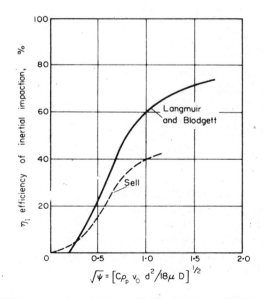

FIG. 7.3. Efficiency of inertial impaction by spheres on spheres, based on the theories of Sell[430] and Langmuir and Blodgett.[296]

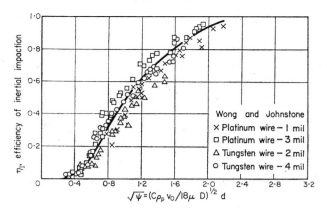

FIG. 7.4. Experimental results of inertial impaction experiments by spheres impacting on wires.[548]

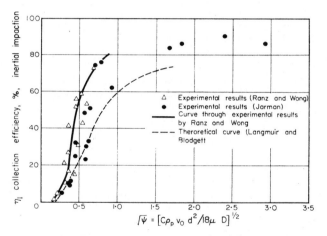

FIG. 7.5. Experimental results for inertial impaction by spheres on spheres by Ranz and Wong,[387] and Jarman,[235] together with the theoretical curve by Langmuir and Blodgett.

Albrecht[5] and later workers have shown that the calculations predict a value of the inertial impaction parameter ψ_{crit} below which the inertial impaction collection efficiency is zero. For cylinders Albrecht gave ψ_{crit} as 0·09, without allowing for a viscous boundary layer. With this allowance, Langmuir[295] obtained ψ_{crit} as 0·27. Subsequent calculations by Langmuir and Blodgett[296] and by Bosanquet[58] gave the critical value of ψ, ψ_{crit} as 0·0625 for cylinders.

The curves for efficiency of inertial impaction on cylinders and spheres, using $\sqrt{\psi}$ as the abscissa, are shown in Figs. 7.2 and 7.3 respectively.

The most extensive measurements of collection efficiencies on cylinders have been made by Wong and Johnstone[548] (Fig. 7.4). The curve drawn through Wong and Johnstone's results, which is included in Fig. 7.2, lies close to the predicted curve by Landahl and Hermann.[289] Also it should be noted, that while practical values for Re_c in fibre filtration are about 0·2, the Re_c values for which the inertial impaction efficiency has been found have been of the order of $13 < Re_c < 330$. Until more realistic determinations of inertial impaction efficiency at low Re_c numbers have been carried out, an efficiency intermediate between the Landahl and Hermann and the Langmuir and Blodgett curves will probably give the best estimate.

Experimental work of collection of particles by spheres is frequently associated with collection of particles by raindrops or artificial water sprays. Experimental points obtained in recent measurements by Jarman[235] together with earlier work by Ranz and Wong[387] are plotted in Fig. 7.5.

7.3. INTERCEPTION

The model considered for inertial impaction assumed particles had mass, and hence inertia, but no size, except when calculating the resistance of the fluid for cross stream movement. In allowing for actual particle size, an interception mechanism is considered where the particle has size, but

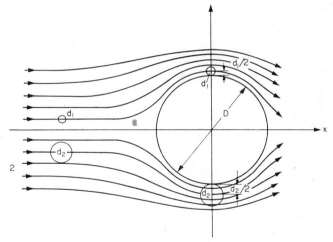

FIG. 7.6. Flow pattern around cylinder, showing interception collection mechanism for spheres of differing sizes.

no mass, and so follow the streamlines of the gas around the collector. If the streamline on which the particle centre lies approaches to closer than $d/2$ to the collector, the particle will touch the collector and be intercepted (Fig. 7.6).

Interception is characterized by a parameter R, which is the ratio of the diameters of the particle d and of the intercepting body D. $(R = d/D)$. If potential flow is assumed, the efficiency of collection by interception, η_c, can be calculated from the relations[387]

$$\eta_c = 1 + R - 1/(1 + R) \tag{7.9}$$
(cylindrical collector)

and:

$$\eta_c = (1 + R)^2 - 1/(1 + R) \tag{7.10}$$
(spherical collector).

Alternatively using Langmuir's viscous flow equation[295] Ranz[385] obtained the interception collection efficiency of a cylindrical target:

$$\eta_c = \frac{1}{2 \cdot 002 - \ln Re_c} \left[(1 + R) \ln (1 + R) - \frac{R(2 + R)}{2(1 + R)} \right] \tag{7.11}$$

This last equation should be used whenever possible, as it allows for the changing flow pattern with different stream velocities.

The two mechanisms of inertial impaction and interception are of course not independent of one another, as has been assumed above. A much better estimate of combined interception and impaction efficiency can be obtained when an allowance is made for those particles whose centres lie on

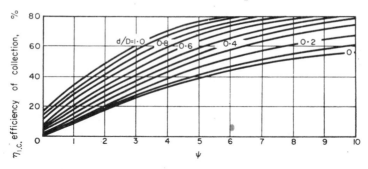

FIG. 7.7. Efficiency of collection by combining inertial impaction and interception for a Re_c value of $0 \cdot 2$.[120] The parameter is $d/D(= R)$.

trajectories closer than the particle radii to the collecting body. This however requires the stepwise calculation of particle trajectories for different values of R and Re_c. Davies[120] has carried out this calculation for $Re_c = 0 \cdot 2$, a typical value for fibrous filters. The curves are plotted in Fig. 7.7 and an equation for the combined efficiency has been fitted to these curves.

$$\eta_{I C} = 0 \cdot 16[R + (0 \cdot 50 + 0 \cdot 8R)\psi - 0 \cdot 1052R\psi^2] \tag{7.12}$$

No further equations, for other values of Re_c have been calculated, so approximate combined efficiencies must be used. As a first approximation, particularly for low individual efficiencies of impaction and interception, the sum of the two can be used. However, as a particle caught by one mechanism cannot be caught again, a better estimate, which allows for this, is:

$$\eta_{IC} = 1 - (1 - \eta_C)(1 - \eta_I) \tag{7.13}$$

7.4. DIFFUSION

Very small particles, in the sub-micron size range, are rarely collected by inertial impaction or interception, because they not only follow the gas streamlines surrounding the collecting body, but also move across them in an irregular way. This erratic, zigzag movement of small particles, caused by their continued, irregular bombardment by molecules of the gas, is called Brownian motion. In a still gas small particles move freely and distribute themselves evenly throughout the gas, and if an object were placed in the gas, some of the particles would settle on it, being thus removed from the gas. In a moving gas, only limited time is available for this process of removal by diffusion, that is while the gas in the streamlines from which diffusion takes place remains sufficiently close to the collector.

The estimation of the number of particles that are removed while the gas flows past the collector then follows one of two methods. One, introduced by Langmuir[295] calculates the average distance moved by the diffusing particle during this time, and finds the efficiency of collection from the volume cleared by diffusion as compared to the total volume flowing past. The other deduces the efficiency of collection by using theories of mass transfer to calculate the rate of diffusion across a "boundary layer" during the time the gas from which the particles are diffusing to the surface remains sufficiently close to it.

In the first method, Langmuir calculated, using "random walk" theory, that the layer of a still gas cleared of particles diffusing to a surface may be found from

$$x = (4\mathscr{D}t/\pi)^{1/2} \tag{7.14}$$

where $\mathscr{D}$ is the diffusion coefficient or diffusivity of the particles.

The *particle diffusivity* may be calculated in two ways. One, introduced by Einstein, applies to particles of a size order, the same as or greater than, the mean free path of the gas molecules. The other, introduced by Langmuir, applies to particles smaller than the mean free path. Einstein,[131] from a consideration of osmotic forces, deduced that the particle diffusivity may be found from

$$\mathscr{D} = kT/F' \tag{7.15}$$

where k = Boltzmann's constant

T = absolute temperature

F' = "fluid resistance to particle" term: $3\pi\mu d$.

In the particle size range considered for collection by diffusion, Stokes' law, corrected for *slip* by the Cunningham correction factor C, can be applied for the fluid resistance, and so equation (7.15) becomes

$$\mathscr{D} = \frac{CkT}{3\pi\mu d} \tag{7.16}$$

Langmuir[295] used the Stephan–Maxwell diffusion theory, which assumes that the gas molecules are not influenced by the particles. This restricts the diffusivity calculated in this way to particles which are much smaller than the mean free path of gas molecules, but still very large compared to the molecules themselves. Langmuir found that the diffusivity can be found from

$$\mathscr{D} = \frac{\bar{u}}{3N(\pi d^2/4)} \tag{7.17}$$

where N = number of gas molecules per unit volume

$\bar{u}$ = average molecular velocity (equation 3.3.).

The number of gas molecules per unit volume is a function of the gas pressure, which may be expressed, at ordinary pressures where the ideal gas law can be assumed, as $N = P/kT$. Substituting for N and $\bar{u}$ in equation (7.17) gives the diffusivity as:

$$\mathscr{D} = \frac{4kT}{3\pi d^2 P}\left(\frac{8RT}{\pi M}\right)^{1/2} \tag{7.18}$$

Some diffusivities calculated from both equations (7.16) and (7.18) are given in Table 7.1.

TABLE 7.1. PARTICLE DIFFUSIVITIES AND SCHMIDT NUMBERS[385]
(air at 20°C, 1 atm pressure)

Particle diameter microns	Diffusivity cm²/sec		Schmidt numbers using $\mathscr{D}$ calculated from	
	eqn. (7.16)	eqn. (7.18)	eqn. (7.16)	eqn. (7.18)
10	$2\cdot4 \times 10^{-8}$	–	$6\cdot4 \times 10^{6}$	–
1	$2\cdot7 \times 10^{-7}$	–	$5\cdot6 \times 10^{5}$	–
0·1	$6\cdot1 \times 10^{-6}$	$7\cdot8 \times 10^{-6}$	$2\cdot5 \times 10^{4}$	$1\cdot9 \times 10^{4}$
0.01	$4\cdot0 \times 10^{-4}$	$7\cdot8 \times 10^{-4}$	$3\cdot8 \times 10^{2}$	$1\cdot9 \times 10^{2}$
0·001	$3\cdot8 \times 10^{-2}$	$7\cdot8 \times 10^{-2}$	$4\cdot0$	$1\cdot9$

Diffusivity has dimensions of (area)/(time), expressed as cm²/sec, if the gas pressure is in dynes/cm². The dimensionless group which includes diffusivity is the Schmidt number, Sc:

$$\mathrm{Sc} = \frac{\mu}{\varrho\mathscr{D}} = \frac{\nu}{\mathscr{D}} \tag{7.19}$$

where ν = kinematic viscosity (μ/ϱ).

Schmidt numbers corresponding to the particle diffusivities have also been listed in Table 7.1.

The other dimensionless group used in these calculations is the Peclet number (Pe), which is a measure of the transport by convective forces compared to the transport by molecular diffusion. For a system involving a gas stream, velocity v, moving past a body, diameter D, this is

$$\mathrm{Pe} = \mathrm{Re}_c \mathrm{Sc} = \frac{v\varrho D}{\mu} \cdot \frac{\mu}{\varrho \mathcal{D}} = \frac{vD}{\mathcal{D}}. \tag{7.20}$$

Langmuir assumed that collection by diffusion will take place from a surface layer, effective width x_e, during the time t that an element of the

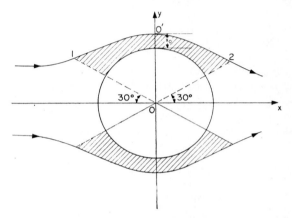

FIG. 7.8. The space near the collecting body from which diffusion is assumed to take place.[295]

fluid moves from a point 1 to 2, (Fig. 7.8) taken as a 60° intercept upstream to a 60° intercept downstream on the collecting body, which is assumed to be a cylinder. At the point O' the fluid element is at a distance x_0 from the collecting body. On the basis of the stepwise integration for viscous flow around a cylinder the effective distance x_e was found to be, as a first approximation.

$$x_e = 1 \cdot 120 x_0. \tag{7.21}$$

While the time for the fluid to move from 1 to 2 was

$$t = \frac{0 \cdot 278 D^2 (2 \cdot 002 - \ln \mathrm{Re}_c)}{v_0 x_0}. \tag{7.22}$$

These values for t and x_e can be substituted in equation (7.14), and on rearrangement a diffusion parameter, Z (similar to the interception parameter) can be found from:

$$Z = \frac{x_0}{D/2} = [2\cdot24(2\cdot002 - \ln Re_c)\mathscr{D}/v_0 D]^{1/3} \qquad (7.23\,\text{a})$$

$$= [2\cdot24 (2\cdot002 - \ln Re_c)/Pe]^{1/3}. \qquad (7.23\,\text{b})$$

Langmuir stated that a more rigorous treatment of the diffusion problem could change the coefficient 2·24, but it would be unlikely to alter very much.[295] Natanson has subsequently suggested that it should be approximately twice Langmuir's value.[348]

The efficiency of collection by diffusion can now be calculated by an equation analogous to Langmuir's equation for interception collection efficiency (7.11).

$$\eta_D = \frac{1}{2\cdot002 - \ln Re_c} \left[(1 + Z) \ln (1 + Z) - \frac{Z(2 + Z)}{2(1 + Z)} \right] \qquad (7.24)$$

Efficiencies of collection calculated for particles moving past a 1 micron fibre at a stream velocity of 10 cm/sec are in Table 7.2.

TABLE 7.2. PECLET NUMBERS AND DIFFUSION COLLECTION EFFICIENCES FOR FIBRES 1 MICRON DIAM., VELOCITY 10 CM/SEC AND AIR 20°C, 1 ATM PRESSURE

Particle size microns	Peclet numbers Pe	Collection efficiency η_D					
		experimental	from eqn. (7.24)	from eqn. (7.25)	from eqn. (7.31)	$\frac{1}{Pe}$	$\frac{\pi}{Pe}$
10	$4\cdot2\times10^4$		$8\cdot8\times10^{-4}$	$1\cdot4\times10^{-2}$	$6\cdot6\times10^{-4}$	$2\cdot36\times10^{-5}$	$7\cdot5\times10^{-5}$
1	$3\cdot7\times10^3$		$4\cdot3\times10^{-3}$	$4\cdot6\times10^{-2}$	$3\cdot5\times10^{-3}$	$2\cdot68\times10^{-4}$	$8\cdot5\times10^{-4}$
0·1	$1\cdot63\times10$	0·18	$3\cdot1\times10^{-2}$	0·22	$3\cdot1\times10^{-2}$	$6\cdot0\times10^{-2}$	$1\cdot91\times10^{-1}$
0.01	2.5		$3\cdot4\times10^{-1}$	1·8	$8\cdot2\times10^{-1}$	0·4	1·26
0·001	0·026		3·4	17	47	37.8	120

Bosanquet,[58] using a similar approach, but assuming the contact distance to be half the perimeter ($\pi D/2$) obtained the collection efficiency for a cylinder:

$$\eta_D = [8\mathscr{D}/v_0 D]^{1/2} = 2\sqrt{(2)}/Pe^{1/2} \qquad (7.25)$$

Efficiencies of collection from equation (7.25) are also given in Table 7.2.

In the same way[473] the collection efficiencies for a sphere and for one side of a strip (width W) can be calculated.

For a sphere:

$$\eta_D = 2\sqrt{(2)}/(PeD)^{1/2} \qquad (7.26)$$

For a strip:

$$\eta_D = (4\mathscr{D}/v_0 W)^{1/2} \qquad (7.27)$$

Because of the mathematical difficulties involved, the calculation of collection efficiencies from mass transfer relations has not been fully developed. The general equation for unsteady state mass transfer, usually referred to as Fick's law, the limited case of which was given in equation (3.1) is:

$$\frac{\partial c}{\partial t} = \mathscr{D}\frac{\partial^2 c}{\partial x^2} \tag{7.28}$$

where c refers to the particle concentration and x the thickness of the zone immediately around the collecting body. If no particle accumulation occurs in this zone equation (7.28) can be integrated to give the rate of particle diffusion per unit area of collector surface:

$$\frac{dc}{dt} = \mathscr{D}\frac{(c_0 - 0)}{x_f} \tag{7.29}$$

where x_f is the width of the zone around the collector in which the particle concentration gradient exists, c_0 is the particle concentration in the bulk of the gas, while at the surface of the collector the concentration is 0.

Johnstone and Roberts[243] suggested that a correlation based on the heat transfer analogy can be used for calculating the collection efficiency by diffusion for a spherical collector:

$$\eta_D = \frac{4}{\text{Pe}}(2 + 0.557\text{Re}_c^{1/2}\text{Sc}^{3/8}). \tag{7.30}$$

Ranz[385] later gave a similar formula for cylinders:

$$\eta_D = \frac{\pi}{\text{Pe}}\left(\frac{1}{\pi} + 0.55\text{Re}_c^{1/2}\text{Sc}^{1/3}\right) \tag{7.31}$$

which was used for $0.1 < \text{Re}_c < 10^4$, and Sc less than 100. Values for the efficiency of collection calculated from equation (7.30) are also presented in Table 7.2.

Landt[293] suggested that the collection efficiency by diffusion could be found from π/Pe, while Davies[120] considered that the reciprocal of the Peclet Number $(1/\text{Pe})$ would have the same efficiency as corresponding values of the inertial impaction parameter ψ. However, neither of these give realistic estimates of collection by diffusion (Table 7.2).

Stern et al.[469] have carried out experiments on the collection efficiency of sub-micron sized polystyrene particles on a filter at reduced pressures, where diffusion is the predominant mechanism. These workers used an equation by Torgeson.[492]

$$\eta_D = 0.775\text{Pe}^{-0.6}(C_{DC}\text{Re}_c/2)^{0.4} \tag{7.32}$$

where C_{DC} is the fibre drag coefficient, and Re_c the fibre Reynold's number. They are characteristic of the filter and are found experimentally from the pressure drop, Δp, the fibre volume fraction α and the filter thickness h. From Chen's formula[92]

$$(C_{Dc}Re_c/2) = \frac{\pi}{4} \frac{\Delta p}{v_0} \left(\frac{1 - \alpha}{\alpha} \right) \frac{D^2}{\mu h} \qquad (7.33)$$

The estimates of diffusion collection efficiency from Langmuir's equation were approximately half of the Torgeson equation estimates. These however were still conservative. For example, at Pe = 36, experimentally η_D was 50 per cent, while Torgeson's estimate was 35 per cent and Langmuir's equation predicted 18 per cent collection. Approximately interpolating Stern's data, for Pe = 163, experimental efficiency is 18 per cent, Langmuir's equation predicts 3 per cent (using the Einstein diffusivity equation) or 6 per cent (using Langmuir's diffusivity equation), Bosanquet's equation predicts 22 per cent, while Torgeson's equation predicts about 15 per cent. Until more extensive experimental data become available, if little is known about the filtering medium, either the Langmuir (equation 7.24) or heat transfer analogy equation (7.31) can be used. If, for a filter, pressure drop, filter density, fibre size and thickness of the bed can be found, Torgeson's equation will give the most reliable estimate.

Langmuir[295] modified his equations (7.21–7.24) for the combination of interception and diffusion. The effective width of the strip which is cleared of particles is actually $d/2$ wider than x_0 in equation (7.23). Because of the other assumptions made this correction is not often warranted except when the surface area for collection becomes very large.

7.5. COMBINATION OF INERTIAL IMPACTION, INTERCEPTION AND DIFFUSION

As aerodynamic capture does not proceed by the isolated mechanisms discussed in the previous sections but by two or more of these together, combined efficiencies must be considered. The fusion of interception with inertial impaction or with diffusion has been discussed in the earlier sections, but for practical calculations all three mechanisms must be combined.

In early attempts to combine the mechanisms, their separate collection efficiencies were simply added together,[460] but this makes it possible, in theory, for a particle to be collected more than once, which is inconsistent. A better approach therefore is to allow only the particles not collected by one mechanism to be collected by the others. This leads to the combined efficiency of collection η_{ICD}

$$\eta_{ICD} = 1 - (1 - \eta_I)(1 - \eta_C)(1 - \eta_D) \qquad (7.34)$$

Another method suggested by Davies[120] has been to combine the inertial impaction parameter (ψ), with the diffusion collection parameter (1/Pe), and to substitute the new parameter in the appropriate equation, e.g. in (7.12).

$$\eta_{ICD} = 0.16 \left[R + (0.50 + 0.8R)(\psi + 1/Pe) - 0.1052(\psi + 1/Pe)^2 \right]$$
(7.35)

A more general approach has been considered by Friedlander[163, 164] who uses the Smoluchowski equation. This describes the rate of collection as the sum of a diffusion term (Fick's Law, equation 7.28), and an impaction term. The equation was too difficult to solve completely, but partial

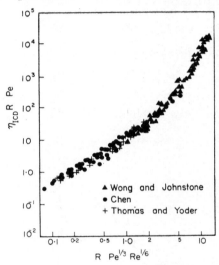

FIG. 7.9. Experimental correlation of combined collection efficiency, Reynolds number, Peclet number and interception parameter $\eta_{ICD}RPe$ vs. $RPe^{1/3}Re^{1/6}$.

solutions, when either the diffusion term or the impaction term were predominant, have been obtained. These were:

(a) *Diffusion term*. The steady flow diffusion equation was written using cylindrical co-ordinates, and then solved using the velocity distributions calculated by Langmuir[295] for viscous flow. This gave a proportionality

$$\eta_D Pe \propto (B'Pe)^{1/3}$$
(7.36)

where B' is a function of the Reynolds number and can be written as $BRe^{1/2}$, while interception is allowed for by multiplying both sides by R; the interception parameter

$$\eta_{DC}RPe \propto (BR^3Re^{1/2}Pe)^{1/3}$$
(7.37)

(b) *Impaction term*. Friedlander shows that the efficiency by impaction can be found from

$$\eta_I = 2B'R^2 = 2BRe^{1/2}R^2$$
(7.38)

Multiplying both sides by PeR:

$$\eta_{IC}RPe = 2BPeRe^{1/2}R^3. \tag{7.39}$$

The combined efficiency can be found by joining the two separate efficiencies; and finding a numerical value for the proportionality from experimental data. This was obtained by plotting $\eta_{ICD}RPe$ against $RPe^{1/3}Re^{1/6}$ on log–log scales together with data from Johnstone and Wong[548] Chen[92] and Thomas and Yoder[488] (Fig. 7.9). The experiments were approximately represented by the expression

$$\eta_{ICD}RPe = 6RPe^{1/3}Re^{1/6} + 3R^3PeRe^{1/2} \tag{7.40}$$

A more useful form of this combined equation is:

$$\eta_{ICD} = 6Sc^{-2/3}Re^{-1/2} + 3R^2Re^{1/2} \tag{7.41}$$

Friedlander and Pascari[164] have replotted the data according to equation 7.41 (Fig. 7.10) and show excellent agreement with available experiments.

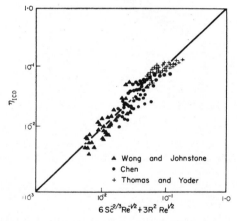

FIG. 7.10. Combined collection efficiency based on experimental results η_{ICD} vs. $\{6Sc^{-2/3}Re^{-1/2} + 3Re^{1/2}R^2\}$.

Another calculation, applying the differential equation of convective diffusion to the deposition process has given similar results[383] and will not be presented here.

If particles of decreasing size moving with constant velocity approach a collector, the inertial impaction and interception efficiencies decrease with size, while collection by diffusion improves. Thus, under specific operating conditions, a particular particle size can be predicted for which the collection efficiency is a minimum. This minimum was indicated in the theories of filtration of Langmuir,[295] Davies,[120] Stairmand[460] and Friedlander,[163] and can readily be shown by differentiating equation (7.40), which has a positive second derivative.[254]

Stairmand,[460] using a simplified model, predicted that the minimum efficiency would occur for a 0·9 micron particle (density 2) collected on 10 micron fibres from a gas stream moving at 3 cm/sec. Similar ideas were used by Landt,[294] while Davies predicted a range of minima for a range of stream velocities (Fig. 7.11).

The existence of the minimum has been confirmed by a number of workers using radioactive particles of known size,[198, 469, 487, 488] but is found to occur at a much lower value than was first predicted by Stairmand. Experimental minima are also shown in Fig. 7.11.

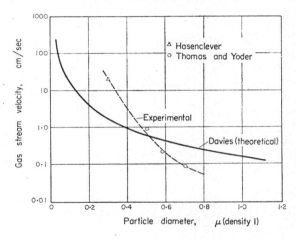

FIG. 7.11. Theoretical[120] and experimental particle sizes for minimum collection efficiency.

7.6. EFFECT OF TEMPERATURE ON THE BASIC MECHANISMS

Although the effect of temperature on inertial impaction, interception or diffusion collection efficiencies has not been investigated, it can be predicted from the temperature dependent terms in the inertial impaction parameter (equation 7.5), the interception efficiency (equation 7.11) and the diffusivity and diffusion collection efficiency (equations 7.18 and 7.31). With increased temperatures, the efficiency of collection by both interception and inertial impaction is reduced, while collection by diffusion increases.

Results of calculations using the equations listed are plotted in Fig. 7.12.[475]

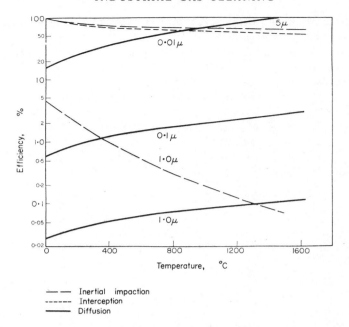

FIG. 7.12. Effect of temperature on the basic collection mechanisms of inertial impaction, interception and diffusion.[475]

7.7. DEPOSITION BY GRAVITATIONAL SETTLING

When a slow moving gas stream passes through a filter, the momentum of the larger particles may not be sufficient for collection by inertial impaction in all cases. Gravity settling may account for an appreciable fraction of the particles collected in this case because of the comparatively long gas stream residence time. For example, settling is a discernible collection mechanism for one micron particles passing through a 10 micron fibre filter bed when gas stream velocities are less than 0·05 cm/sec.

The efficiency of separation by settling can be calculated from the gravity settling parameter $\mathscr{G}$ suggested by Ranz and Wong:[387]

$$\eta_G = \mathscr{G}\, \frac{gD}{v^2}\, \psi = \frac{Cd^2\varrho_p g}{18\mu v} \qquad (7.42)$$

This equation shows that settling becomes significant when gD^2/v^2 is greater than ψ.

Sedimentation has been found to play an important part in the deposition that occurs in the passage of gases through packed beds at low velocities.

Filtration efficiency for large particles was greater for downward flowing gases than for upflowing gases.[488] Typical curves for the penetration of dioctyl phthalate droplets into a lead shot column are shown in Fig. 7.13.

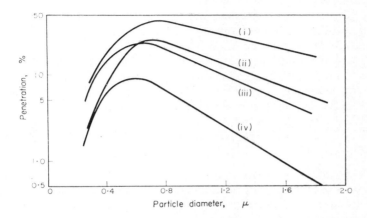

FIG. 7.13. Penetration of dioctylphthalate droplets into a lead shot tower. The increased penetration when the flow is downwards indicates that gravitational settling may influence collection.[488]

(i) Flow up column 1·49 cm/sec.   (ii) Flow up column 0·745 cm/sec.
(iii) Flow down column 1·49 cm/sec.   (iv) Flow down column 0·745 cm/sec.

In the case of spray towers and scrubbers, the relative velocities of particles and droplets are almost always too large for gravitational settling to be important.

7.8. ELECTROSTATIC FORCES

The theories of aerodynamic capture of particles given in the earlier sections have avoided the effect of electric forces which may be present either on the particles, the collectors, or both. The fact that electrostatic forces can assist filtration has been recognized since about 1930,[194] and has led to the development of resin impregnated filters with enhanced efficiency. More recently, attention has been focused on the selection of filter fabrics with the best electrical properties for collection of specific dusts,[162] and mechanical electrostatic charging has also been used.[445]

Electrostatic charges in filter fabrics can be induced by friction; for example, wiping a lucite rod over the fabric,[445] or by the simple passage of the gas stream laden with particles through the fabric. Charges of the order of 1·2 kV are produced when air with a velocity of 170 to 200 cm/sec (330–400 ft/min) is passed through a chemical fibre fabric.[136]

The analysis of the effect of electrostatic forces, and the combination of this with the basic capture mechanisms is exceptionally difficult. Two attempts have met with some success. Gillespie[171] employed Langmuir's approach to particle capture[295] with the addition of static charges present during interception and diffusion, and the use of potential flow to estimate the flow velocities past the collector. The resulting equations were very complicated and will not be given here.

The graphical solutions presented by Kraemer and Johnstone[274] are much easier to apply. The calculations are based on whether the aerosol particle, the collector, or both are charged. The collection efficiencies have been found by solving the potential and viscous flow equations in these cases with the aid of a digital computer.

There are four aspects of electrical forces acting in a system of particles approaching a collector which have to be considered.

(i) When both the particles and the collector are charged, coulombic forces of attraction or repulsion act, depending on whether particles and collector have unlike or like charge. These are considered as point charges. The coulombic force has magnitude F_{EC}.

(ii) A charged collector induces an image charge on the particle surface, opposite in sign to the charge on the collector. This force has magnitude F_{EI}, and is an additional force on the particle.

(iii) If a particle is charged, it, in turn, induces an image charge opposite in sign, on the collector. This results in a force F_{EM}. This also is an additional force between particle and collector.

(iv) The particles charged in the same sense, produce a repulsion force among themselves, F_{ES}. This is called the space charge effect.

The force F_{E1} between a charged aerosol particle and a charged spherical collector (with *constant charge*) is given by:

$$F_{E1} = F_{EC} + F_{EI} + F_{EM} + F_{ES} \tag{7.43}$$

where

$$F_{EC} = \frac{Qq_1}{4\pi\epsilon_0 r^2} \tag{7.44}$$

$$F_{EI} = -\left(\frac{\epsilon - 1}{\epsilon + 2}\right)\frac{d^3 Q^2}{16\pi\epsilon_0 r^5} \tag{7.45}$$

$$F_{EM} = \frac{q_1^2 D}{8\pi\epsilon_0 r^3} - \frac{2q_1^2 D r}{\pi\epsilon_0 (4r^2 - D^2)^2} \tag{7.46}$$

$$F_{ES} = -\frac{q_1^2 D^3 N}{24\epsilon_0 r^2} \tag{7.47}$$

where q_1 = charge on particle

Q = charge on collecting body

r = distance between particle and collector

N = particle concentration per unit volume

ϵ = dielectric constant or aerosol particle

ϵ_0 = specific inductive capacity of space

= $8\cdot85 \times 10^{-21}$ coulomb^2 dyne^{-1} cm^{-2}.

When there is a constant voltage V_1 on the spherical collector, then an additional term F_{ET} is required for the force F_{E2} between the particle (charge q_1) and the total charge induced on the collector by all the surrounding particles within a radius $\mathscr{R}$,

$$F_{E2} = F_{EC} + F_{EI} + F_{EM} + F_{ES} + F_{ET} \tag{7.48}$$

Where the constituent forces, in terms of the voltage V_1 are:

$$F_{EC} = \frac{V_1 q_1 D}{2r^2} \tag{7.49}$$

$$F_{EI} = -\left(\frac{\epsilon - 1}{\epsilon + 2}\right) \frac{V_1^2 D^2 \pi \epsilon_0 d^3}{4r^5} \tag{7.50}$$

$$F_{EM} = \frac{q_1^2 D}{8\pi \epsilon_0 r^3} - \frac{2q_1^2 Dr}{\pi \epsilon_0 (4r^2 - D^2)} \tag{7.51}$$

$$F_{ES} = -\frac{q_1^2 D^3 N}{24\epsilon_0 r^2} \tag{7.52}$$

$$F_{ET} = -\frac{q_1^2 D^2 \pi N \mathscr{R}^2}{8\pi \epsilon_0 r^2} \tag{7.53}$$

These forces are expressed in terms of force parameters, K, which are obtained by dividing the various forces by the Stokes–Cunningham equation, force $F = 3\pi \mu d v_0 / C$ (equation 4.22). The force constants and their definition are listed in Table 7.3.

Approximate equations for the collection efficiency can be obtained if only one term of the electrostatic force relations (7·43 or 7·48) are considered and if the interception parameter R is assumed to be zero. The approximate solutions are listed in Table 7.4. These solutions are, however, very limited. They do not consider the joint action of two or more forms of electrostatic force; cannot be applied to the case of an uncharged collector; and omit the interception effect. Moreover, the collection efficiencies are based on reasonable assumptions only when the efficiencies are much greater than one[274] (efficiency being y_{lim}/frontal area of collector).

TABLE 7.3. ELECTROSTATIC FORCE PARAMETERS (KRAEMER AND JOHNSTONE)[274]

Collector shape	Type of force	Charge type	Equation No.	Parameter symbol	origin	Definition
Sphere	Coulombic attraction between charged particle and charged collector	Constant charge	7·44	K_E	F_{EC}/F	$\dfrac{q_1 Q_{ac} C}{3\pi\mu d v_o \epsilon_o}$
		Constant voltage	7·49	K_E	F_{EC}/F	$\dfrac{q_1 V_1 2C}{3\pi\mu d v_o D}$
Sphere	Force caused by image of electrical charge on collector in the particle	Constant charge	7·45	K_I	F_{EI}/F	$\left(\dfrac{\epsilon-1}{\epsilon+2}\right)\dfrac{d^2 Q_{ac}}{3\mu v_o D \epsilon_o}$
		Constant voltage	7·50	K_I	F_{EI}/F	$\left(\dfrac{\epsilon-1}{\epsilon+2}\right)\dfrac{8CD^2 V_1^2 \epsilon_o}{3\mu v_o D^3}$
Sphere	Force caused by image of electrical charge on particle in the collector	—	7·46, 51	K_M	F_{EM}/F	$\dfrac{C q_1^2}{3\pi^2 \mu d v_o \epsilon_o}$
Sphere	Force caused by space charge	—	7·47, 52	K_S	F_{ES}/F	$\dfrac{C q_1^2 DN}{18\pi\mu v_o d \epsilon_o}$
Sphere	Force between particle and charge induced on collector by other particles	Constant voltage	7·53	K_G	F_{ET}/F	$\dfrac{C q_1^2 NR^2}{3\pi\mu d v_o \epsilon_o D}$
Cylindrical Dipole	Coulombic attraction	—	—	K_c	—	$\dfrac{2q_1 m C}{3\pi^2 \mu d D v_o \epsilon_o}$

F = Stokes–Cunningham resistance force to motion of particle = $3\pi\mu d v_o/C$

Q_{ac} = charge per unit area on collector surface

m = dipole moment of collector

TABLE 7.4. APPROXIMATE COLLECTION EFFICIENCIES[274]

Collector Shape	Electrostatic Force	Electrostatic Equation	Collector Charged	Aerosol Charged	Collection Efficiency
Sphere	Coulombic	7·44	Yes	Yes	$-4K_E$
Sphere	Image	7·50	Yes	No	$\left(\dfrac{15\pi}{8} K_I\right)^{0\cdot4}$
Cylinder	Coulombic	—	Yes	Yes	$-\pi K_E$
Cylinder	Image	—	Yes	No	$\left(\dfrac{3\pi}{4} K_I\right)^{1/3}$
Plane	Coulombic	7·44	Yes	Yes	$\left(\dfrac{-K_E}{1-K_E}\right)^{2/3}$
Plane	Image	7·45	Yes	No	$\left(\dfrac{K_I}{1+K_I}\right)^{1/3}$
Dipole Cylinder	Coulombic	—	Yes	Yes	K_C

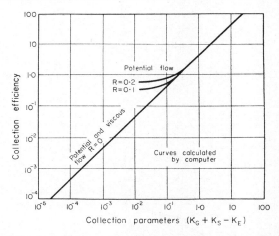

FIG. 7.14. Collection efficiency when both spherical particle and spherical collector are charged.[274]

Much more realistic solutions were obtained by using the complete force balances for the particles, and either potential or viscous flow relations for the streamlines around the collector. These were solved numerically with a digital computer and graphs of the results for three possible cases are shown:

(i) Both particles and collector charged (Fig. 7.14).
(ii) Charged collector with uncharged particles (Fig. 7.15).
(iii) Uncharged collector with charged particles (Fig. 7.16).

These calculations give lower efficiencies than those calculated by the summation of approximate efficiencies for the different mechanisms. The difference varies between 1 and 25 per cent, averaging about 5 per cent. Experimental results agreed well with the theory (Fig. 7.17) although the theory tended to underestimate the efficiencies when these were very low. Calculations and experiments show that much improved collection efficiencies are obtained when both the aerosol and the collecting body are

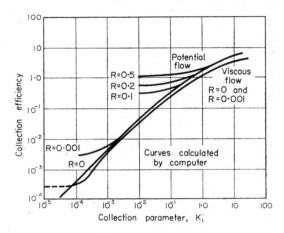

FIG. 7.15. Collection efficiency when uncharged particles are collected by a charged collector.[274]

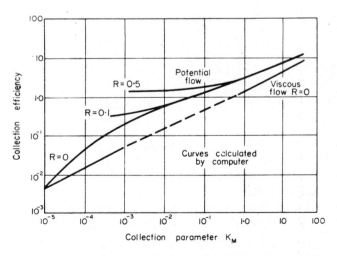

FIG. 7.16. Collection efficiency when charged spherical particles are collected by an uncharged spherical collector.[274]

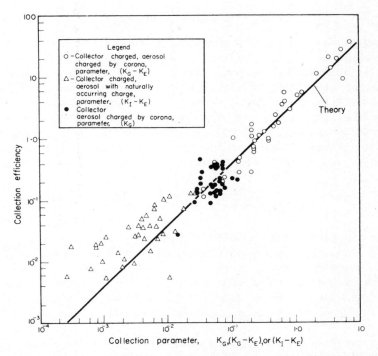

Fig. 7.17. Comparison of theory of charged particles and collectors with experimental results: the collection of dioctylphthalate aerosol on a spherical collector.[274]

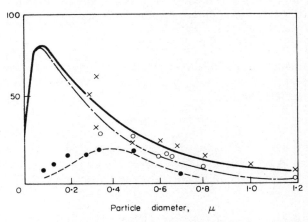

Fig. 7.18. Effect of electrostatic charges on particle diameter for maximum penetration.[171]

Experimental
- ● Charged aerosol–charged filter (polystyrene particles–irradiated resin wool).
- ○ Uncharged aerosol–charged filter (Stearic acid–irradiated resin wool).
- × Uncharged aerosol–uncharged filter (Stearic acid–resin wool).

Calculated
- $----$ heterogeneous charged aerosol–charged filter 0·014 esu/cm.
- $-\cdot-\cdot-$ homogeneous aerosol–charged filter 0·014 esu/cm.
- —— homogeneous aerosol–uncharged filter.

Superficial gas velocity – 11·3 cm/sec.

charged, while charging of even one of the elements leads to improved collection.

On the other hand, Gillespie[171] was able to show that the presence of electrostatic charges increased the particle diameter for maximum penetration into a bed (Fig. 7.18). This may account in part for anomalous results such as those of Humphrey and Gaden[224] who found that the size for maximum penetration for *B. Subtilis* spores which carried some electrostatic charge was 1·15 microns, this being greater than would be expected from the values in Fig. 7.11 for both theoretical and experimental maxima.

7.9. MULTIPLE COLLECTORS

In previous sections the collection of particles on a single collecting body has been discussed. In gas cleaning plants such as fibre filters or spray towers, particles encounter a number of collectors during their passage through the plant. Two separate models will be considered. In one the collecting bodies are all identical and act independently of one another, while in the other, size, orientation and interference effects will be considered.

An example of the first type is a *spray tower* (Chapter 9) where a large number of almost identical spray droplets are produced. These droplets are essentially spheres falling through a slow upward moving gas stream. When the combined collection efficiency of a single spherical droplet η_{ICD} has been found, the overall efficiency, η_0 can be found from

$$\eta_0 = 1 - (1 - \eta_{ICD})^n \tag{7.54}$$

where n is the number of collecting droplets encountered by the particles.

In most practical cases, n is large (greater than about 25), and equation (7.54) can be modified:

$$\eta_0 = 1 - e^{-n\eta_{ICD}} \tag{7.55}$$

For a spray tower the value of n can be estimated if the gas flow rate, scrubbing liquid rate and average droplet size is known, and, if it is assumed that for effective collision the droplets must cover the whole of the tower cross section:

$$n = \frac{Q_L H}{Q D} \cdot 7{\cdot}8 \times 10^4 \tag{7.56}$$

where Q_L = liquid flow rate (gal/min)

Q = gas flow rate (ft³/min)

H = tower height (ft)

D = average droplet diameter (microns)

Equation (7.56) shows that a smaller droplet or a larger liquid flow will increase the value of n.

If a fibre filter is likewise assumed to consist of a number of identical cylindrical collectors, evenly spaced, with no inter-fibre interference, at right angles to the gas flow, equation (7.54) can also be used.

Actually *fibrous filters* consist of randomly oriented fibres with a range of diameters. It may be assumed that for fabric filters of the type used in bag filters, and other industrial filters with low resistance to the gas flow, that the fibres are relatively far apart and staggered in relation to one another. Consider an area of filter dA at right angles to the gas flow, and depth dh. If the free space velocity of the gas stream is v_S, and the packing density of the fibres is α, then the average velocity v of the gases within the filter pad is

$$v = v_S/(1 - \alpha) \tag{7.57}$$

If the average diameter of a fibre is D, the total length of fibres L, and, if the overall collection efficiency of a fibre within the bed (allowing for streamline interaction) is η_α then the number of particles removed by the fibres in unit time is:

$$vN \, dA \, dh \, \eta_\alpha \, DL \tag{7.58}$$

where N = number of particles entering the element of filter per unit volume.

The change in particle concentration is also given by

$$-v_S \, dA \, dN \tag{7.59}$$

Substituting for v_S in (7.59) and combining with (7.58) gives

$$-\frac{dN}{N} = \frac{dh}{1 - \alpha} \eta_\alpha DL \tag{7.59}$$

Which, on integration, gives

$$\ln N/N_0 = \frac{H}{1 - \alpha} \eta_\alpha DL \tag{7.60}$$

where H = bed depth

N_0 = initial concentration

N = final concentration.

Now the actual volume of fibre in a unit volume of filter, which is the packing density, is given by

$$\alpha = \pi D^2 L/4 \tag{7.61}$$

Substituting for L from (7.61) in (7.60) gives

$$\ln \frac{N}{N_0} = \frac{4H}{\pi D} \left(\frac{\alpha}{1 - \alpha}\right) \eta_\alpha \tag{7.62}$$

Chen[92] points out that the average fibre diameter D to be used in equation (7.62) should be based on the ratio (D_S^2/D) where D_S is the *surface* average fibre diameter (considering total surface area) and D is the arithmetric mean diameter.

Fibre interference effect: When fibres are close together in a filter bed, there will be increases in velocity with greater packing density of the fibres. Also a change in flow pattern around a fibre will result because of neighbouring fibres. Both of these effects increase the collection efficiency from interception and inertial impaction. A higher velocity, however, will decrease diffusion collection, although the flattened streamlines may help to reduce this effect.

To obtain a measure of the interference effect, Davies assumed that the interference effect would be the same for all mechanisms. Solving the equations of motion to find the lateral displacement of the streamlines by the collectors, Davies calculated that the efficiency for interception by a single fibre in a bed of packing density α will be:

$$\eta_\alpha = R(0{\cdot}16 + 10{\cdot}9\alpha - 17\alpha^2) \tag{7.63}$$

Davies then proposed that equation (7.63) should be combined with equation (7.35) to give the combined collection efficiency for a single fibre embedded in the filter:

$$\eta_\alpha = (0{\cdot}16 + 10{\cdot}9\alpha - 17\alpha^2) [R + (0{\cdot}5 + 0{\cdot}8R) (\psi + 1/\text{Pe})$$
$$- 0{\cdot}1052R(\psi + 1/\text{Pe})] \tag{7.64}$$

However, because of the difficulty of obtaining a satisfactory average fibre diameter by direct measurement, it was suggested that this could be better deduced from a pressure loss relation based on d'Arcy's equations (8.7 and 8.10).

Chen[92] determined the fibre interference effect experimentally for values of α less than 0·10. Here

$$\eta_\alpha = \eta_0(1 + 4{\cdot}5\alpha) \tag{7.65}$$

This gives values for the fibre interference effect less than that calculated from Davies' equation (7.64), but because of its experimental basis should be used for low packing density fibre filters.

7.10. RETENTION OF PARTICLES ON COLLECTORS

In the previous sections it has been postulated that when a particle hits a collecting body it will stick and not be removed. When the particle is a mist droplet, and the collecting body a liquid, either the same as or miscible with the droplet, then the two will coalesce, forming a single body. If the collecting body is a solid or a liquid with which a particle or a mist droplet is not miscible, then the particle or droplet will sit on the surface of the collector. It may then stay where deposited, slide along to a point where it will fix itself, such as the crossing over of two fibres, or be torn off again by the gas stream moving past the collector.

The forces retaining the collected particle may be[273] surface tension forces, London–van der Waals forces, which arise from the interactions between the molecules, or electrostatic attraction. Condensed moisture, even at low relative humidities can partially enclose a particle and secure the particle by surface tension effects to the surface, and if either the particle or collector are partially soluble and form ions, these may assist in the particle retention. The London–van der Waals forces are comparatively small and by themselves may not be sufficient to hold particles on a surface from which the gas stream is attempting to remove them. However, in dry conditions fibrous filters invariably have some electrostatic attractive forces and these will retain most collected particles. In humid conditions, if both particle and collector are wetted by the humidifying liquid, surface tension will make a major contribution to particle adhesion. If one of the materials is hydrophobic, this influence will be reduced. Adhesive forces are especially high if the particles and collecting bodies acquire ionic charges in the presence of a polar liquid.

Photographic studies of impacting droplets indicate that particle and droplet adhesion is relatively independent of gas velocity.[174] At low velocities the drag is insufficient to detach particles even lightly adhering to the surface, while at high velocities a much greater area of contact is produced on impact to ensure adhesion.

Gillespie[171] has suggested that the critical parameter for particle retention is the angle at which a particle strikes the collecting body. When the angle of strike is greater than a certain value, the particle will not be retained by the collecting body. This concept has been incorporated in a "slippage" coefficient, i.e. the fraction of particles which do not stick on contact. The "slippage" coefficient theory has proved useful for correlating experimental data by a number of workers although it is not necessarily founded on realistic physical interpretation of the filtration process.[185]

CHAPTER 8

FILTRATION BY FIBROUS FILTERS

8.1. INTRODUCTION

The process of filtration of gases to remove particulate matter has been shown to be a combination of the mechanisms of inertial impaction, interception and diffusion. Additional factors, such as gravitational, electrostatic or thermal forces, when present, also have great influence on collection efficiency. In general, fine fibres are more effective collectors than coarse ones because of their larger inertial impaction and interception parameters, as well as their provision of a larger aggregate surface area per unit volume for diffusion to take place. Closer packing of fibres also tends to improve collection because of favourable fibre interference effects. Close packed fibres will however increase the pressure losses, and this may not be economically desirable.

The presence of electrostatic charges on either particles or fibres will enhance collection efficiency, while if both carry charges of opposite sign, even greater efficiencies can be obtained. Conversely, if the charges on both are of the same sign, and the resultant coulombic repulsion is greater than the image force attraction, the collection efficiency will be reduced.

The fibres can be used loosely packed, pressed together in felt form or spun and woven into cloth. They can be metal, natural or chemical fibres, cellulose or glass fibres. The selection of a particular filter medium depends on the application. Thus, if the particle concentration is high, as in the waste gases from smelting, the filters have to be cleaned continuously or at frequent intervals, and a strong fabric has to be provided, able to withstand frequent cleaning. If, on the other hand, particle concentrations are low, for example in filtering air, the filter may not be loaded for many months and will not be re-used. Loosely packed fibre may then be more suitable.

Mist collecting filters are made of fibres from which the collected drops will run to a collecting point. The fibres must be sufficiently rigid to withstand the droplet load and gas pressure without matting, which reduces efficiency and increases pressure drop. High temperatures and corrosive conditions restrict the range of fibres that can be used. Glass fibres do not deteriorate at temperatures up to 600°F (316°C), and some chemical fibres and wool stand up to mildly acid conditions while other chemical fibres have a long life in alkaline conditions.

This chapter discusses the construction of filter plants and filter media application to industrial waste gas cleaning. Fibre filters for mist collection and air cleaning are also dealt with briefly as they present a major field of filter application.

8.2. CONSTRUCTION OF INDUSTRIAL FILTER PLANT

The first gas filters used commercially consisted of long filter sleeves hung in rows, tied together at the bottom, while the dirty gases were ducted into the top. At intervals the sleeves were shaken manually and emptied. The sleeves were called bags, and the building containing them "bag houses",

FIG. 8.1. Early automatic bag house.[226]

which is the name still applied to installations of this type. Equipment of the type described is still found in some industries where the duty is light and the scale of application small, as for example in the collection of sawdust from a motorized saw-bench.

An obvious development of the rudimentary bag house described was to motorize the shaking of the bags, and install the plant in a small, separate and easily transportable housing. This was introduced in a German patent in 1881, where a mechanized shaking device, which slackened and tautened the bags was described, and the bags were enclosed in a wooden box (Fig. 8.1). This equipment was able to handle much larger gas volumes

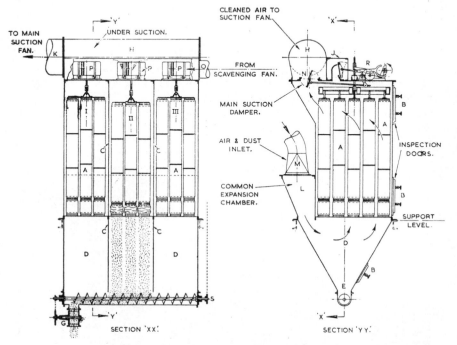

FIG. 8.2. Rectangular three compartment bag house with circular filter sleeves.[505]

than the traditional plant, in a smaller space, because of the frequent dust removal. Unfortunately the wooden housing of this early model tended to dry out and the cracks permitted excess air to be drawn in, reducing the amount of gas filtered. Since this early patent a large number of improvements, particularly with regard to dust removal, have been introduced by the manufacturers of "bag houses", and a modern plant will cope with high dust concentrations, large volumes, and comparatively high temperatures up to 316 °C (600 °F).

The filter sleeves used can be divided into two categories. The one consists of long, circular sleeves, which are directly descended from the early "bags", while the other contains flat filter sleeves, which have the advantage that a greater filter area can be packed into a housing of smaller volume than could be used for the round sleeves.

Circular filter sleeves, where the gas flow is usually from inside to outside, do not, under these conditions, require internal support, although some rings to prevent total bag collapse during shaking are often provided. The bags are mostly suspended in a regular pattern in a rectangular steel casing, although cylindrical containers are often used. In the case of the rectangular containers (Fig. 8.2) the complete "bag house" is made up of a number of

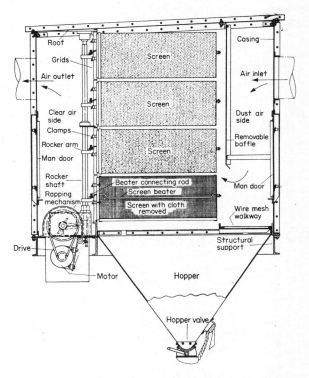

FIG. 8.3. Rectangular bag house with flat filter sleeves.[360]

similar standardized sections, each with the same number of bags and each able to be shaken separately. In the case of cylindrical containers there are usually fewer bags, but greater filter areas are obtained by using several cylindrical sections in the casing and longer bags.

When flat sleeves are used, these are supported on wire frameworks and the gas flow is from outside the sleeve inwards. The housing is invariably of rectangular design, and a number of housing units make up a complete installation (Fig. 8.3).

8.2.1. Dust cake removal methods

When the dirty gases pass through the filter cloth, the particles being removed from the gases first collect on the fibres, by the mechanisms discussed in the previous chapter. Then a cake builds up on the collected particles, and the pressure drop through the fabric increases. When the cake has built up to an optimum thickness for removal, it must be loosened from the filter cloth by some means and allowed to drop into the collection hopper.

In the first automatic unit (Fig. 8.1) the bag tension was released, the bag collapsed, and the dust cake fell through the wide sleeve into the hopper. Because the filter surface area that can be provided by wide bags was limited, the tendency has been to use narrower sleeves, which enable a much greater surface area to be fitted into the same size bag house. However, the cake tends now to be held up by the collapsed filter sleeve, and so the

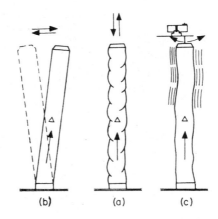

FIG. 8.4. Methods of shaking cylindrical filter sleeves:

(a) Vertical filter sleeve movement.

(b) Gentle sideways movement.

(c) Sideways vibration of filter sleeve.

sleeves are stiffened at intervals by retaining rings which prevent their total collapse, and allow the cake to fall.

Besides vertical bag motion (Fig. 8.4a), sideways movement is used (Figs. 8.4b and 8.4c), the most effective form of this being the rapid sideways shaking which loosens the cake while vibrating the filter sleeve. At high temperatures, where the fibres are weaker, the mechanical vibration may reduce the strength of the filter cloth, and gentle sideways shaking may be preferred. Sonic vibrations and low pressure shock waves have been used

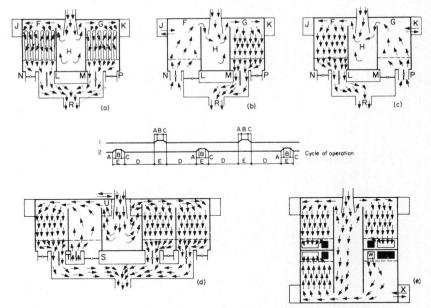

FIG. 8.5. Arrangements of gas flows to obtain reverse flow in one compartment of multicompartment filters.[448]

Two-section type:

This filter is divided into two sections F and G (Drawing (a)–(c)). Each section has its own bag shaking device with motor drive (J and K). A centre classifier (H) is highly desirable for (1) better distribution of dust-laden air, (2) more convenient dust pipe location, (3) considerable settling of dust, especially the larger particles, thereby relieving the filters of a portion of the load.

The clean air chambers of both filter sections have main dampers (L and M) and small reverse air-flow dampers (N and P). Each main damper and reverse air-flow damper are connected by linkage to a small gearhead motor. A timer controls opening and closing of the dampers; whenever a main damper closes, the corresponding reverse air-flow damper opens. The two main dampers lead to a common fan duct (R) for connection to the exhaust fan.

(a) Both filter sections F and G handle the dust-laden air. This is period D in the Operation Cycle described below.

(b) Main damper L is closed, small damper N is open for reverse air-flow through filter F. This air assists shaker drive J, which is in operation removing dust from bags.

(c) Main damper M is closed, small damper P is open for reverse air-flow through filter G. This air assists shaker drive K, which is now in operation removing dust from bags.

Cycle of operation 1 and 2 represent the two sections (F and G above).

A — About 1 minute allowed for closing damper, shutting of one section.

B — Two to four minutes operation of bag shaking device.

C — About 1 minute allowed for opening damper.

D — From 15 minutes to several hours when both filter compartments are in use.

E — From 4 to 6 minutes when one or the other compartment is shut off for bag shaking.

Four or more sections:

Filters of larger capacities may be subdivided into four or more sections with a common classifier. Each section has its own shaker drive, main damper and reverse air-flow damper. With a one-hour cycle, one section will be shaken every 15 minutes so that each compartment gets its turn every hour. As illustrated, filters may be arranged in single or double file, as dictated by available space.

Single file (d):

Four filter sections with second section from left closed. Main damper S is closed, small damper T is open for reverse air-flow to assist shaker drive U in removing dust from bags.

Double file (e):

Another four-section filter arrangement. Control dampers are bottom mounted. Main damper V is closed, small damper W open for reverse air-flow to assist shaker X which is in operation removing dust from bags in lower right section.

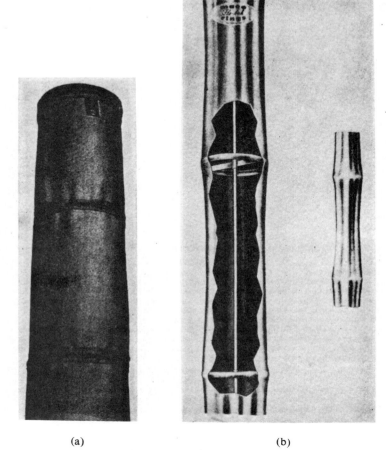

(a)   (b)

FIG. 8.6. Internal support for filter tubes.

(a) Rings sewn on the bags. (b) Rings held separately on rods. [338]

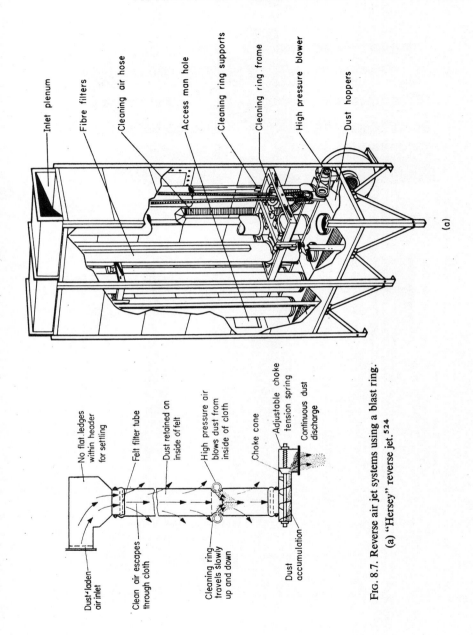

Inlet plenum

Fibre filters

Cleaning air hose

Access man hole

Cleaning ring supports

Cleaning ring frame

High pressure blower

Dust hoppers

(a)

No flat ledges within header for settling

Felt filter tube

Dust retained on inside of felt

High pressure air blows dust from inside of cloth

Choke cone

Adjustable choke tension spring

Continuous dust discharge

Dust-laden air inlet

Clean air escapes through cloth

Cleaning ring travels slowly up and down

Dust accumulation

Fig. 8.7. Reverse air jet systems using a blast ring.
(a) "Hersey" reverse jet.[524]

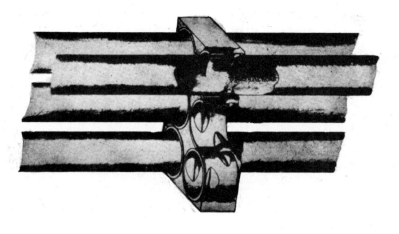

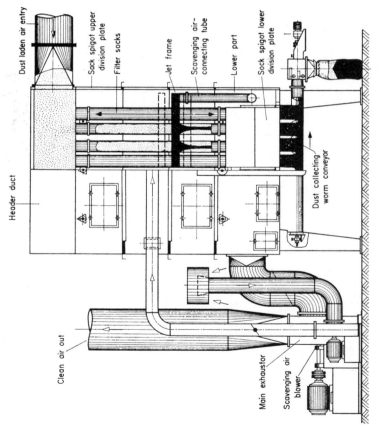

Dust laden air entry

Sock spigot upper division plate

Filter socks

Jet frame

Scavenging air-connecting tube

Lower part

Sock spigot lower division plate

Header duct

Dust collecting worm conveyor

Clean air out

Main exhaustor

Scavenging air blower

(b)

Fig. 8.7 (continued)

(b) "Junckmann" reverse jet. [464]

in recent years, but few details of performance are available. For high temperature operation or in corrosive atmospheres, where mechanical linkages could seize and corrode rapidly, these methods which do not require mechanical movement of the bags appear to be very suitable.

In many installations the bag shaking is assisted by reversal of the gas flow in the section being cleaned (Fig. 8.5). The bags are either kept circular by rings sewn on the bags (Fig. 8.6a) or by rings held in position by

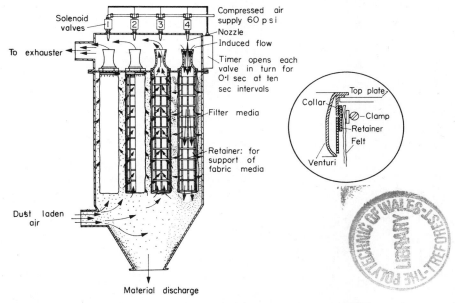

FIG. 8.8. Reverse air jet for separate filter sleeves: the Micro-Pulsaire system.[382]

rods hanging down the axis of the bags. This latter system is particularly useful for high temperature filters (Fig. 8.6b).

Besides shaking combined with gentle gas flow reversal, the filter cake can also be blown off by a strong blast of reverse air. Three systems of this type have been developed. In the first (Fig. 8.7a), an external ring, slightly smaller than the filter sleeve, with a slit facing inwards, is slowly and continuously moved up and down the filter sleeve. This is billowed out with the normal gas stream, so that the ring, being smaller than the sleeve, squeezes it, loosening the cake, and then the strong blast of air from the slit in the ring blows the cake off.[216] Instead of individual rings, a framework, shown in Fig. 8.7b, can be used. In the second system, the normal gas flow direction is reversed, being from outside inwards into a bag, supported on a framework and closed at the bottom (Fig. 8.8), while the cleaned gas escapes at the top. Intermittently a high velocity jet, blown through a

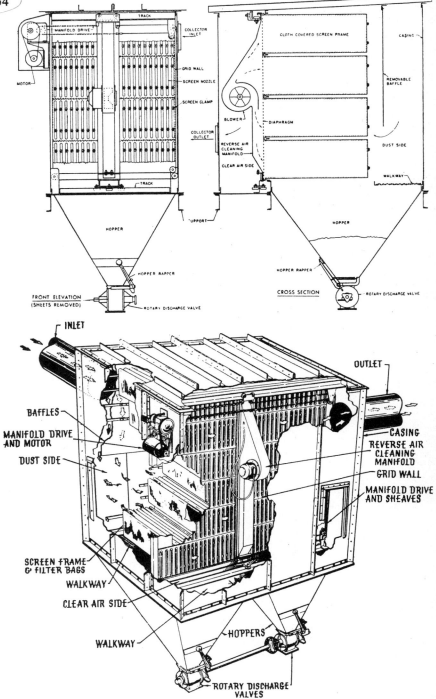

FIG. 8.9. Continuous reverse air cleaning system for flat filter sleeves.[360]

nozzle and a converging–diverging section at the top of the filter sleeve temporarily reverses the gas flow, and dislodges the collected cake, which falls into the hopper. The third system has been developed for flat filter sleeves, and as in the second system a reverse air flow is used, but in this case it is directed between two sealing off rollers which move from one sleeve to the next (Fig. 8.9).

8.2.2. Suspension and support of filter sleeves

The system of suspending and supporting filter sleeves depends on the direction of gas flow and the method of dust removal. If the filter sleeve is tubular, and the gas flow is from inside the tube outwards, the tube will not collapse during normal operation. The method of shaking, the velocity of

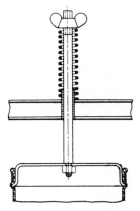

FIG. 8.10. Spring tensioning system for filter sleeves.

gas during reverse flow (if this is used) and the length of the tubes, then determine whether rings are required for bag support during removal of the collected dust. The provision of supports adds to the cost of the filter sleeve.

When flat filter sleeves are used, the gas flow is always from the outside inwards, and the sleeves have to be supported on a framework. Flow in the opposite direction tends to blow the sleeves outwards and adjoining sleeves may contact and wear. When a reverse flow cleaning system of the second type (Fig. 8.8) is used with circular bags, a supporting frame for the tubes is also essential.

One end of the filter sleeve is fastened round a hole through which gases enter or leave the filter sleeves. The fabric must be sealed at this point, usually by extending a short tube inside the sleeve and fastening the sleeve over this with a screw-clip or patented connection. This tube must be carefully designed, for example with a ridge, so that the bag cannot slip off during shaking. This is also the place where the greatest stresses and maximum wear occur on the sleeve, and it is frequent practice to strengthen this section. Long filter sleeves can be individually tensioned by a screw–spring system of the type shown in Fig. 8.10. Short filter sleeves may not require this.

8.2.3. Housing

The casing used for a bag filter system depends on the type of gas, gas temperature and direction of gas flow, and the type of dust cake removal system used. If the gases are of no further value, non-corrosive, non-toxic, and are brought to the inside of the filter bags, which are simply shaken, without gas flow reversal, for cake removal, then, the housing for the bags serves merely as weather protection for the sleeves and shaking mechanism. Simple corrugated steel sheets, probably zinc coated against atmospheric corrosion, can then be used for weather protection, and the cleaned gases

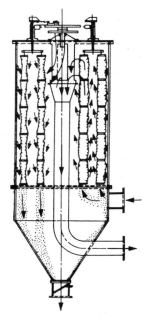

FIG. 8.11. Cylindrical housing for filter sleeves, where centrifugal separation is used for initial coarse particle separation.[464]

can be allowed to escape through openings in the building. If reverse gas flow is provided by suction within the bags, then a similar simple structure will also often be found adequate.

When the gases are of some value and are required for further processing, or when they are toxic, then the "bag house" must be carefully sealed, and if the pressure in the system is inadequate, an extraction fan must be used to exhaust the gases. This system has an advantage over the open bag house in that the fan used will handle the cleaned gases, with low fan blade erosion and a long fan life, while the fan used to push the gases through the filter sleeves of the open bag house operates on the dirty gases with resultant blade erosion and other problems associated with fans in dirty gases.

When the fan exhausts the housing, the housing must be strengthened to resist the external pressure. A cylindrical housing (Fig. 8.11) may be more economical in this case, particularly for small installation. Tangential entry into cylindrical casings also removes coarse particles by centrifugal forces. Careful sealing of the housing is necessary to reduce leaking in of excess air. In filter houses where the dirty gas is on the outside of the filter sleeves (Flat sleeves or reverse jet type Fig. 8.8), the housing has to withstand internal pressures of the order of several inches water gauge. In this case leaks in the housing will distribute dirty gases to the surroundings.

The housing is usually made of steel, which may be treated for corrosive or humid conditions by galvanizing, painting or lining with rubber or polyvinylchloride. Some of these materials are unsuitable at high temperatures, and stainless or special steels may be required. It is frequently necessary to insulate the installation to reduce heat losses and keep the gases above their dew point.

8.3. FILTER MATERIALS

It has been emphasized that the fibres used in filter materials should be fine and that if they do possess an electrostatic charge, it should be of the right type for the dust to be collected. Other factors must also be considered, such as the orientation of the fibres, which should be perpendicular to the direction of gas flow for maximum efficiency, and the mechanical strength of the filter cloth which must be able to withstand shaking or vibration. The fibres must also withstand chemical attack from the constituents of the gases, which can be acidic or alkaline, oxidizing or reducing. When the plant is closed down mould growths can occur and in some cases (particularly with untreated wool) insects and bacteria may attack the cloth. The filters used may be of natural fibres (cotton, flax, wool, silk, asbestos or glass) or chemical fibres. There are a number of these (listed in Table 8.1), with different chemical composition and a large number of trade names by which they are normally referred to.

All natural fibres are short fibres, called staple fibres, which are either pressed into felts or first spun into yarn and then woven into cloth. The chemical fibres are made either in the form of staple fibre or as long filament yarn, the latter being much stronger mechanically. For example,

TABLE 8.1. TRADE NAMES OF FIBRES USED AS FILTER MEDIA

Chemical name	Fibre type	Trade names
Polyamide fibre	Staple fibre and filament yarn	Nylon Perlon Phrilon
Polyacrylonitrile	Filament yarn and staple fibre	Orlon: Type 42, staple fibre Type 81, filament yarn PAN Dralon-T Redon
Polyester fibre (Polyethylene tetraphthalate)	Filament yarn and staple fibre	Terylene Dacron Diolen Trevira
Polyethylene fibre	Filament yarn	Polythene Alkathene
Polytetrafluorethylene fibre	Filament yarn	Teflon PTFE Hostaflon
Polyvinylchloride	Filament yarn	Vinyon Rhovylfibro
Vinylidene chloride (90%) Vinyl chloride (10%) Copolymer fibre	Filament yarn	Saran
Vinyl chloride (60%) Acrylonitrile (40%) Copolymer fibre	Filament yarn	Dynel

polyester fibre filament yarn has approximately twice the strength of the staple fibre yarn of the same diameter.

Essentially two types of woven cloths are made for gas filtration. These are simple, unraised fabrics or raised (mercerized) fabrics, where the raised fabric faces the dirty gas stream. The pores in woven cloths are those between the threads and between the fibres, the latter making up 30–50 per cent of the voids in the cloth. When a gas is drawn through the cloth most of the flow initially will be through the holes between the threads, while only a small fraction of the gas stream passes through the interstices between the fibres, where effective particle collection takes place. The more tightly twisted the yarn the less gas in fact can pass through the fibre interstices.

After a while, with a plain cloth, coarse particles will be caught in the inter-thread holes, and the gas stream is then forced through the interstices between the fibres. The cloth then acts as a most effective filter for both fine and coarse particles, and a cake builds up. Plain, unraised fabrics tend to release the dust cake more easily on shaking the cloth, while the cake tends to be interlocked with the fibres on a raised fabric. After cake removal, the efficiency of filtration and the pressure drop with a plain cloth are again low until the first filtration stage of closing the gaps between the threads has been achieved.

When a raised or "napped" fabric is used, the particles are collected predominantly by the nap—coarse particles by inertical impaction and fine particles by diffusion—the weave acting largely as a mechanical support. The particles which penetrate the nap are either lodged in the weave or are lost. Those lodged in the weave are unlikely to be dislodged during shaking, and an increasing pressure drop, with some increase in efficiency is observed in the early stages of filter cloth life. Some of the nap fibres are torn away when the cake is shaken off, and in time the nap will be removed completely. The cloth will then act as an unraised cloth, although sometimes the nap can be reformed.

The nap is formed by passing the cloth over "nappers", which tear the surface fibres from the threads in the weave. Conventional wire nappers have proved the most satisfactory, while sanders or sueders cause "pilling" of the fibres, which is not very desirable. If cloth is to be raised, a yarn with a twist that does not exceed 5 turns/in. should be selected, or napping becomes difficult. When dust loads are low, a heavier cloth (4 ply, 17 oz/yd^2) has a high initial efficiency with an acceptable pressure drop, while with high dust loads a lighter cloth (13 oz/yd^2) has better pressure drop characteristics.[503]

Non-woven fabrics or "felts" are different to woven fabrics because they present a uniform array of fibres right through the cloth, and get their mechanical strength from the interlocking of fibres. Strong felts can only be made from crimped staple fibre. The fibres are first carded, forming a web, which is then cross lapped to build up a batt, with depth and a random fibre distribution. The fibres are mechanically locked together by passing the batt through a needle loom, and the felt is then treated with heat and chemicals to shrink the material as well as to proof it against mould and insects if necessary.

At present felts are made of wool, polyester fibres or mixtures of these. The filtration efficiency tends to be uniformly high, although the pressure drop increases with use as more particles are lodged in the cloth and not shaken off or removed with reverse gas flow. Even if reverse flow does dislodge a particle within the felt, it is likely to be recollected before reaching the felt surface.

8.3.1. Properties and application of fibres

Cotton. Cotton is the cheapest fabric available commercially. It is strong at ambient temperatures and may be used up to 80 °C (175 °F). At higher temperatures cotton filter cloths rapidly lose strength, and tend to degrade in superheated steam. Cotton cloths have little chemical resistance in the case of alkaline or oxidizing conditions, or the presence of formic acid, organic solvents and hydrogen peroxide. Cotton fibres are relatively coarse and are not recommended for the collection of particles in the sizes below about 10 microns.

Wool. Wool fibres are much finer than cotton fibres and woollen cloths and felts have been widely used for gas filtration for many years. The cost of wool cloth is approximately twice that of cotton in most countries. Like cotton, wool is not suitable for use at elevated temperatures and continuous use above 95 °C (203 °F) is not recommended. Wool degrades in steam and alkaline conditions, but is stable in mild acid conditions. Wool can be mixed with polyester fibre to give the cloth greater strength and the filter sleeve a longer life.

Flax and *Silk* cloths are not commonly used as filter media and no data are available.

Asbestos. Asbestos fibres are exceptionally fine and are very suitable for fine particle collection (section 8.5.3), as well as being stable at high temperatures. Unfortunately the fibres cannot be satisfactorily spun and woven or felted into a cloth strong enough for making into filter sleeves. Mixing the asbestos fibre with 5–10 per cent cotton gives a cloth, which, although weaker than cotton at ambient temperatures, does retain some strength up to 400 °C (775 °F). This strength however is much lower than glass fibre cloths, whose use is to be preferred for high temperature applications.[312]

Glass. For temperatures between 150 and 300 °C, which is the range of temperatures where nearly all natural and chemical fibres are degraded, fine glass fibres make the most suitable filter fabric. The strength and flexibility of the fibres, compared to other high temperature resistant fibres such as aluminium silicate fibres, is such that conventional bag houses with gentle shaking mechanisms can be used. The glass fibres are made from alumina-boro-silicate glass (Pyrex) or very occasionally from soda glass.[331] The basic glass constituents are melted together in a glass furnace and then cast into marbles. These are re-melted in a small furnace, and the liquid glass then flows through orifices to form continuous filaments which are attenuated, sized and wound on to high speed cylinders. Glass staple fibres can be formed by playing a jet of air on the filaments flowing from the re-melting tank. The staple is collected on a drum and spun into yarn which is woven into cloth (grey goods). The grey goods are frequently treated again to remove the size by passing through a furnace at 530 °C for 5–20 sec. The size burns away, the glass is annealed and a permanent crimp sets into the fibres. The fibres are finally covered with a silicone resin finish, which is cured, and the finished cloth is then sewn into sleeves. The silicone resin is derived from phenyl-methyl or dimethyl silane.

The chemical resistance of the glass cloth is excellent, as it is not attacked either by acids or alkalis. Even fluoride gases with hydrogen flouride, silicon tetraflouride or boron triflouride require moisture to attack the glass, and this is not available at the temperatures used.

Because filter cake release characteristics of fibre glass cloths are excellent, gentle shaking and bag collapse or sonic vibration is found adequate and tends to lengthen the life of the filter cloths. Failure of the bags is probably caused by abrasion between the fibres. This seems to be verified by the greatly increased bag life at 600°F when the bags had been treated with colloidal graphite as a lubricant.[312]

TABLE 8.2. SUMMARY OF RELATIVE PROPERTIES OF CHEMICAL FIBRES
(ARRANGED IN ORDER OF PERFORMANCE)

(a) Polyamide fibres   (b) polyacrylonitrile fibres
(c) Polyester fibre   (d) polytetrafluorethylene fibre

Resistance to dry heat	Resistance to moist heat	Tensile strength	Resistance to acids	Resistance to alkalis	Resistance to oxidizing and reducing agents	Resistance to rot and mildew	Flex and abrasion resistance	Cost
(d)	(d)	(a)	(b)	(d)	(d)	(d)	(a)	(d)
(c)	(b)	(c)	(d)	(a)	(c)	(c)	(c)	(c)
(b)	(a)	(b)	(c)	(c)	(b)	(b)	(b)	(b)
(a)	(c)	(d)	(a)	(b)	(a)	(a)	(d)	(a)

Some workers consider that the burning off of the size reduces the mechanical strength of the cloth, and good results have been obtained with the untreated grey goods.[451] Some case histories for installations with glass bags are given here.[451]

(i) Non ferrous metals: (a) Lead oxide fumes at 205°C were filtered at 1·2 ft/min. (b) Zinc oxide fumes, filtered at 230°C, 1·6 ft/min velocity; using 10 ft bags, 5 in. dia. Aggregate area 222,000 ft² of fibre glass bags. Bag cleaning by collapse every ½ hour, supplemented by mechanical shaking every 8 hours. Bag life was over 2 years.

(ii) Carbon Black: Filter velocities 1·5 ft/min at gas temperatures 205 to 260°C. 5 in. dia. bags 11½ ft long commonly used. Cleaned by collapse with supplementary shaking.

(iii) Cement: Filter velocities 2·1 ft/min at 260°C. 11½ in. dia. woven glass tubes 25 ft long are used. Volumes of 90,000 ft³/min are handled by a 12 compartment filter with 48 tubes per compartment. Pressure

TABLE 8.3. PROPERTIES OF FIBRES AND CONDITIONS FOR PRE-

Fibre	Type	Cost*	Tenacity g/dernier at 20°C	Melting or sublimation temperature °C
Cotton	—	1	3·6	—
Wool	—	2	1·4–1·5	—
Polyester	Yarn	1·8	staple 3·5–4 filament 6–7	softens at 260°
Polyamide	Yarn	2·2	6.	250°
Polyacrylonitrile	Yarn	2·2	5·5	sticking temperature 255°
Polytetrafluorethylene	—	—	1·68 (1·4 at 260°)	sublimes over 800°

* Relative Costs in the European Common Market in September, 1962 (Cotton = 1)[139]

drop is 3 in. W. G. Filters are cleaned by bag collapse at 60 min intervals.
(iv) Electric arc steel furnace: Filter velocity 1·8 ft/min at 260°C: 11½ in. dia. filter tubes 25 ft long; volume treated 105,000 ft³/min. Cleaned by bag collapse.

Chemical Fibres: The chemical fibres (Table 8.1) are generally stronger and more resistant to heat and chemical attack than the natural fibres, wool and cotton. A comparison of their various properties is given in Table 8.2 (qualitative) and Table 8.3 (quantitative). Polytetrafluorethylene (PTFE) yarns are comparatively weak and coarse and are therefore infrequently used for gas cleaning filter fabrics, although the material is chemically very inert.

Polyester and polyacrylonitrile fabrics are resistant to acids, organic solvents, oxidizing and reducing agents, but are attacked by alkalis, while polyamide fibres are resistant to alkalis but degrade rapidly in acidic conditions. The vinylidene chloride copolymer fibres have not yet been used for gas cleaning applications.

Experiments with polyamide fibre cloth[513] show that the material will not break up at 120°C (248°F) but the filtration efficiency is reduced after use at this temperature and yellow spots are observed. Similarly, a cloth consisting of a mixture of polyester fibre with 30 per cent cotton, although retaining mechanical strength when heated above 100°C (212°F) will break down locally in the fibre structure and show reduced collection performance.

Filter sleeves made of chemical fibres shrink at elevated temperatures. This alters fabric dimensions, and porosity and causes cloth stiffness. When the material is to be used at elevated temperatures it must be carefully

SHRINKING SYNTHTIC FIBRE CLOTHS FOR USE AT HIGH TEMPERATURES

Useful working temperature °C	Conditions for pre-shrinking (°C)	
	(i) overfeed pin tenter	(ii) gas heated oven
below 80°	—	—
below 95°	—	—
usually below 120° but have been used to 140°C	220° for 1 min	220° for ½ min
—	205–220° for ½ min	205–220° for ½ min
100°	260° for 1 min	240° for ½ min
245°	290–320° for 1 min	320° for 1 min

finished and preshrunk. The cloth should be boiled off under relaxed conditions using rope, Hinneken or book scours, and then dried under relaxed conditions at 150–160°C (300–320°F). If the fabric consists of filament yarn it can then be napped and is then pre-shrunk in an overfeed pin tenter or gas heated oven. The temperatures and shrinking times are listed in Table 8.3. The fabric should be supported on rolls so that the only tension in the fabric is warpwise as it runs through the oven. Approximately 15 per cent shrinkage occurs and must be allowed for. In all cases the pre-shrinking temperature is higher than the recommend in-service temperatures, and pre-shrinking eliminates any further shrinkage of the cloth.

Chemical fibre cloths are usually much lighter in weight than wool cloths (only 5–7 oz/yd²). It is important that the filter sleeves are sewn with a thread of the same material or one with the same shrinkage and heat and chemical resistance.

Some typical case histories of chemical fibre applications are outlined.

(i) Filtration of 17,000 ft³/min at 135°C (275°F) waste gases from grey iron cupola. A five compartment conventional bag house was installed using gas to cloth ratios of 2·3 ft³/min (5 compartments) or 2·9 ft³/min (4 compartments). 15 min intervals between shaking in each compartment. Shaking for 1 min. The filter material was a polyacrylonitrile fibre, and the average inlet dust concentration was 1·42 gr./ft³ (60°F) during charging. The filter system was virtually 100 per cent effective.[379]

(ii) Filtration of zinc oxide fumes containing some sulphur dioxide at 135°C (275°F), using an automatic type shaker bag house. Polyacrylonitrile filter cloth had a life of 12 months, compared to cotton (2 weeks) and wool (3 months).

(iii) Filtration of non ferrous oxide fumes from furnace gases with some sulphur dioxide at 140°C (284°F). Polyester fibre cloth was used, without replacement for a period exceeding 12 months.

(iv) Abrasive dust with high moisture content. Polyacrylonitrile cloth lasted for 4½ years.

Other examples of case histories have been published by Walter.[513] These include comparison of cotton and wool (both raised) as well as felts of synthetic fibres strengthened by woven fabrics.

8.4. FILTER PLANT OPERATION

8.4.1. Gas flow rates: gas to cloth ratios

The size of a filter plant is primarily determined by the area of filter cloth required to filter the gases. The theory of filtration requires a low gas velocity if diffusion is the predominant mechanism and a high velocity if inertial impaction and interception are predominant. The choice of a filtration velocity must also consider other factors. High velocities give greater particle penetration of the cloth, and make cake removal more difficult. This also tends to increase the pressure drop through the filter. Higher filtration rates however reduce the filter area required, and consequently smaller plants are required to handle the same volume.

Practical experience has led to the use of a series of *gas to cloth ratios* for various materials collected and types of equipment. Smaller plants tend to use higher filtration velocities than large ones, but this is probably due to the difficulty of getting even gas distributions in large bag houses, and within a very long filter sleeve.

The *gas to cloth ratio* is commonly taken as the cubic feet per minute of gas filtered per square foot of filter area, and is expressed as feet per minute (ft/min). The ratios used vary from about 1–25 ft/min. For fine dusts in a conventional tube or flat sleeve installation 2–3 ft/min are usual. Typical rates for a number of materials are listed in Table 8.4. For coarser materials rates up to 6 ft/min can be used, while with coarse materials which are easy to handle, such as dust from wood sanding machines, 10 ft/min can be employed in conventional plant.

In the reverse jet type of plant, where the period between cake removal blows is brief, higher velocities have been found practicable. Thus 6–7 ft/min are used for fine fumes, 9–18 ft/min for fine dusts, and velocities up to 22 ft/min for coarse dusts. Although the construction of these units is more

TABLE 8.4. AIR TO CLOTH RATIOS IN SIMPLE BAG HOUSES

Type of dust	Air to cloth ratio ft/min*
Abrasives	2–2½
Asbestos†	2½–3
Blast cleaning	3–3½
Carbon	2–2½*
Cement—mills	1½–2
Cement—conveying and packing	2–2½
Clay	2–2½
Coal	2–2½
Feed	2½–3
Graphite	1½–2
Grinders	3–3½
Gypsum	2–2½
Lamp black	1½–2
Limestone	2–2½
Rubber	2–2½
Salt	2½–3
Sand	3–3½
Silica flour	2–2½
Soap	2–2½
Soapstone	2–2½
Talc	2–2½
Wood flour	2–2½

* For glass fibre installations lower air to cloth ratios 1·2–1·8 ft/min are used.

† In a recent large installation[64] it was recommended that 2·5 ft/min should not be exceeded.

complicated than the simple bag house, the high velocities have reduced the filter area required, and so this type of filter has become commercially feasible.[196]

8.4.2. Timing intermittent dust cake removal

When a new filter cloth is first put into operation, it does not contain any dust, but after dirty gases have passed through the cloth and it has been shaken or had reverse air blown through it, some of the dust collected remains in the filter. After some time the amount of dust retained remains approximately constant, and this is called the equilibrium dust content of the cloth. This depends on the type of filter material, dust sizes, and the timing and type of filter cake removal system being used.

If, in a single compartment filter, a constant gas velocity is maintained, the pressure drop increases with increasing build up of the filter cake. More commonly, a fan can maintain a constant pressure drop across a cake, and then the velocity decreases as the cake builds up.

It has been found experimentally, that with constant gas velocity, the pressure drop Δp_{CF}, measured in inches water gauge, is a linear function of the total dust content of the cloth, x, measured in grains per square foot of cloth:

$$\Delta p_{CF} = a + bx \qquad (8.1)$$

where a and b are empirical constants, and x is greater than x_e, the equilibrium dust content. When the gas velocity, u_0 ft/min, varies, the pressure loss Δp is:

$$\Delta p = u_0 \, \Delta p_{CF} \qquad (8.2)$$

The amount of dust collected when filtering V ft³ of gas per square foot of filter cloth, is a function of the dust concentration, c gr./ft³.

Therefore, from equation (8.1)

$$\Delta p_{CF} = a + b(x_e + cV) \qquad (8.3)$$

Combining equations (8.2) and (8.3), and noting that the face velocity with constant pressure drop is a time dependent function of the total gas flow V, dV/dt, the face velocity u_0 is:

$$u_0 = \frac{dV}{dt} = \frac{\Delta p}{\Delta p_{CF}} = \frac{\Delta p}{a + b(x_e + cV)} \text{ ft/min} \qquad (8.4)$$

Integrating (8.4) for constant pressure drop gives a relation between time and total flow:

$$t = \frac{V}{\Delta p} (a + bx_e + bcV/2) \qquad (8.5)$$

In an actual example[177] it was found that the equilibrium dust content of a cloth was 247 gr./ft² and the relation for constant velocity was:

$$\Delta p_{CF} = 0 \cdot 00195x - 0 \cdot 4 \qquad (8.6)$$

Instantaneous and average face velocities were calculated for a filter with a dust burden of 2 gr./ft³ in the gases and a constant pressure drop of 1 in. w. g., and these are given in Table 8.5. The table shows the high initial velocity obtained of 12·5 ft/min, which decreases to 5 ft/min after four minutes and 2 ft/min after 27 min.

The results of the calculation show that if a filter cloth is used, such as a felt, which gives a high initial filtration efficiency, more frequent dust removal results in higher effective filtration velocities. Thus, if 27·5 min shaking intervals are used, the average velocity is 3·6 ft/min, but this could be increased to 6 ft/min with 6 min intervals or even 10 ft/min for 2½ min shaking intervals. This is one of the main reasons why the reverse jet filters, with their frequent cleaning cycles are able to operate at much higher face velocities.

Shorter filtration cycles, followed by brief shaking periods can also be succesfully applied to conventional filters. Experiments have shown that 85 per cent of the total dust in the cloth is removed in the first 5 sec of shaking, while 30 sec remove a further 3 per cent, and 2 min shaking only another 1 per cent.[465] These experiments were also able to show that the amount of dust removed varies with the position in the filter tube. More (95 per cent) is removed from near the top than from the centre down (80 per cent). This leads to uneven filtration rates and excess wear in certain parts of the filter tube, particularly near the top.

For minimum filter area and long cloth life a combination of short filtration cycles coupled with brief shaking times are therefore advantageous.

TABLE 8.5. INSTANTANEOUS AND AVERAGE FILTERING VELOCITIES FOR A TYPICAL BAG FILTER INSTALLATION OPERATING AT CONSTANT PRESSURE DROP

Volume of gas filtered per ft² of cloth ft³	Time required min	Face velocity at time t min ft/min	Average face velocity after time t min ft/min
0	0	12·5	—
10	1	8·4	12·5
20	2·4	6·3	10
30	4·1	5·1	8·4
35	5·2	4·6	6·7
50	8·9	3·6	5·6
60	11·8	3·2	5·1
100	27·5	2·1	3·6

If however, filtration immediately after shaking is not very efficient, and a cake has to build up for effective performance then the large intial flow has the advantage that the cake first builds up rapidly, and an extended effective cleaning period follows before the flow rate is reduced to an uneconomically low rate. This method of operation is often used for very high temperature glass fibre filters where low filtering velocities and long cycling times are used.

8.4.3. Pressure losses in filter media

For the complete design of a filter plant, including the selection of the best fan, it is necessary to know the pressure drop through the filter medium. In many cases this is known from experiments on similar installations, or even from simple tests with a piece of filter material.

When it is not possible to obtain the pressure losses which occur experimentally, or if it is necessary to extrapolate existing results to higher temperatures, then theoretical or semi-empirical methods for calculating the pressure drop must be used. These methods are based on two approaches.

(i) The pressure drop is due to the friction of the gas moving through channels in the filter.
(ii) The pressure drop is due to the friction drag of the fibres placed in the gas stream.

The channel model is better for tightly packed beds while the friction drag on the fibres model is more applicable to loose fibre systems.

Channel Theory: The fibre beds are essentially slabs through which interconnected pores pass, and the pressure drop, Δp, is found from D'Arcy's formula:

$$\Delta p = \varkappa L \mu u_s \qquad (8.7)$$

where L = depth of bed (bed thickness),

μ = gas viscosity,

u_s = superficial gas velocity

$\varkappa$ = permeability coefficient.

This coefficient has been related to the specific surface area of the packing A and the bed porosity ϵ by Carman[86] in cases where orientation is not important by the equation

$$\varkappa = k_1 A^2 (1 - \epsilon)^2 / \epsilon^3 \qquad (8.8)$$

Here k_1 is a constant which was found to be 4·5 (using c.g.s. units) for spheres, and which will vary around this value for fibrous beds[159,295,479,542] where an orientation factor must also be included. Thus, Sullivan and Hertel[479] have suggested that for porosities (ϵ) less than 0·88, equation (8.8) can be modified to include a ratio of a shape factor parameter k_2, which increases with porosity and an orientation factor k_3, which is unity for flow parallel to the fibres and 0·5 for flow normal to the fibres:

$$\varkappa = \frac{k_2}{k_3} A^2 \frac{(1 - \epsilon)^2}{\epsilon^3} \qquad (8.9)$$

The ratio k_2/k_3 is as follows:

k_2/k_3 = 6·04 when fibres are normal to the direction of flow.

k_2/k_3 = 3·07 for fibres which are parallel to the direction of flow.

k_2/k_3 = 5·5 for the usual case of a fibre blanket where most of the fibres are normal to the direction of flow.

An empirical correlation which applies in the streamline flow region
($\text{Re}_c < 1$) has been suggested by Davies[120] for the permeability coefficients.

$$x = \frac{64}{D^2}(1 - \epsilon)^{3/2}\{1 + 56(1 - \epsilon)^3\} \qquad (8.10a)$$

This relation is based on a large number of materials, as shown in Fig. 8.12,
for which the porosity is less than 0·98.

Davies has also suggested a correlation for fibre mats with a porosity
greater than 0·98, based on measurements of wool, cotton, rayon, glass,

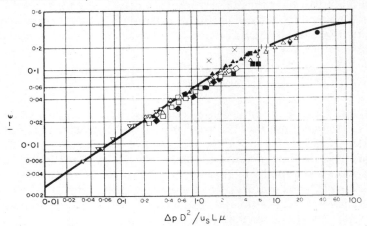

FIG. 8.12. Correlation of bed density ($1 - \epsilon$, where ϵ = voidage) with a function of pressure drop Δp and superficial gas velocity u_s: $(\Delta p D^2/u_s L \mu)$.[120]

Fluid flow through fibrous material.

◯ Glass wool.	△ Kapok.	▢ Cotton wool.
● Glass wool and copper wire.	▲ Merino wool.	◼ Camel hair.
+ Glass (fibres perpendicular to flow).	◇ Cotton wool.	▽ Down.
× Glass (fibres parallel to flow).	◆ Rayon.	▼ Glass wool.

wool and steel wool pads, where the fibre size varied from 0·8 to 40 microns.

$$x = \frac{70}{D^2}(1 - \epsilon)^{3/2}\{1 + 52(1 - \epsilon)^{3/2}\} \qquad (8.10b)$$

The fibre diameter D in equations (8.10) is the effective fibre diameter.
This can be found by measuring the pressure drop when gases flow through
a filter pad, and it is the diameter required in the filter efficiency equations
in Chapter 7. At high porosities the effective and actual mean fibre diameter is almost the same, but at low porosities, where fibres clump together, the effective fibre diameter is likely to be greater than the mean diameter.

A relation based on a regular array of fibres which was derived by Langmuir[295] is not given here as it is more difficult to apply, without gaining greater precision than is found by using Davies' equations.

The equations of Carman and Sullivan and Hertel can only be applied to very dense beds, where the porosity is less than 0·95, while the empirical equations by Davies (and also Langmuir's equation) will give realistic pressure drops at higher porosities, which occur in practical filters.

Fibre Drag Theory: Because the channel theory cannot be applied to practical gas filters,[71] several formulae have been derived which consider the drag on individual fibres in relation to the surrounding fibres.[92, 225] The most satisfactory of these is Chen's equation[92] which incorporates a modification for the gas stream interaction of a fibre in a tank composed of other fibres.[527] This gives

$$\Delta p = \frac{4k_4}{\pi \ln\{k_5/(1 - \epsilon)^{1/2}\}} \cdot \frac{1 - \epsilon}{\epsilon} \cdot \frac{\mu u_s L}{D_s} \qquad (8.11)$$

where k_4 and k_5 are constants, which were found experimentally to be 6·1 and 0·64 respectively and D_s is the mean fibre diameter based on the surface area of the fibres.

The effect of absolute pressure on the pressure drop in a filter has been investigated experimentally by Stern *et al.*[469] at pressures between 17 and 1000 millibars (13–760 mm Hg). The following empirical relation held to a high degree of accuracy in this range and can probably be extrapolated to pressures somewhat greater than atmospheric:

$$\Delta p = \frac{u_s \cdot 0\cdot00634}{1 + 13\cdot75/P} \qquad (8.12)$$

where Δp = pressure drop in inches water gauge

P = absolute pressure in millibars

and the velocities, u_s, were less than 200 ft/min.

8.4.4. Electrostatic charges in fibre filtration

The theory of the effect of coulombic and image charges was discussed in Chapter 7. The practical effects of these charges in actual gas filters has not been investigated in detail until recently.[162]

In the case of air conditioning filters and other filters where the collected material is retained in the filter fabric, the problem of particle release on shaking or blowing an air jet does not arise, and the fact that the charged particles are firmly held to the fibres adds to the usefulness of the filter. In the case of an industrial filter, where the collected particles have to be frequently removed, the strong electrostatic attractive forces between par-

TABLE 8.6. TRIBOELECTRIC SERIES FOR FABRICS[162]

Electrostatic
units

Positive		
+ 25		
		Wool felt
+ 20		
+ 15		Glass filament, heat cleaned and silicone treated
		Glass spun, heat cleaned and silicone treated
		Wool, woven felt
+ 10		Nylon 66, spun
		Nylon 66, spun, heat set
		Nylon 6, spun
		Cotton sateen
+ 5		Orlon 81, filament
		Orlon 42, needled fabrics
		Arnel, filament
		Dacron, filament
		Dacron, filament, silicone treated
0		Dacron, filament M.31
		Dacron, combination, filament and spun
		Creslan, spun: Azoton spun
		Verel, regular, spun: Orlon 81 spun (55,200)
		Dynel, spun
− 5		Orlon 81 spun
		Orlon 42 spun
		Dacron, needled
− 10		Dacron, spun: Orlon 81 spun (79475)
		Dacron, spun and heat set
		Polypropylene 01, filament
		Orlon 39B, spun
− 15		Fibraryl, spun
		Darvan, needled
		Kodel
− 20		Polyethylene B filament and spun
Negative		

Polystyrene, Saran and Vinyon are at the far negative end of the series.[446]

ticles and fibre prevent particle release, and hinder filter operation by assisting the rate of plugging of filter pores.

The type and quantity of charge acquired by a filter medium is a function of the filter type and the method of charging. The rate at which a fabric looses its charge is also an important consideration. This not only depends on the conductivity of the fibres, but also on the humidity of the gases passing through the filter. Thus fabrics which are poor conductors retain a charge much longer than good conductors, while in humid conditions a fabric acquires a surface film of moisture which also acts as a conductor.

Charges are induced in fabrics by friction, and the type and extent of charging that a particular material acquires relative to others can be measured by charging a series of materials in the same way. The usual technique consists of placing a strip of the material on an insulated ring and rubbing it with a strip of the reference fabric which is mounted on an insulating rotating disk.[162] The charge on the test strip is measured after a standardized number of turns of the charging disc, and again after a period (frequently 2 min) to find the rate of charge leakage. The maximum charge, measured immediately after charging enables the materials to be placed in relation to one another in a *triboelectric series* (Table 8.6).

Dust particles can be arranged into a similar series of positions relative to one another and to filter fabrics, and this can assist in the selection of filter fabrics with the most favourable charge characteristics for both particle collection and particle release, if the particles are to be removed by shaking, vibration or blowing.

Particles can be allotted to one of three categories.[4] Those which acquire a charge and do not agglomerate (Class I); those that acquire a charge and agglomerate (Class II), these being the active classes; and those which are not affected by the charge on the filter (Class III), being inactive. The active groups are divided into fine and coarse particles. Coarse particles do not present a problem in filtration as they are easily collected on the surface layers of the fabric, usually form a loose cake, and are easily shaken off. Fine particles are much more difficult to collect because they tend to penetrate the filter medium and often leak through. By selecting a highly charged filter medium, fine particles in Class II will be agglomerated, their collection improved, and they should form a loosely agglomerated cake on the fibre filter surface. If the filter has a high rate of charge loss under these conditions, cake release will also be assisted.

Several dusts in the various categories have been experimentally investigated,[162] and their performance is listed in Table 8.7.

When filters are used for air conditioning, it is usually important that the fibres retain their charge for a long time, as the filters are only replaced at long intervals. This led to the early development of resin impregnated wool filters which gave improved performance with only a small rise in pressure drop.[407] Other methods of obtaining a persistent charge in a filter medium were the impregnation of fibres with polystyrol, the covering of glass fibres with polystyrol or polyethylene, or the use of shredded polyethylene.[136,520]

It was assumed by Endres and van Orman[137] that these impregnated materials were self charging. Subsequent experiments by Silverman *et al.*[446] have shown that generally mechanical friction is required, because a clean gas stream does not charge a filter, while the friction from small particles

TABLE 8.7. RELATIONS OF FABRIC REQUIREMENTS TO DUST PROPERTIES AND DUSTS IN THE CATEGORIES LISTED[162]

Dust classification	IA	IB	IIA	IIB	III
Relative particle size	Fine	Coarse	Fine	Coarse	Fine and Coarse
Electrostatic properties	Active	Active	Active	Active	Inactive
Agglomerating tendencies	Little or none	Little or none	Positive	Positive	—
Criteria for filtration: Leakage	P_x	Const[1]	P_x to P_c^2	P_x to P_c^2	Fabric Construction dictates performance
High Flow low Δp	Const[1]	P_m	P_x	P_x	
Criteria for cleaning: Leakage control	D_e	Const[1]	P_x to P_c^2	P_x to P_c^2	
Ease of cake removal	D_h	D_h	D_h	D_h	
Material	Calcined Calcium Silicate	Flux Calcined Diatomaceous Earth, Commercial Finished Cement, Ball Clay	Processed Natural Diatomacious Earth, Wheat Starch, Taconite, Zinc oxide, Fume, Nickel furnace fume, Magnesite, Cellulose, Acetate, Molybdic oxide, Sugar	Carbon SRF	Kaolin

1. Fabric construction determines property.
2. Requires low density, rapidly agglomerating dust forming large aggregates.

P_x = maximum P.D. dust and fabric.　P_c = controlled P.D. dust and fabric.　P_m = minimum P.D. dust and fabric.

D_h = high rate of charge dissipation.　D_e = low rate of charge dissipation.　[P.D. = Potential Difference] passing through the filter is not adequate. Filter media which are in themselves non-conducting can become charged when charged particles are deposited on them. Electrical fields are formed all over the surface of the filter, with concentrations at places where, due to filter weaknesses, a larger

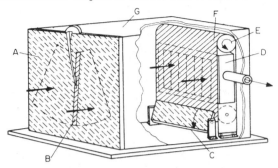

FIG. 8.13. Two-stage filter electrostatically charged by mechanical friction.[446]

A: Fabric A screen.
B: Fabric B covered windshield wiper blade.
C: Fabric A covered paddle.
D: Lucite box.
E: Lucite roller.
F: Fabric B belt.
G: Masonite box.

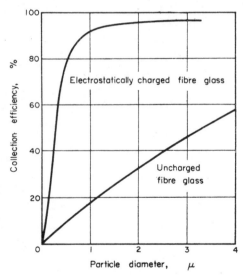

FIG. 8.14. Comparative fractional efficiency curves for charged and uncharged fibre glass filters.

proportion of the gas stream passes. This may have been the basis of the "self-charging" filter.

Mechanical charging of filters (Fig. 8.13) has been tried by Silverman *et al.*[446] These workers achieved some increase in filtration efficiency with no increase in pressure drop. However, the improved efficiency obtained was not comparable with the efficiencies of the "absolute" filters required for radioactive waste collection. It was also found that when air with an absolute humidity exceeding 120 gr. water per pound of dry air was passing through the filter, the filter would not retain a charge sufficiently long to be effective.

Electrostatic charging has been introduced in some bonded fibre glass filter media in commercial production, recommended for air conditioning installations. The efficiencies for uncharged and charged media with the same type of fibre are shown in Fig. 8.14.

8.5. FIBRE FILTERS FOR SPECIAL APPLICATIONS

Fibre filters of special designs are used for a number of industrial and commercial applications which have not been covered in the discussion of bag houses. These are for use at very high temperatures, for decontamination of radioactive waste gases, for collection of mist droplets and for air conditioning installations.

8.5.1. Filters for very high temperatures (above 400 °C)

Conventional filter sleeves, even those of glass fibres, cannot be used at temperatures above 350–400 °C ($\sim$660–750 °F) because of the reduced mechanical strength of the cloth at these and higher temperatures. Mechanical support to the glass fibres has been obtained by winding the fibres on a metal former. The resultant filter gave satisfactory service for long periods at temperatures of 400 °C.[397]

An alternative approach is to use a fibre blanket supported on a steel mesh, which is continuously replaced when an optimum amount of dust and fume has been collected. This type of filter has been extensively investigated by Silverman et al.[47,48,49,50,51] at the Harvard University Air Cleaning Laboratory for open hearth furnace fumes, fly ash, acid gases and mists. Spun blast furnace slag, where 50 per cent of the fibres were less than 5 microns, 90 per cent less than 10 microns and 99 per cent less than 30 microns dia, was used in filter beds from 1–5 cm thick (0·4–2 in.). The chemical composition of the slag wool was: SiO_2, 40 per cent, Al_2O_3, 10 per cent; CaO, 39 per cent; MgO, 8 per cent, and Fe_2O_3, 1 per cent.

Laboratory studies were carried out with temperatures ranging from 320 to 650 °C (610–1200 °F), with gas velocities between 100–220 ft/min. High fibre packing densities and high gas velocities favoured collection, indicating that inertial impaction is the controlling collection mechanism. With favourable conditions in the laboratory, collection efficiencies better than 90 per cent were consistently obtained, while in some cases efficiencies as high as 97–98 per cent were noted.

Extension of this work to the continuous pilot plant scale, however, met with considerable difficulties and collection efficiencies tended to average 60 per cent (by weight). In the first design used (Fig. 8.15) the slag wool, in the form of a slurry, was fed on to a continuous steel chain conveyer belt, where it was drained, dried to a web by the hot clean gases from the clean-

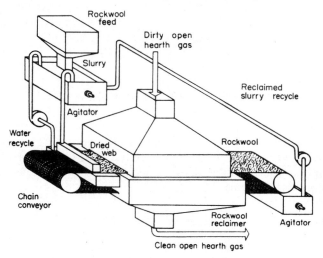

FIG. 8.15. Continuous slag wool filter — chain belt type.[47]

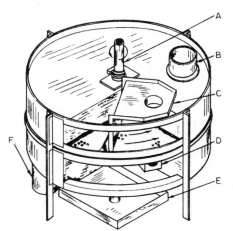

FIG. 8.16. Continuous slag wool filter — circular disk conveyor type.[51]

A. Shaft on which disk of 10 gauge perforated steel sheet is mounted.
B. Point of entry for furnace gases.
C. Tray from which slurry is introduced to disk.
D. De-watering suction box.
E. Sump for water.
F. Exit for clean gases.

ing section of the filter in one section, and then used as the filtering medium for the dirty gases. A later model was based on the same sequence of operations but used a rotating disc instead of the conveyer belt (Fig. 8.16). This model was even less efficient, averaging 44 per cent. This was improved, by placing the unit in series with a screw conveyer agglomerator, to 60 per cent. Stationary beds gave efficiencies similar to those which had been obtained in the laboratory.

The difficulty of cleaning the stationary bed filter has been approached by using a low pressure shock wave operating at sonic velocities to shake the dust from the fibres. The shock wave is generated by the explosion of a paper diaphragm. The agglomerated material, after being shaken off the fibres is re-entrained and collected by a mechanical collector, for example a cyclone.

Recent studies in fly ash collection at temperatures to 980°C (1800°F) have used an aluminium silicate fibre which melts at 1750°C (3190°F).[253] Collection efficiencies up to 90 per cent were achieved. Finer fibres and higher fibre bulk densities tended to give better collection. Very high velocities — between 146 and 690 ft/min (74–350 cm/sec) were used, and the rising gas velocities gave reduced efficiencies, suggesting that re-entrainment took place at these velocities. Similarly, lower efficiencies were obtained when the filter contained a large amount of dust. The temperature limitation in this case was not imposed by failure of the fibre, but of the fibre support. If a refractory support for the fibre were provided, then this material could be used to temperatures up to 1500°C (2730°F).

8.5.2. Mist filters

The most important difference between filtering solid particles and mist droplets is that no shaking or other particle removal method has to be provided for the latter because they agglomerate, run together, and finally run off the filter. The construction of a mist filter does, however, have to make provision for draining away the collected liquid.

Typical applications for mist filters are for the coarse mists produced in packed absorption and distillation towers. Some types of tower packing which are very effective liquid distributors are also effective liquid entrainers and must be followed by efficient mist collectors. Other applications are on the tail gases of acid plants, and below the bottom plate of a vacuum distillation column to prevent entrainment of asphalt droplets which would contaminate the product streams being taken off at the various stages of the column.

Mist eliminators for coarse droplet collection are usually made of woven metal wire, or more recently, polytetrafluorethylene. The wire is first woven and then crimped to a standard width strip of about 4–6 in. The strip is then coiled into circular sections or other suitable shapes. For installation within

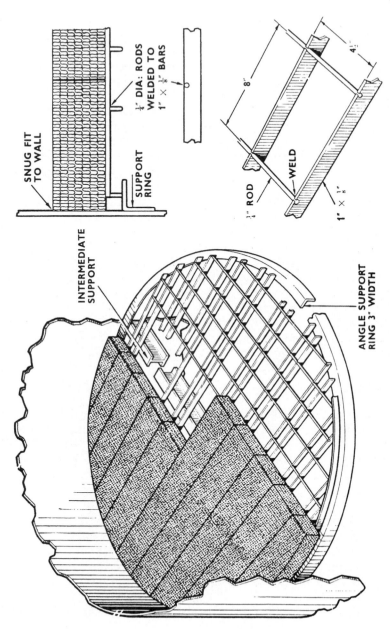

FIG. 8.17. Knitted metal wire demister for absorption tower or spray column.[265]

distillation columns the sections are made so that they can be fitted together in the column, and readily removed for cleaning (Fig. 8.17). Various wire winding patterns are used to give mesh densities suitable for different operating conditions. Typical specifications are given in Table 8.8.

TABLE 8.8. WIRE MESH MIST ELIMINATOR SPECIFICATIONS

Application	Free volume per cent	Surface area ft²/ft³	Density lb/ft³ (steel)
General purpose	98	100	10
Moderate velocities and clean liquids	97·5	120	12
High velocity, dirty liquids	99	60	6
High velocities, dirty liquids and particles	98·5	70	7

When droplets are to be collected at the top of a column a two stage mist eliminator is recommended practice. The lower stage is a high density mesh (12 lb/ft³) which acts as droplet agglomerator while the upper stage is a low density mesh (6–7 lb/ft³), which collects the enlarged mist droplets. For effective agglomeration, flooding conditions should exist in the lower mesh. This helps to scrub the gases and increase the droplet velocity, assisting collection by inertial impaction on the upper mesh. The two stages are separated by a distance of about three quarters of the tower diameter.

The optimum design superficial vapour velocity to be used can be calculated from the liquid and vapour densities using an equation based on the Souders–Brown equation.

$$u_S = 0.35 \sqrt{\left(\frac{\varrho_L - \varrho_V}{\varrho_V}\right)} \qquad (8.13)$$

where u_S = superficial vapour velocity (ft/sec)

ϱ_L = liquid density lb/ft³

ϱ_V = vapour density lb/ft³.

Operating vapour velocities should be in the range between 30 and 110 per cent of the optimum. Pressure losses through steel and polytetrafluorethylene grids for various velocities can be found from Fig. 8.18.

The meshes are made of mild and stainless steel wire as well as Monel, other nickel alloys, titanium and tantalum alloys and polytetrafluorethylene-monofilament, which will withstand 200 °C (392 °F) at very low rates of corrosion. The mesh is supported on stainless steel or other steel bars, but these can be made of other alloys or polyvinylchloride coated metals.

A typical application for a wire mesh mist eliminator made of Hastelloy C (54 nickel, 15·5 chromium, 16 molybdenum, 4 tungsten, 2·5 cobalt, 5 iron)

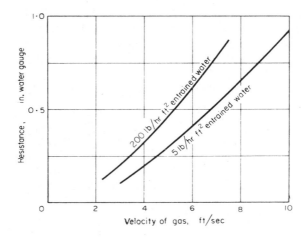

FIG. 8.18. Resistance–gas flow characteristic for 4 in. thick wire mesh demister (12 lb/ft³) at standard conditions.[265]

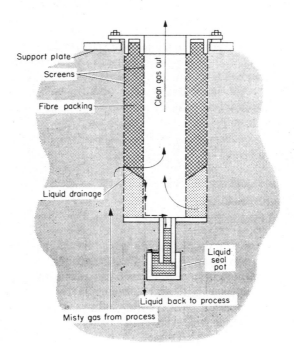

FIG. 8.19. Fibre demister candle.[69]

was on the tail gases of a contact sulphuric acid plant. With vapour velocities of 15–18 ft/sec, the acid concentration was reduced to a satisfactory 0·03–0·06 g/m³ at a pressure drop of 1·5–2 in. water gauge.[332]

When the droplets are much finer than in the above applications, a more efficient mist collector is required which uses finer fibres than wire mesh. Special filters packed with silicone treated glass fibre or polyester fibre have been developed[69, 146] (Fig. 8.19). The filter "candles" can be made by

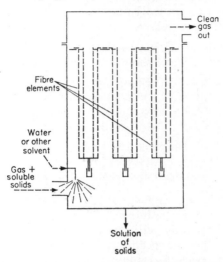

FIG. 8.20. Fibre demister candles arranged in vessel suitable for pressure or vacuum operation.[69]

wrapping the fibre on a frame or packing in a double walled framework, which can be made of steel, PVC, or steel coated with PVC. Figure 8.20 shows the arrangement of these units in a tank for service under pressure.

If the collected material contains solid particles as well as mist droplets, the candles can be irrigated with individual water sprays directed into each unit to wash the particles off the fibre.

The efficiency of a filter pad was found to be better than 99·5 per cent for the tail gases from a sulphuric acid plant,[146] and the exit concentrations obtained were about 1·0 g/1000 m³ (0·4 gr./1000 ft³). Other industrial plants gave the following performances:[353]

(i) Sulphuric acid mist from a Kachkaroff acid plant. Inlet concentration of 0·25 g/m³ was reduced to 0·004 g/m³ sulphur trioxide, being an efficiency of 98·6 per cent with 7 in. W.G. pressure drop. The plant needed no maintenance because of filter deterioration for over 1½ years.

(ii) Sulphuric acid mist from a contact acid plant. Inlet concentration of 0·175 g/m³ sulphur trioxide, was reduced to 0·0025 g/m³, an efficiency of 98·5 per cent. Pressure drop built up from 9–11 in. W.G. over nine months due to deposition of insoluble particles on the fibre.

(iii) Sulphuric acid mist from calciners. Inlet concentration of 0·090g/m³ sulphur trioxide reduced to 0·007 g/m³, an efficiency of 92·1 per cent. The mist was exceptionally fine, and a pressure drop of 5 in. W.G. was used in the pilot plant.

Note: Ceramic filters which have been normally used for this application tend to block up after about 3 months and have to be replaced.

(iv) Phosphoric acid mist.[68] Fibre mist eliminators reduce inlet concentration of 17 gr./ft³ (60°F) to 0·3 gr./1000 ft³ (60°F) on a plant producing 20,000 ft³/min waste gases. In general, the mist eliminators remove 99 per cent of the fume below 3 microns and virtually 100 per cent above 3 microns.

8.5.3. Filters for decontamination of radioactive gases

Radioactive particles are produced at all stages of treatment of the radioactive ores; mining, milling, refining, fuel element fabrication, and in atomic reactors. While the radioactive particle concentrations are comparatively dilute during the mining and milling stages, and conventional gas cleaning equipment, carefully applied, is adequate, when the radioactive materials are concentrated in fuel elements, and in reactors, very great care has to be taken as not only are the small particles from the fuel elements radioactive, but dust particles from the atmosphere also become contaminated. It therefore becomes vital to clean carefully not only the hot gases from gas cooled reactors, but also the ordinary air which is used to condition reactor buildings. These protective filters also have to protect the reactor building surroundings in case of accidents. The air for radiochemical laboratories, where high concentrations of radioisotopes are being treated, also has to be carefully cleaned for the same reasons.

The filters for radioisotopes must have the following specifications:

(a) The collection efficiency must be of the order of 99·99 per cent for sub-micron sized particles, as it has been found that the radioactive particles are predominantly in the range 0·2–0·7 microns.
(b) Low initial flow resistance.
(c) Minimum maintenance requirements during operation.
(d) A life expectancy in years.
(e) High resistance to fire.
(f) Containment of materials which will not cause a secondary disposal problem.

It is usual to refer to equipment performance for efficiency of capture of radioactive particles in terms of the *decontamination factor* (D.F.) rather than efficiency, where D.F. = 1/(1 − efficiency) A D.F. of 10 is equivalent to a particle capture efficiency of 90 per cent, while a D.F. of 1000 is equal to an efficiency of 99·9 per cent. D.F. values of 10^6 are frequently required for applications in cleaning waste gases from reactors.

FIG. 8.21. Two stage glass fibre, cotton asbestos filters.[345]

For cleaning the air entering reactor buildings, and similar applications, the Esparto grass–asbestos fibre filters have been developed, and are discussed in section 8.5.4 in connection with air conditioning filters. For reactor gas cleaning deep beds of asbestos and glass fibres are in use. These give innumerable surfaces for inertial impaction and diffusion.

The initial practice of the United Kingdom Atomic Energy Authority was to use canisters 13 in. dia., 55 in. long, filled with a mixture of asbestos and wool fibres, each having a throughput of 36 ft³/min with a pressure drop of 1 in. W.G. These had a methylene blue test efficiency of 99·99 per cent. However, the small volume flows led to the development of two stage filters (Fig. 8.21) filled with cotton and asbestos, with a fibre glass pre-filter, with a throughput of 200 ft^3/min and subsequently to a three stage unit, consisting of a pre-filter and two absolute fibre glass filters, with a throughput of 1000 ft^3/min, at a total pressure drop of 2·7 in. W.G. This type has a methylene blue efficiency of 99·997 per cent, and floor space requirements of only 2 ft square.[345]

United States practice has led to the use of deep bed fibre glass filters, for which the decontamination factor (D.F.) can be calculated from the empirical equation[56]:

$$\text{D.F.} = \mathscr{C}L^a\varrho_F^b u_s^c \tag{8.14}$$

where $\mathscr{C}$ = constant

   L = depth of bed (in.)

   ϱ_F = fibre bed density

   u_s = superficial velocity

a, b and c = constants (Table 8.9).

The empirical constants have been determined experimentally and are given in Table 8.9.[57]

TABLE 8.9. EMPIRICAL CONSTANTS FOR CALCULATION OF DECONTAMINATION FACTORS FOR FIBRE GLASS FILTERS[57]

Fibre classification	Fibre size microns	$\mathscr{C}$	a	b	c
AA	1·3	4·6	0·9	1·0	− 0·2
B	2·5	—	—	—	− 0·25
55	15	0·085	0·9	1·1	− 0·4
115K	30	0·054	0·9	0·9	− 0·4
450	115	—	—	—	− 0·5

Two types of multilayer deep bed filters have been in use, one for venting a process vessel, and the other for decontamination of effluent ventilation. The process vessel venting filter (Fig. 8.22) was designed for a flow volume of 250 ft^3/min, and for an efficiency of 99·99 per cent with a pressure drop of 4 in. W.G.

The design calculation is shown in Table 8.10.

Evaluation of this filter in service indicated that efficiencies were better than 99·9 per cent probably near the predicted value of 99·99 per cent.[57]

The filter for ventilation air consisted of 84 in. of freely packed 115K fibre, followed by two 0·5 in. sections of B and AA fibres in series (Fig. 8.23).

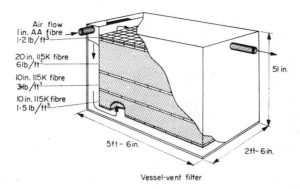

Air flow
1 in. AA fibre
1·2 lb/ft³

20 in. 115K fibre
6 lb/ft³

10 in. 115K fibre
3 lb/ft³

10 in. 115K fibre
1·5 lb/ft³

51 in.

5 ft - 6 in.

2 ft - 6 in.

Vessel-vent filter

FIG. 8.22. Vessel vent filter for use on vessels with radioactive process materials.[57]

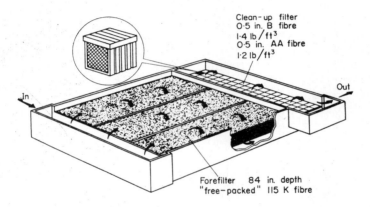

Clean-up filter
0·5 in. B fibre
1·4 lb/ft³
0·5 in. AA fibre
1·2 lb/ft³

In

Out

Forefilter 84 in. depth
"free-packed" 115 K fibre

Ventilation-air filter

FIG. 8.23. Multistage fibre glass filter for ventilation air for radioactive process operations.[57]

TABLE 8.10. PREDICTION OF COLLECTION EFFICIENCY OF FIBRE GLASS
FILTER FOR RADIOACTIVE VENT GASES[57]

Layer	Fibre class	Fibre size microns	Packing density lb/ft³	depth in.	Pressure drop in. W.G.	Predicted Efficiency %
Bottom	115K	30	1·5	12	0·10	39
Second	115K	30	3·0	10	0·24	53
Third	115K	30	6·0	20	1·34	93
Top	AA	1·3	1·2	1	2·20	99·9
				43	4·0	99·99

Efficiencies of 99·9 per cent, with a 4 in. W.G. pressure drop were predicted for this unit, and experimentally the radioactivity counts gave efficiencies of 99·84 per cent.

8.5.4. Filters in air conditioning

The removal of atmospheric dust from air is an essential part of air conditioning. The degree of cleanliness required varies with the application. Ordinary office and commercial air conditioning require less rigid standards than the air used in rooms for certain precision engineering operations or the manufacture of pharmaceuticals and photographic film. The amount of dust encountered in the atmosphere varies with the place, and some typical dust concentrations are given in Table 8.11.

The atmospheric dust concentrations, which are removed by the filters are much lower (about one ten-thousandth part) of the dust and fume concentrations encountered in industrial waste gases, and so it takes a very long time for an appreciable dust load to collect in the filter.

It is therefore one practice to build a filter installation of a number of small units which can be readily replaced at intervals, which vary from 1 to 12 or more months, depending on filter type and dust conditions. The

TABLE 8.11. ATMOSPHERIC DUST CONCENTRATIONS

Locality	Concentration	
	mg/m³	gr./1000 ft³
Rural or outer suburban	0·4–0·8	0·17–0·35
Commercial	0·8–1·5	0·35–0·65
Light industrial	1·0–1·8	0·45–0·8
Heavy industrial	1·5–3·0	0·65–1·3
Dusty workplaces	Over 3	Over 1·3

used filters may be of the type that can be cleaned for further use or may be discardable. In other installations, particularly useful for heavier dust burdens, provision is made for more frequent automatic replacement of the filter surface, using either a continuous cleaning bath, or a new section of cloth unwound from a roll. A low pressure drop is essential for air cleaning filters because very large volumes are handled, and the power consumption costs have to be kept to a minimum.

Instead of fibre filters, positive corona electrostatic precipitators are often used (Chapter 10). These units are greater in initial cost than conventional filters, but do not require the elements to be replaced as they can be washed down at intervals to remove the accumulated dust on the plates.

Air cleaning filters are made of a number of materials: metal wire or turnings, glass or chemical fibres, asbestos or paper. The fineness of the fibre determines the filter performance. Thus, metal turnings collect only comparatively coarse particles while asbestos fibre filters are effective collectors of particles in the sub-micron size range.

Metal wire is woven into gauze, chevron crimped, and layered, so that the direction of crimping is reversed in successive layers. The wire is retained in a 2 in. wide metal surround by an expanded wire grid. When metal

Fig. 8.24. Viscous filter cell.

turnings are used these are simply supported between the wire gauze walls. The most common size of the cells is 20 in. square (Fig. 8.24), although other sizes varying from 12 in. × 12 in. to 20 in. × 30 in. are made. A 20 in. square filter cell weighs about 25 lb, and the cells are clipped into sectioned frameworks.

Face velocities between 300 and 550 ft/min are used, and a velocity of 430 ft/min, giving a throughput of 1200 ft³/min for a 20 in. square cell is recommended by most manufacturers. Resistance to gas flow varies with flow rate and the dust load on the filter. A resistance–flow rate characteristic for a clean filter is shown in Fig. 8.25a, while the variation of resistance with dust load is shown in Fig. 8.25 b. The dust used in this experiment was a mixture of fly ash and lamp black, which is recommended for filter testing by the American Society of Heating and Ventilating Engineers.

The metal wire in these filters is usually covered with a film of a soluble oil, which serves two purposes. It holds the collected particles on the wire

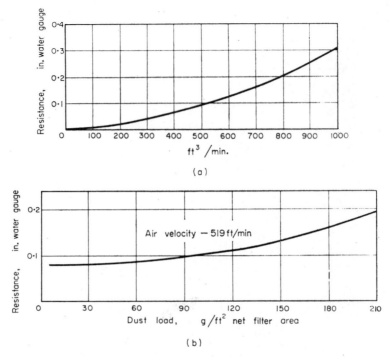

(a)

(b)

Fig. 8.25. (a) Resistance–flow rate characteristic for a clean 2 in. thick metal viscous filter.[505]
(b) Resistance–dust load characteristic of a 2 in. thick metal viscous filter at 519 ft/min face velocity.

(A.S.H. and A.E. Test method: Flow rate: 519 ft/min. Test dust: 80% Pocahontas fly ash. 20% Lamp Black. Feed rate: 5·4 gr./1000 ft³).

and it prevents corrosion. These filters are often referred to as viscous filters. One manufacturer interleaves the metal wire with cotton gauze which helps to keep the oil in the filter as well as acting as a filter on its own. When the filters are dirty they are exchanged, steam cleaned and recoated with oil. The simple filters have a comparatively low efficiency; an overall gravimetric efficiency of about 90 per cent, and a typical fractional efficiency curve is shown in Fig. 8.26. The low efficiencies for the small particles indicates that inertial impaction is the predominant collection mechanism, and these filters are only satisfactory when a comparatively low degree of cleaning is required.

When dust burdens are very high, a unit where the filter cells are continuously cleaned can be used. The cells are built on an endless moving belt or curtain arrangement (Figs. 8.27a and 8.27b), where the cells are dipped into an oil bath at regular intervals, normal practice being one complete

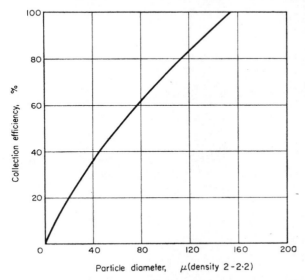

FIG. 8.26. Typical fractional efficiency curve for a metal viscous filter (2 in. thick).[505]

revolution of the belt every day. The units are built in panels 3 ft or more wide and between 5 and 15 ft high, increasing in 4–5 in. steps, depending on cell construction. Face velocities are about 550 ft/min and the pressure drop varies, depending on cell structure, between 0·35 and 0·45 in. W.G. The efficiency of these systems is similar to the fixed wire mesh panels.

When better cleaning than that provided by the wire mesh filter is required, glass or chemical fibre media are used. In their simplest form, these consist of disposable cells of standard dimensions (20 in. square and 1, 2 or 4 in. deep), packed loosely with the filter medium, which may be treated to cross link the fibres, and which is retained between cardboard or metal punched plates. The cross linkage treatment is a low volatility plastic resin, and is necessary where damp atmospheres cause matting together of the loose fibres. The face velocities recommended for these filters are about 300 ft/min, although special cells can be obtained which operate at velocities 50 per cent higher, similar to metal viscous filters. The recommended velocity should not be exceeded or internal break-

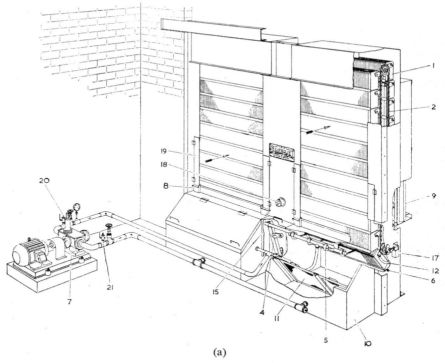

(a)

FIG. 8.27. Continuously cleaned metal viscous filter.
(a) Automatic continuously cleaned filter cells.[505]

1. Filter cells.
2. Cell conveyor chains.
3. Filter drive motor.
4. Reciprocating lever.
5. Reciprocating header with nozzles.
6. Cell tilting pin.
7. Main oil pump.
8. Oil traps.
9. Oil eliminators.
10. Oil tank.

11. Removable strainer screens.
12. Cell guides.
13. Cell conveyor chain tensioning bolts.
14. Worm gear.
15. Removable guard for reciprocating lever.
16. Safety cut-out switch.
17. Limit switch.
18. Hand drive.
19. Loading doors.
20. Hose union for filling oil tanks.
21. Hose union for emptying oil tanks.

down of the filter material occurs as well as re-entrainment, and filtration efficiency is reduced permanently. The resistance of this type is somewhat greater than the metal viscous filter, and a pressure drop–flow rate curve is shown in Fig. 8.28.

The collection efficiency characteristic for a typical fibre glass filter, tested under British Standard test conditions[76] is shown in Fig. 8.29. The test dusts used have average particle sizes of 18 microns (No. 2 test dust), 7 microns (No. 3 test dust) and 0·3 microns (Methylene blue fume). The efficiency is high (80–85 per cent) for new filters for test dusts 2 and 3, but falls off with high dust loads, indicating that re-entrainment occurs at this stage.

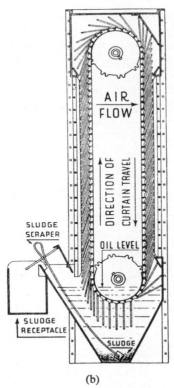

(b)

FIG. 8.27 *(continued)*

(b) Curtain type of filter cells.[12]

The retention of sub-micron sized particles is very inefficient, as indicated by the 10 per cent efficiency with methylene blue, and these filters cannot be used for clean rooms for photographic, biological or radiochemical work.

To improve the efficiency of this type of filter, it is important to avoid high dust loads, and an automatic filter medium replacement unit has been developed (Fig. 8.30). The actual medium is a comparatively close packed layer of glass or chemical fibre, bonded together, and supported on a loose woven cloth. The clean filter medium is exposed to the dirty gases, and either after a predetermined time or after the pressure drop has reached an optimum value (0·35–0·40 in. W.G.) an automatic mechanism exposes a new surface to the gases, rolling up the dirty medium. Face velocities of 500 ft/min are recommended, and 95 per cent collection is frequently achieved with dusts comparable with the British Standard dust Nos. 2 and 3, with loadings up to 40 g/ft² (which gives filter resistances of the order of 0·36–0·40 in. W.G.). For coarser dusts higher fabric loadings up to 100 g/ft² can be tolerated without the pressure drop exceeding 0·40 in. W.G.

An alternative solution to improving the filter efficiency with high dust loads is to increase the filter surface area, by stretching the filter cloth over a number of frames, as shown in Fig. 8.31. The superficial face velocity of this type of unit is about 300 ft/min, which gives a velocity of about 23 ft/min through the filter fabric, which is sufficiently low to avoid re-

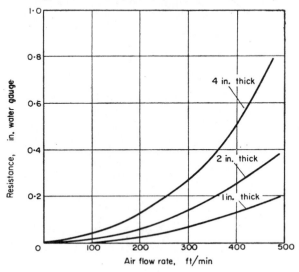

FIG. 8.28. Resistance–air flow characteristic for fibre glass filter pack.[506]

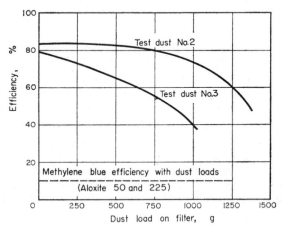

FIG. 8.29. Efficiency of fibre glass filter packs with standard test conditions (B.S. 2831) showing effect of reduced efficiency with high dust loads.[506] (Air flow: 300 ft/min.)

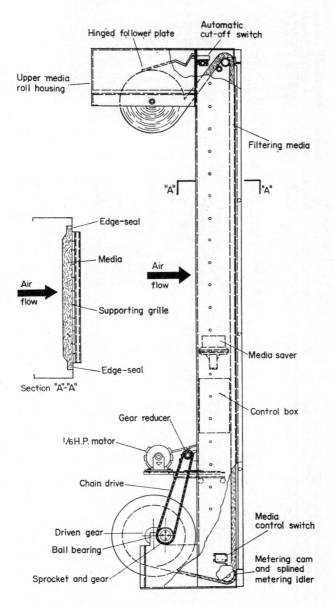

FIG. 8.30. Automatic filter cloth roll system.[99]

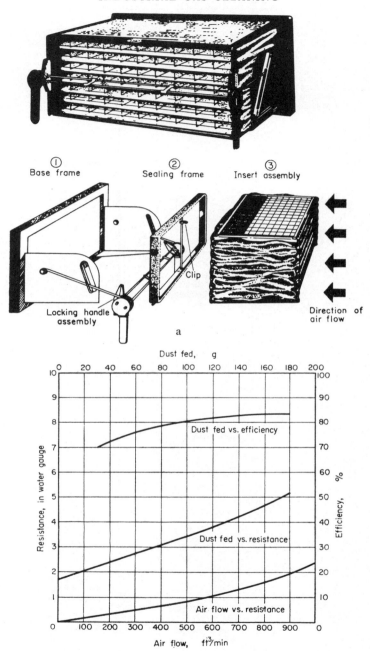

a

FIG. 8.31. (a) Multilayer filter, showing one method of assembly.[506] (b) Typical operating characteristics for multilayer type filter.

entrainment. The resistance of this filter is about 0·15 in. W.G. for a new filter fabric.

Some manufacturers supply a heavier filter medium with higher efficiencies and superficial face velocities of 200 ft/min. This reduces the velocity through the cloth to 15 ft/min, with a pressure drop of 0·3 in. W.G. The efficiency of this filter has been shown to be 97 per cent for the A.S.H. and V.E. test and about 88 per cent for the methylene blue test.[54]

If the filter medium is of chemical fibre, the cloth can sometimes be washed in special dry cleaning tanks and re-used. However some fibre matting and felting is likely to occur in the cleaning process, and there may be enlargement of pores between the fibres so that these will pass air preferentially without removing particles. Washing the filter medium is therefore not recommended if high efficiencies are to be maintained.

When even higher efficiencies are required than is possible with the multilayer filter, it becomes necessary to construct the filter medium of very fine fibres. Asbestos fibres in particular have proved suitable for this

TABLE 8.12. EFFICIENCIES OF FILTER MATERIALS USED IN AIR CONDITIONING FILTERS (D.O.P. OR METHYLENE BLUE TESTS)

	Flow rate ft/min at paper surface	Resistance in. W.G.	Efficiency %
Asbestos bearing paper[457]			
at start	5·25	0·8	99·980
after 205 min	5·25	0·95	99·993
Commercial "absolute" filters[506]			
Esparto grass–asbestos	4	1·1	99·95
glass fibre–asbestos	4	1·1	99·99
glass fibre (suitable to 550°C)	4	1·1	99·99
cellulose paper–asbestos	4	0·35	90
Esparto grass only	4	0·25	65
(For use in photographic industry where asbestos is undesirable)			
Glass fibre pads			
3 micron fibres loose 0·5 in.	33	0·05	63
1·3 micron fibres loose 0·5 in.	29	0.60	91
1·3 micron fibres loose 1 in.	27	1·5	99·4
$\frac{1}{2}$ in. 3 microns followed by $\frac{1}{2}$ in. 1·3 microns	30	0·90	94
Vacuum cleaner bag paper[457]	14	0·3	30
Woven glass fibres[457]			
fine weave fabric	5	0·06	48
coarse weave fabric	5	0·02	22
Wool Felt (reverse jet system)[457]			
at start	20	0·8	30
after 840 hr (constant)	20	2·8	92

because of their fire resistance as well as very fine fibres. Instead of methylene blue American workers prefer dioctylphthalate (DOP) smoke which has a mean particle size of 0·3 microns, similar to the methylene blue, and so is directly comparable with it.

Asbestos bearing filter papers have DOP efficiencies of 99·85 per cent for new papers, which increase to 99·999 per cent after 2 hr use, with flow rates of 5·25 ft/min,[457] and pressure drop of 0·95 in. W.G. To get practicable flow rates, face velocities of 125 ft/min, the papers are folded into compact panels, 24 in. square and 8 in. deep. The panel is able to handle 500 ft³/min, with a velocity through the paper of about 4 ft/min. These filters, which are in commercial production, are usually called "absolute" filters. They are made of Esparto grass and carded asbestos. Atomic Energy Authorities require their filters to be fireproof and able to withstand 550 °C (1020 °F), and are of an all glass fibre paper. These filters are in commercial production and have DOP efficiencies slightly below the experimental types. For slightly less rigorous duties, and where asbestos fibres are undesirable, an Esparto grass filter can be obtained. The efficiencies of various filters in common use are listed in Table 8.12.

For use in pharmaceutical work and the food industry, the efficiency of capture, or alternatively the penetration of micro-organisms is of interest, and the effectiveness of these filters towards bacteria (1·0 microns) and viruses (0·03 microns) is listed in Table 8.13.

TABLE 8.13. PENETRATION OF MICRO-ORGANISMS THROUGH FILTER MEDIA[345]

Type of filter	DOP penetration %	Bacteria (1·0 microns) penetration %	Virus (0·03 microns) penetration %
Glass paper	0·01	0·0001	0·0036
Asbestos—cellulose paper	0·05	0·0002–0·0003	—
Asbestos—cellulose (lower grade)	5·0	0·4	3·5
Cotton–asbestos cannister	0·001	0·005	—

CHAPTER 9

PARTICLE COLLECTION BY LIQUID SCRUBBING

9.1. INTRODUCTION

The effectiveness of rain in removing airborne dust from the atmosphere has been recognised for a very long time. Industry has used the idea of this natural process to develop a variety of liquid scrubbing equipment. The wet collection of particles has a number of advantages compared to dry methods, such as reduced dust explosion risk, as well as a number of disadvantages, largely associated with plant corrosion and effluent liquid disposal. These are summarized in Table 9.1.

The collection mechanisms in scrubbers are the same as in filters: inertial impaction, interception and diffusion, which were discussed quantitatively in Chapter 7. In addition, condensation effects and particle entrainment may play important parts in collection.

Although some electrostatic charge is produced on spray droplets during atomization, this has been shown to be too small to be a major aid in collection,[150] except when the droplets are deliberately charged by an external source.[274] Similarly, thermal precipitation is unlikely to be a major force in attracting particles, because the droplets are volatile, and the temperature difference for effective thermal precipitation is such that the droplets would evaporate. Where spray towers are used for hot gases they perform the multiple task of gas cooling and humidification as well as coarse particle collection, before passing the gases to a unit for fine particle removal.

The condensation effect is probably of great importance in the venturi scrubber where care is taken to use gases which have been saturated before passing through the reduced pressure zone in the venturi throat where more liquid is added. The subsequent condensation takes place in the diffuser where the pressure rises, as the velocity is reduced.[277] The dust particles tend to act as nuclei for the condensing vapour, increase in size, agglomerate and are more easily separated in the collection chamber. Entrainment of particles can occur in the wake of droplets, and may lead to particle capture when the droplets are collected.

It is not possible to classify scrubbers by the principal collection mechanism which is used in each case, giving one type a particular application.

TABLE 9.1. ADVANTAGES AND DISADVANTAGES OF WET AND DRY COLLECTION[152]

Wet	Dry
Advantages:	
(1) Can collect gases and particles at the same time.	(1) Recovery of dry material may give final product without further treatment.
(2) Recovers soluble material, and the material can be pumped to other plant for further treatment.	(2) Freedom from corrosion in most cases.
(3) High temperature gases cooled and washed.	(3) Less storage capacity required for product.
(4) Corrosive gases and mists can be recovered and neutralized.	(4) Combustible filters may be used for radioactive wastes.
(5) No fire or explosion hazard if suitable scrubbing liquor used (usually water).	(5) Particles greater than 0·05 microns may be collected with long equipment life and high collection efficiency.
(6) Plant generally small in size compared to dry collectors such as bag houses or electrostatic precipitators.	
Disadvantages:	
	(1) Hygroscopic materials may form solid cake and be difficult to shake off.
(1) Soluble materials must be recrystallized.	(2) Maintenance of plant and disposal of dry dust may be dangerous to operatives.
(2) Insoluble materials require settling in filtration plant.	(3) High temperatures may limit means of collection.
(3) Waste liquids require disposal which may be difficult.	(4) Limitation of use for corrosive mists for some plants (e.g. bag houses).
(4) Mists and vapours may be entrained in effluent gas streams.	(5) Creation of secondary dust problem during disposal of dust.
(5) Washed air will be saturated with liquid vapour, have high humidity and low dew point.	
(6) Very small particles (sub-micron sizes) are difficult to wet, and so will pass through plant.	
(7) Corrosion problems.	
(8) Liquid may freeze in cold weather.	

It has in fact been shown that improved scrubber performance, being the ability to collect particles of decreasing sizes, is a function of the energy consumed in the plant.[431] Thus, low resistance scrubbers such as spray towers collect coarse particles, while high pressure loss units of the venturi type are very effective with fine fumes. Here scrubbers will be classified primarily by the method of droplet formation, and secondly by the mechanism used to collect the droplets. Thus, in simple spray towers, the droplets are formed by atomizing sprays, and are collected by gravitational attraction, while in centrifugal spray scrubbers, the droplets, still formed by atomizing sprays, are collected by centrifugal forces. In other scrubbers the gas stream is used to break up the liquid and form droplets. Irrigated or wetted wall collectors, where the liquid serves mainly to prevent particle entrainment but not initially to collect the particle, are excluded from the present discussion. These have been included with the principal mechanism used in particle collection. For example, irrigated cyclones have been found to have a better performance characteristic in comparison to ordinary cyclones.

9.2. SPRAY TOWERS

The simplest type of scrubber is a spray tower. Liquid droplets are produced by spray nozzles, and are allowed to fall downwards through a rising stream of dirty gases. In order not to be entrained by the gas stream, the droplets must be sufficiently large to have a falling speed greater than the upward velocity of the gas stream, which, in practice, is about 2 to 4 ft/sec. Droplets smaller than 1 mm, in the case of water, tend to be approximately spherical, and their falling speeds can be estimated from the falling speeds of spheres in still air (Table 5.1).

Because the droplets used in spray towers are of the order of 0·1–1 mm dia., the particles collected by these droplets are comparatively large and the predominant collection mechanisms are inertial impaction and

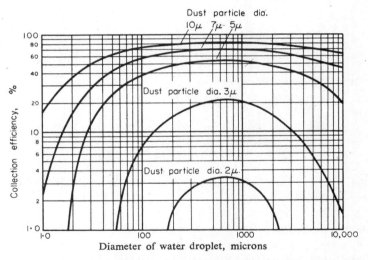

FIG. 9.1. Optimum droplet size for collection by inertial impaction by droplets falling in the earth's gravitational field, i.e. in a simple spray tower.[460]

interception. Stairmand[460] has calculated that the maximum collection efficiency by inertial impaction for droplets falling under gravity through still air is independent of the collected particle size, and is obtained when the droplets are about 0·8 mm (800 microns) dia. (Fig. 9.1): 0·8 mm dia. droplets have a falling speed of over 10 ft/sec while 0·4 mm drops fall with a relative velocity of 5·17 ft/sec, so a nozzle producing a coarse spray with droplets just below 1 mm is the most satisfactory for a simple spray tower. For these an impingement type nozzle (section 9.4) has been found to be suitable as it is very robust and has little tendency to block up or wear when the scrubbing liquid is re-circulated and contains a certain fraction of solid material.[199] In practice about 30–35 per cent of the liquid is recycled in the case of blast furnace gas scrubbers,[519] this leading to a reduced load

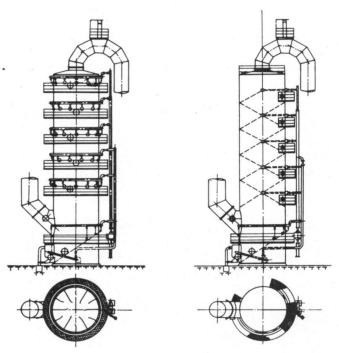

FIG. 9.2. Spray tower with circum-ferentially placed sprays.[199]

FIG. 9.3. Spray tower with axially placed sprays.[199]

on the water purification plant. It is also thought, although no evidence will confirm this at present, that the solids content of the scrubbing liquid reduces the surface tension, improves the wetting characteristics and so assists in collection.

A typical large spray tower is shown in Figs. 9.2 and 9.3. The design shown is 16 ft dia., has an effective height of 53 ft and in the original pattern had 5 circumferentially arranged rings of sprays with 14–16 sprays per ring (Fig. 9.2). The tower handled 1·75 million ft³/hr, and the gas velocity was about 2·5 ft/sec. The second arrangement (Fig. 9.3) shows the same tower with 9 centrally placed solid cone impact sprays, which reduced the solids concentration in the gas from 2·2 g/Nm³ to 0·22 g/Nm³, an efficiency of 90 per cent, compared with 73 per cent achieved with the circumferentially placed sprays. The central sprays had a service life of 18 months, and were found to be effective in towers up to 25 ft. dia. handling 7 million ft³/hr (gas velocity 3·7 ft/sec).

Water consumption for spray towers can be found from the data in Fig. 9.4, which plots specific water consumption (in l./Nm³) for exit dust concentrations using inlet concentrations as parameters, in the case of blast furnace gas dusts.

When a counter-current spray tower acts as a gas cooler as well as particle collector, the design of the tower from first principles presents a number of problems, as the droplet size decreases because of the evaporation which takes place. To carry out the calculation it is necessary to divide the tower into a number of sections, each with one ring of spray nozzles, and then find the evaporation which takes place within this zone, based on the

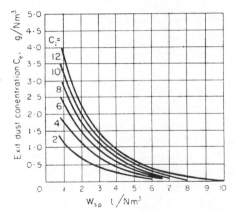

Fig. 9.4. Specific water consumption correlation for a simple spray tower.[199]

C_i = dust concentration at inlet gr./Nm³.
C_e = dust concentration at exit gr./Nm³.
W_{sp} = specific water consumption l./Nm³.

gas temperature and the droplet residence time. The first region to be tackled is the one at the top of the tower, where exit gas conditions are specified, and new droplets are introduced. From the evaporation in this zone the conditions at the top of the penultimate zone can be found, but in this zone we have both freshly-introduced droplets and falling partially evaporated ones. A complete calculation has not yet been attempted.

The rate of evaporation from pure water droplets travelling at their terminal velocity, which is a reasonable initial assumption, can be estimated from the graphs plotted by Marshall,[327, 328] one of which is shown in

Fig. 9.5. The complex problem of evaporation from drops with some dissolved solids has also been attempted by Marshall as part of his studies on spray drying, and if detailed calculations are to be carried out, the monograph[327] on this subject should be referred to.

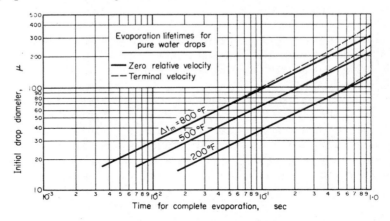

FIG. 9.5. Relation between water drop diameter
and time for complete evaporation.[328]

9.3. CENTRIFUGAL SPRAY SCRUBBER

The efficiency of collection of particles smaller than those recovered in a simple spray tower can be improved by increasing the relative velocity of the droplets and the gas stream. The force on the droplets can be increased by using the centrifugal force of a spinning gas stream rather than the gravitational force in the simple tower. For example, when gases are spinning with a tangential velocity of 57 ft/sec at a radius of 1 ft, the centrifugal force is 100 g. Johnstone and Roberts[243] calculated the efficiency of collection by inertial impaction of particles by droplets of various sizes under the influence of a force of 100 g (Fig. 9.6). The curves show that droplets of about 100 microns are most effective, larger droplets have smaller inertial impaction parameters while smaller droplets are entrained in the gas stream. The curves also show the vastly improved collection efficiency of the centrifugal spray type scrubber compared to the gravity spray tower, particularly in the 1–10 micron particle size range. Collection by diffusion is not very effective, except for particles less than 0·001 microns. Commercial centrifugal spray scrubbers have operating efficiencies of 97 per cent or better for particles greater than 1 micron. A selection of performance data is listed in Table 9.2.

Commercially designed centrifugal spray scrubbers are of two patterns. In the first, the spinning motion is imparted to the gas stream by a tangen-

TABLE 9.2. PERFORMANCE DATA FOR CYCLONIC SPRAY SCRUBBER[264]
(PEASE–ANTHONY TYPE)

Source of gas	Type of dust or mist	Particle size range microns	Dust loadings gr./ft³		Efficiency %
			inlet	outlet	
Boiler flue gas	Fly ash (pulverized coal)	>2·5	0·49–2·58	0·02–0·046	88–98·8
Blast furnace (iron)	Iron ore coke	0·5–20	3–24	0·03–0·08	99
Lime kiln (Kraft mud)	Lime	1–25	7·7	0·25	97
Lime kiln (raw stone)	Lime	2–40	9·2	0·08	99
Reverbatory lead furnace	Lead compounds	0·5–2+	0·5–2	0·023–0·04	95–98
Rotary dryer	Ammonium nitrate	large, unstable agglomerates	...	...	99+
Superphosphate den and mixer	Fluorine compounds	mist	0·14	0·003	97·8
Air bodying of castor oil	Castor oil	mist	0·0027	0·0006	78

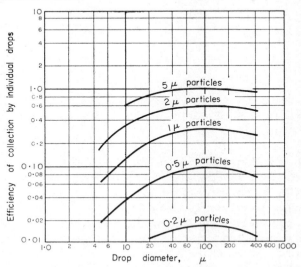

FIG. 9.6 Optimum droplet size for collection by inertial impaction when droplets are moving in field of $100 \times g$: i.e. a centrifugal spray tower.[243]

tial entry with velocities between 50 and 200 ft/sec. The liquid is directed outwards from sprays set in a central pipe[264] (Fig. 9.7a). In the second type (Fig. 9.7b) the spinning motion is given to the gas stream by fixed vanes, and the water spray in the chamber is directed downwards from a centrally placed single nozzle. Both types of plant are built to handle volumes ranging from 500 to 40,000 ft³/min.

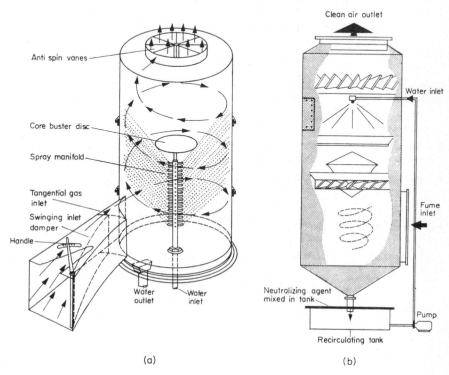

(a)   (b)

FIG. 9.7. Centrifugal spray scrubber.
(a) Tangential entry, centrally placed sprays (Pease–Anthony design).[246]
(b) Vane entry.

A third type of centrifugal scrubber, not in commercial production, has been extensively tested by First *et al.*[152] This is essentially a conventional cyclone, but with the gas entry at the base of the cylindrical section, and water sprays directed across the entry. High pressure water jets from a swirl atomizer proved most effective, a collection efficiency of 90 per cent being obtained with micronized talc test dust. A similar unit has been tested elsewhere,[376] and a 95 per cent efficiency was obtained with a coarse dust (85 per cent greater than 10 microns), a loading of 2 gr./ft³ and a pressure loss of 2·1 in. W.G.

The liquid droplets in these centrifugal scrubbers are much smaller than in the simple gravitational spray towers, and it is therefore not desirable to have further droplet evaporation taking place in the scrubbers as they would no longer act effectively. It is usual practice to saturate the gases before they enter the scrubber, particularly if they are warmer than the liquid, to reduce droplet evaporation.

9.4. SPRAY NOZZLES

Spray scrubbers require droplets which are fairly closely sized in order to avoid entrainment and act most effectively. As the scrubbing liquid is often re-circulated to reduce liquid consumption and the provision of very large separation tanks, the nozzles must be capable of handling liquids with a fairly high solids concentration. The most extensive study of nozzles for this type of duty has been in connection with spray drying[327] and also blast furnace gas cleaning.[199] Six nozzle types are in use:

(i) Impingement type.
(ii) Spiral spray nozzle.
(iii) Spinning disk type.
(iv) Two liquid jet impingement nozzle.
(v) Pneumatic nozzle.
(vi) Sonic nozzle.

(i) In *impingement nozzles* a high velocity liquid jet is directed at a solid target. The jet is disintegrated by the impact and the liquid attenuation caused by the jet's change of direction. Depending on the type of target, either a directional spray or a hollow cone spray is produced. The two targets used are either a solid wall (Fig. 9.8a) for the directional spray, or the point of a hook, inserted in the axis of the nozzle (Fig. 9.8b) for the hollow cone spray. The nozzles are cheap, robust and simple in construction and are widely used where coarse sprays are required, as for example in the blast furnace gas spray towers.[199]

(ii) The atomizing action in *swirl type nozzles* is caused by the spinning motion imparted to the liquid before it leaves the nozzle. This spinning motion is obtained from a spin chamber within the nozzle, the liquid entry to which consists of a series of tangential holes (Fig. 9.9a). The entry holes have a tendency to block up, and this nozzle is not recommended where a suspension is being re-cycled. Droplet sizes from this nozzle (with 50 lb/in.^{2} water pressure), vary between 150 and 400 microns, depending on the orifice diameter[373] (Fig. 9.9b). With somewhat higher pressures (400 lb/in.^{2}) this type of nozzle has proved most effective for centrifugal spray scrubbers because of the large proportion of droplets about 100 microns which are produced.[238]

(iii) *Spinning disk atomizers* are disks from which liquid droplets are discharged after being accelerated to a high velocity on a rotating disk (Fig. 9.10). The disk can be driven by the liquid or mechanically and the liquid can move radially through tubes or across the flat disk. The droplets produced are uniform in size, and the size can be controlled by changing the disk speed and flow rate, which makes these atomizers most useful in producing the droplets for fundamental studies of their behaviour and performance. Details of their construction can be found elsewhere.[165] At

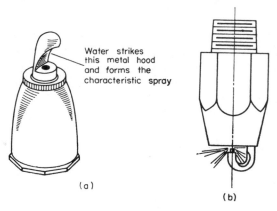

Water strikes this metal hood and forms the characteristic spray

(a)

(b)

FIG. 9.8. Impingement type nozzles.
(a) Fixed wall — directional spray.
(b) Hook type — hollow cone spray.[327]

present spinning disk atomizers are not used in commercial spray towers, but may find an application in scrubber developments where closely sized droplets are required.

(iv) When two liquid jets impinge, a ruffled sheet of liquid forms and then disintegrates intermittently to form groups of drops which appear to originate from the waves formed in the liquid at the point of impingement. The frequency of the waves increases with the jet velocity and with decreasing impingement angle, and rises to 4000 cycles/sec, forming large numbers of fine droplets. The viscosity of the liquid affects the spray formation characteristics, although these seemed to be little affected by the surface tension.[327] These atomizers, which are called *liquid jet impingement nozzles* have the advantage that fine droplet sizes can be produced without the complex mechanical construction of the two foregoing types, or the wearing surfaces of the impingement nozzles. They are not yet used in commercial scrubbers.

(v) In the case of *pneumatic* or *two fluid atomization*, the liquid spray is produced by the impact of a gas stream on a liquid jet rather than of two liquid jets. Pneumatic nozzles produce very fine droplets, which were

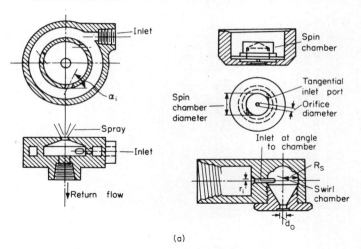

(a)

(a) Nozzle designs with swirl chamber.[327]

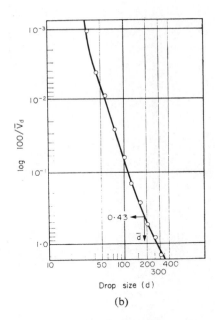

Fɪɢ. 9.9. Swirl type spray nozzles.

(b) Droplet size distribution from swirl type nozzle.

$$\bar{V}_d = 100 \, e^{(-d/\bar{d})q} \quad \text{where } \bar{V}_d = \text{volume per cent oversize.}$$

d = droplet diameter. $\bar{d}$ = Rosin Rammler mean. q = dispersion coefficient (slope of line in Fig. 9.9(b).)

(After Fraser and Eisenklam, *Trans. Inst. Chem. Engnrs.* (London), **34**, 294 (1956).)

FIG. 9.10. Typical disk in spinning disk atomizers.[327]

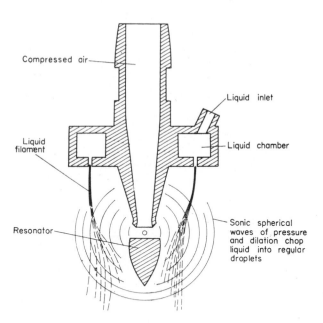

FIG. 9.11. Sonic spray nozzle.[18]

found in practice to be unsuitable for centrifugal scrubbers.[238] The fact that a high pressure air or steam supply has to be provided as well as the water or other liquid adds to the installation and maintenance costs, and they are therefore not normally used for scrubbers.

The droplet formation in pneumatic sprays has been studied in considerable detail, largely because of its relevance to the action of a venturi scrubber, where, essentially, a gas stream impinges on a liquid wall. The average drop size D and surface area of the drops per unit volume of gas can be estimated from the empirical equations of Nukiyama and Tanasawa.[356]

$$D = \frac{585 \sqrt{\sigma}}{u \sqrt{(\varrho_L)}} + 597 \left(\frac{\mu_L}{\sqrt{(\sigma \varrho_L)}}\right)^{0.45} \left(\frac{1000 Q_L}{Q}\right)^{1.5} \tag{9.1}$$

where D = average droplet diameter (surface diameter) (microns)

    u = relative velocity between air and liquid stream (m/sec)

    Q_L/Q = ratio of liquid volume flow to gas volume flow at the venturi throat.

    ϱ_L = liquid density (g/cm³)

    σ = liquid surface tension (dynes/cm)

    μ_L = liquid viscosity (poise)

For the air–water system, equation (9.1) simplifies to:

$$D = \frac{16050}{u} + 1.41 L_1^{1.5} \tag{9.2}$$

where L_1 = gallons of water/1000 ft³ air.
The specific surface of the droplets, A (ft²/ft³ of gas) can be obtained from

$$A = 244 L_1/D. \tag{9.3}$$

Experimental studies reported by Houghton[221] were in excellent agreement with the predictions of the above equations for pneumatic nozzles, while fair agreement was obtained for venturi atomizers.[303]

(vi) *Sonic spray nozzles*, recently developed, have a number of advantages over the traditional high pressure liquid or pneumatic types. The construction is shown in Fig. 9.11. The liquid flows out of a simple annular chamber through holes under low pressures (10 lb/in.²), and the liquid filaments are shattered by the sound waves (at a frequency of 9·4 kilocycles/sec), producing very uniform droplets. The sound waves are produced by the impingement of a jet of compressed air or steam (15–60 lb/in.²) impinging on the resonator placed centrally between the holes. The liquid throughput of the nozzle is about 6 lb/min.[18]

9.5. SCRUBBERS WITH SELF-INDUCED SPRAYS

In many types of scrubbers the droplets which scrub the gases are formed by the gas stream breaking through a sheet of liquid or impinging on a pool. The simplest unit of this type, which is often applied to cupola furnaces, has water running over a cone shaped disk, forming an annular water sheet, which is broken up by the furnace gases (Fig. 9.12). This system has a low pressure drop, less than 0·25 in. W.G., and can be installed very cheaply, and without induced draught fans. The efficiency with coarse dusts is claimed to be high.

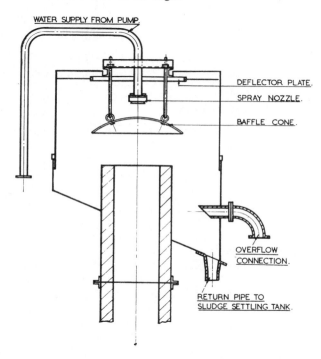

FIG. 9.12. Cupola top scrubber.[376]

A more elaborate device is shown in Fig. 9.13, where the gas stream breaks through a pool of liquid, and then creates a liquid curtain because of the specially designed orifices. The complete unit is shown in Fig. 9.14, and a similar idea in Fig. 9.15. In the former (Rotoclone type N) the impingement gas velocity is about 50 ft/sec, which creates droplets of 300 to 400 microns, while in the latter (Doyle scrubber) the impingement velocity varies between 120 and 180 ft/sec.[129]

FIG. 9.13. Action of a self-induced spray scrubber (Rotoclone N).[12]

FIG. 9.14. Self-induced spray type scrubber (Rotoclone N).[12]

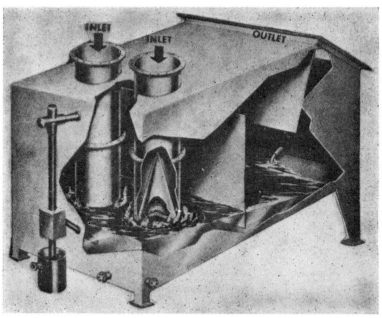

FIG. 9.15. Self-induced spray type scrubber (Doyle).[129]

FIG. 9.16. Automatic sludge ejector as fitted
to a large self-induced spray scrubber.[12]

These plants are extensively used in the metallurgical industry for dusts
and sticky materials such as metal buffings, as well as for the collection of explosive dusts. Power requirements are between 2·2 and 3 h.p. per 1000 ft³/min
gas, while water is needed only to make up the losses by evaporation and
entrainment. The plants can be rubber or PVC lined for operating with
corrosive gases. The collected material settles out and can be removed
from the bottom of the unit with a hopper in which a drag type sludge
ejector is placed (Fig. 9.16) or alternatively, by sluicing the sludge to a cen-

tral disposal unit. In very small units, or where the dust loading is small manual methods may be used. Typical operating characteristics for a wide variety of applications are listed in Table 9.3.

TABLE 9.3. PERFORMANCE DATA ON SELF INDUCED SPRAY COLLECTORS

Source of dust	Inlet conc. gr./ft^3	Outlet conc. gr./ft^3	Efficiency %	Water consumption gal/1000 ft^3 min
		Doyle scrubber[129]		
Boiler, coal fired (P.F.)	10·1	0·150	98·4	5·0
Lead sinter crusher	0·833	0·0031	99·6	1·0
Lead sinter preparation wet mix dryer	2·08	0·044	97·9	1·7
Phosphate rock dryer cyclone in series	7·63	0·205	97·4	2·4
Coal dryer cyclone in series	1·93	0·0278	98·6	1·7
		Type N Rotoclone[55]		
Electric arc furnace	0·27	0·064	75·5	
Fly ash	1·3	0·005	99·4	
Brown coal dust	1·74	0.017	99	
Sinter dust	3·0	0·020	99·3	
Carbon black	0·22	0·0022	99	
Asbestos fibres	0·43	0·002	99·5	
Granite dust	4·3	0·020	99·5	
Limestone	4·3	0·175	96	
Ceramic polishing	0·4	0·008	98·8	
Sandblasting	0·6	0·024	96·9	
Metal polishing	0·12	0·013	90	

9.6. IMPINGEMENT PLATE AND PACKED BED SCRUBBERS

If the dirty gas stream encounters a series of liquid films or impinges on a succession of pools, then better collection, particularly for small particles, is achieved than for the simple scrubbers with self-induced sprays, but with greater pressure drop. The design of units incorporating these ideas follows the pattern either of modified sieve plates, or of a packed bed scrubber.

The conventional sieve plate, with impingement baffles directly above the holes in the trays, is the usual modification (Fig. 9.17), and superficial gas velocities 5 times the velocities used for distillation are used for particle collection. Also fewer holes are provided in the trays so that the velocity through the orifices is of the order of 15–20 ft/sec. The gas–liquid mixture on the trays is formed into jets which impinge on special baffles, in contrast to bubbles rising through the liquid on the trays of a conventional gas absorption or distillation column. For maximum particle collection efficiency

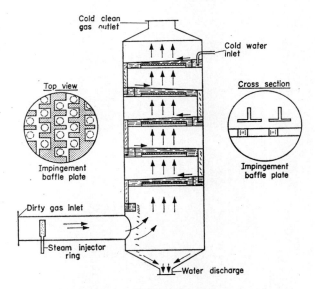

FIG. 9.17. Impingement plate scrubber (Peabody).[388]

the gas should be saturated before entering the sieve plate section of the column, using water or steam jets.

Similar principles are used in the plant shown in Fig. 9.18 where expanded metal is used instead of sieve plates and baffles. The unit is made to handle gas flows varying between 1,200 and 24,500 ft/min. For cleaning the exhaust air from polishing and grinding the unit is filled with a low vapour pressure oil as a collection fluid, while with water as a scrubbing liquid it is used for mist collection. It has been used, after lining with PVC, for sulphuric acid mists, which were effectively reduced from concentrations of 25 gr./1000 ft³ to 3 gr./1000 ft³ (88 per cent).[55]

Because of its high resistance to gas flow, the conventional packed bed is rarely used for particle collection, although sometimes used for mist collection because there is no problem of particle removal from the packing. The packings usually encountered are coke, Raschig rings, saddles or stone. A modified unit has been applied to particle collection. Here low density spheres are contained between grids (Fig. 9.19), and the bed tends to float on the rising gases. In some ways the action is similar to the sieve plate column because little jets are formed between the spheres and impinge on

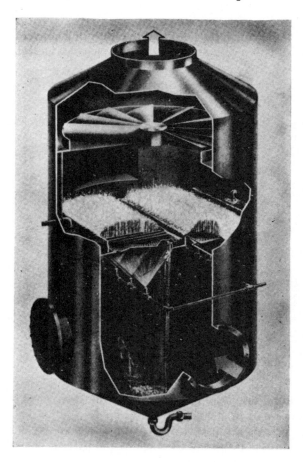

FIG. 9.18. Impingement plate scrubber (Impinjet).[448]

the sphere above. The fluidized state of the bed prevents plugging, and so avoids the chief problem of operating a sieve plate scrubber for particles and sticky materials. The pressure losses for the floating bed scrubber average 4 in. W.G., and the efficiencies obtained are similar to the other systems mentioned in this section.

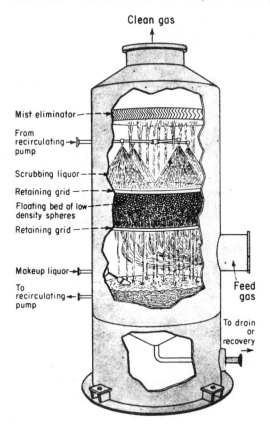

FIG. 9.19. Floating bed scrubber.[2]

9.7. DISINTEGRATOR SCRUBBERS

The scrubbers mentioned in the previous sections are all used for dealing with particles in the size ranges greater than 1 micron, but for collecting sub-micron sized particles a scrubber must provide a very finely dispersed liquid so that the droplets are sufficiently small to have a low inertial impaction parameter, and together provide a very large surface area for diffusion to take place. One method of providing these fine liquid droplets is by shearing the liquid between a stator and a rapidly moving rotor and allowing the gas to pass through the apparatus. This is done in the disintegrator scrubber (Fig. 9.20), where water is injected axially and separated into fine droplets by the bars of the rotor and stator while the relative velocity of the gas is maintained at 200–300 ft/sec through the system. The particles, particularly those larger than 10 microns, tend to erode the vanes of the scrubber, and it is frequent practice to pre-clean the gases to a concentration below 1 gr./ft³ before passing them to the disintegrator. Power consumption is high: of the order of 16–20 h.p. per 1000 ft³/min of gas treated. The scrubber is very effective, removing 90 per cent of the 1 micron

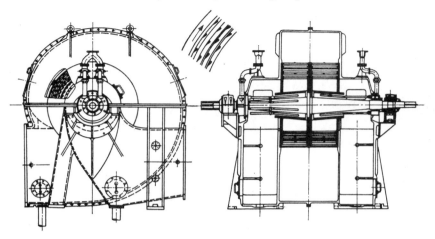

Fig. 9.20. Disintegrator scrubber.[199]

particles present and 70 per cent of the 0·5 micron particles, and has the additional advantage of being very small compared to other types of plant with similar efficiencies handling the same gas volumes. It is therefore often used as a standby unit for electrostatic precipitators on blast furnace gas treatment.

9.8. VENTURI SCRUBBERS

While in the disintegrator scrubber the atomization of the liquid is caused by the mechanical action of the rotor and stator, in the venturi scrubber the velocity of the gases alone causes the disintegration of the liquid. The energy required for the plant is therefore almost wholly accounted for by the gas stream pressure drop through the scrubber, apart from the small amount used in the liquid sprays. The other factor which plays a part in the effectiveness of the venturi scrubber is the condensation effect mentioned in the introduction to this chapter. If the gas in the reduced pressure region in the throat is fully saturated (or preferably supersaturated) condensation will occur on the particles (acting as nuclei) in the higher pressure region of the diffuser. This helps the particles to grow, and the wet particle surface tends to help agglomeration and subsequent collection. The venturi scrubber was first patented in 1925,[200] but the modern version was not put into use for another twenty years, when a Pease–Anthony design venturi scrubber was installed as a pilot plant for the recovery of sodium sulphite from the waste gases of a Kraft recovery furnace. Since then the venturi scrubber has been widely applied to gas absorption and particle removal problems in the metallurgical and chemical industries.

The detailed particle collection mechanism in the venturi scrubber has been investigated by Johnstone *et al.*[241, 242, 243] and more recently by Barth.[36] Johnstone and Roberts[243] found that the specific surface area of the liquid in the scrubber calculated from equation (9.3) gave a good correlation with the particle collection efficiency, and also the rate of sulphur

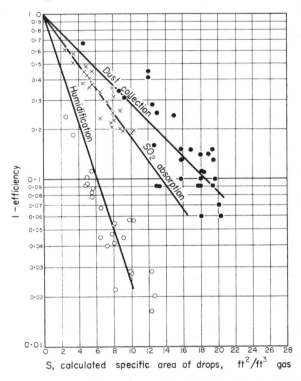

FIG. 9.21. Correlation of venturi scrubber efficiency for absorption, humidification and dust collection with the calculated surface area of drops.[243]

dioxide absorption or humidification of air (Fig. 9.21). In fact, the number of transfer units, N_t (where $N_t = -\ln(1 - \eta)$), equation (9.9), for humidification can be found from the slope of the line in Fig. 9.21. This is greater than the slope for sulphur dioxide absorption by a factor of 2·2, corresponding to the ratio of the diffusivities of water vapour and sulphur dioxide in air.

It was further found that the predominant mechanism in the venturi scrubber of conventional design is inertial impaction,[242] and the following equation correlates the experimental results. The efficiency of collection is given by:

$$\eta = 1 - \exp\left(-Kn\sqrt{\psi}\right) \tag{9.4}$$

where n = concentration of droplets

K = constant, which is a function of path length and specific surface area of droplets

ψ = inertial impaction parameter.

A graph of the correlation of the experimental results with equation (9.4) is shown in Fig. 9.22.

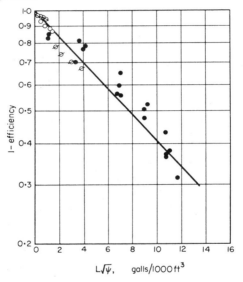

FIG. 9.22. Correlation of venturi scrubber efficiency on the basis of inertial impaction.[242]

L = Liquid flow rate – gal./1000 ft³.

ψ = inertial impaction parameter.

● 10-Micron dibutyl phthalate (Eckman).

⊘ 1·22-Micron ammonium sulphite.

○ 0·58-Micron dibutyl phthalate.

⊘ 0·27-Micron ammonium chloride.

Further experiments showed that to collect sub-micron size particles effectively, high throat velocities between 300 and 400 ft/sec were needed, but for given efficiencies with larger particles, lower throat velocities would suffice if the liquid consumption were very high.

In a much more fundamental approach to estimating collection efficiency Barth considers the relative velocity of droplet and gas as the droplet is released in the venturi throat and then accelerated. So far this has not led to a correlation which is easily applied to the prediction of venturi scrubber efficiency. In general however it appears that effective scrubbing is directly related to the energy expended in the process. The change in kinetic energy, ΔE_K on liquid–gas impact can be found from

$$\Delta E_K = \frac{1}{2} \frac{m_G m_L}{m_G + m_L} (U_G - U_L) \tag{9.5}$$

where m_G and m_L are the mass of gas and liquid respectively used per unit
    time,
and U_G and U_L are the gas and liquid velocities before impact, along the
    axis of the venturi.

This relation shows that if the liquid is sprayed across the throat, high energy losses occur because U_L is zero. However, if the liquid is sprayed from a central nozzle facing downstream, with a high velocity U_L, the energy requirements are much lower. In practice the principal difference between venturi scrubbers is the way in which the liquid is introduced and subsequently removed.

In the first design developed by Anthony et al.[247] and called the Pease–Anthony scrubber, the liquid is sprayed in at right angles to the throat, and is removed by a cyclone separation chamber (Fig. 9.23 a), or a turbine entry

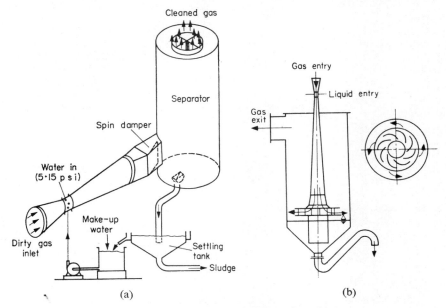

FIG. 9.23. Pease–Anthony type venturi scrubber:
(a) Tangential entry to separating chamber.[246]
(b) Turbine entry to separating chamber.[190]

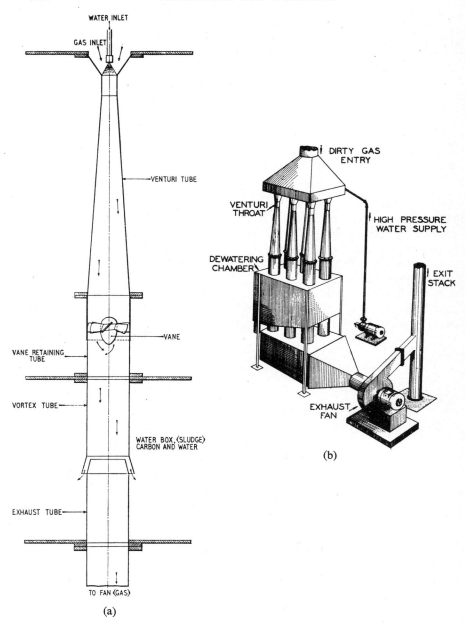

FIG. 9.24. Pontifex cone spray multiple tube venturi scrubber, using straight
through cyclone separation chamber:

(a) Single tube showing spray and separating section.[29]
(b) General arrangement of plant.[250]

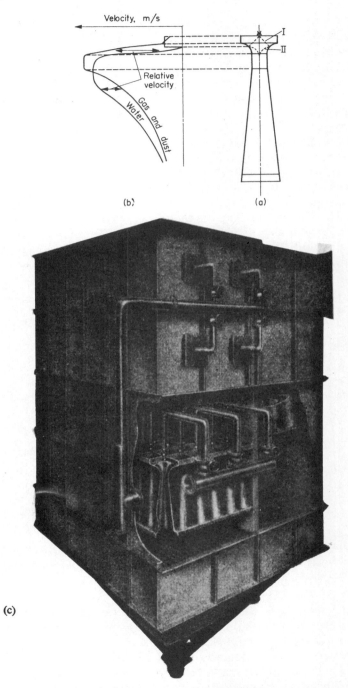

FIG. 9.25. Waagner–Biro cone spray multiple tube scrubber:[359]
(a) Cone spray showing double cone.   (b) Relative velocities of gas, dust and water.
(c) General arrangement of plant.

cyclone settling chamber (Fig. 9.23 b). In the second design, the liquid is introduced from a cone spray just ahead of the throat, and is subsequently removed using either a straight through cyclone separator in the Pontifex pattern[29] (Fig. 9.24) or a fairly deep settling tank in the Waagner–Biro design.[359] (Fig. 9.25). The third type uses a jet spray directed through the venturi throat, and by employing a steam or air pressure nozzle the scrubber can produce its own draft instead of forcing the gases through the throat. This design (Fig. 9.26) developed by Schutte and Korting,[518] is an effective odour and organic vapour collector, but has low efficiency with respect to particles. In the fourth design, by the Svenska Flaktfabriken, called the S.F. venturi (Fig. 9.27) the water is not directed across the throat by nozzles, but is accelerated through the converging section, where it forms a film on the wall, and then across the throat by the gas itself. The final direction is given by a lip at the edge of the throat. There is no power input into the liquid, but the pressure drop by the gas stream is very high, being

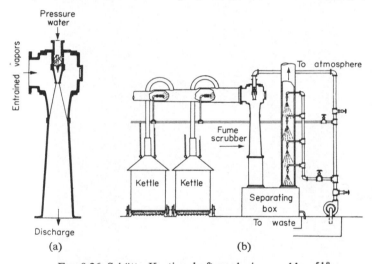

FIG. 9.26. Schütte–Korting draft producing scrubber:[518]
(a) Details of scrubber.
(b) General arrangement of plant for varnish kettles fumes. The spray nozzles at each juncture of the collecting lines prevent possible flame propagation between kettles.

of the same order as in the Pease–Anthony venturi scrubber. The S.F. venturi has been widely used for waste gases from calcium carbide furnaces, cement kilns and steel making processes.

When a cone spray is introduced before the throat it has been shown that the gas stream breaks up the spray, and this is a first scrubbing of the gases by the coarse droplets, which have a high velocity relative to the gas stream.

When the coarse droplets enter the throat the high throat velocity disintegrates them, and the fine droplets moving with the gas stream collect particles by a combination of condensation and agglomeration as well as impingement. This pattern uses more liquid than the Pease–Anthony model but this is compensated for by the lower pressure drop in the unit.

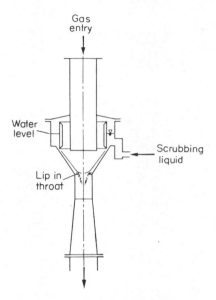

Fig. 9.27. S–F venturi scrubber with self-induced spray.[190]

TABLE 9.4. Applications of Venturi Scrubbers in Industry

Application	Type of scrubber	Reference	Year
Electric arc furnace	Pease–Anthony	Hohenberger[220]	1961
Oxygen lancing pig iron in ladle	Pease–Anthony	Gledhill, Carnall and Sargent[179]	1957
	Irsid	Septier[434]	1958
L. D. Furnaces	Pease–Anthony	Baum[39]	1959
	Pease–Anthony	Harr, Wagner and Willmer[195]	1959
	Pease–Anthony	Krijgsman[276]	1960
	Waagner–Biro	Pallinger[359]	1962
Open hearth	Pease–Anthony	Jones[246]	1949
Carbon black	Pontifex	Bainbridge[29]	1961
Salt cake	Pease–Anthony	Collins, Seaborne and Anthony[97]	1948
Sulphuric acid mist	Pease–Anthony	Jones and Anthony[247]	1952
Phosphoric acid mist	Pease–Anthony	Brink and Contant[70]	1958

TABLE 9.5. PERFORMANCE DATA ON PEASE–ANTHONY VENTURI SCRUBBER[91]

Source of gas	Dust or mist	Particle size microns	Loading (gr./ft³) inlet	Loading (gr./ft³) exit	Average efficiency of collection %
Iron and Steel Industry					
Gray iron cupola	Iron, coke, silica dust	0·1–10	1–2	0·05–0·15	95
Oxygen steel converter	Iron oxide	0·5–2	8–10	0·05–0·08	98·5
Steel open hearth furnace (scrap)	Iron and zinc oxide	0·08–1·00	0·5–1·5	0·03–0·06	95
Steel open hearth furnace (oxygen lanced)	Iron oxide	0·02–0·50	1·0–6·0	0·01–0·07	99
Blast furnace (iron)	Iron ore and coke dust	0·5–20	3–24	0·008–0·05	99
Electric furnace	Ferro-manganese fume	0·1–1	10–12	0·04–0·08	99
Electric furnace	Ferro silicon dust	0·1–1	1–5	0·1–0·3	92
Rotary kiln—iron reduction	Iron, carbon	0·5–50	3–10	0·1–0·3	99
Crushing and Screening	Taconite iron ore dust	0·5–100	5–25	0·005–0·01	99·9
Chemical Industry					
Acid—humidified SO₃	Sulphuric acid mist				
(a) scrub with water		—	0·13	0·0007	99·4
(b) scrub with 40% acid		—	0·176	0·0012	99·3
Acid concentrator	Sulphuric acid mist	—	0·058	0·0014	97·5
Copperas roasting kiln	Sulphuric acid mist	—	0·087	0·0009	99
Chlorosulfonic acid plant	Sulphuric acid mist	—	0·325	0·0034	98·9
Phosphoric acid plant	Orthophosphoric acid mist	—	0·084	0·0016	98
Dry ice plant	Amine fog	—	0·011	0·0009	90
Wood distillation plant	Tar and acetic acid	—	0·467	0·025	95
Titanium chloride plant, titanium dioxide dryer	Titanium dioxide, hydrogen chloride fumes	0·5–1	1–5	0·05–0·1	95

Table 9.5 (continued)

Source of gas	Dust or mist	Particle size microns	Loading (gr./ft³)		Average efficiency of collection %
			inlet	exit	
Spray dryers	Detergents, fume and odor	—	—	—	95
Flash dryer	Furfural dust	0·1-1	1-1.5	0·05-0.08	95
Non Ferrous Metals Industry					
Blast furnace (sec. lead)	Lead compounds	0·1-1	2-6	0·05-0.15	99
Reverberatory lead furnace	Lead and tin compounds	0·1-0.8	1-2	0·12	91
Ajax furnace— magnesium alloy	Aluminium chloride	0·1-0.9	3-5	0·02-0.05	95
Zinc sintering	Zinc and lead oxide dusts	0·1-1	1-5	0·05-0.1	98
Reverberatory brass furnace	Zinc oxide fume	0·05-0.5	1-8	0·1-0.5	95
Mineral Products Industry					
Lime kiln	Lime dust	1-50	5-10	0·05-0.15	99
Lime kiln	Soda fume	0·3-1	0·2-5	0·01-0.05	99
Asphalt stone dryer	Limestone and rock dust	1-50	5-15	0·05-0.15	98
Cement kiln	Cement dust	0·5-55	1-2	0·05-0.1	97
Petroleum Industry					
Catalytic reformer	Catalyst dust	0·5-50	0·09	0·005	95
Acid concentrator	Sulphuric acid mist	—	0·059	0·0014	97·5
TCC catalyst regenerator	Oil fumes	—	0·330	0·0035	98
Fertilizer Industry					
Fertilizer dryer	Ammonium chloride fumes	0·05-1	0·1-0.5	0·05	85
Superphosphate den and mixer	Fluorine compounds	—	0·134	0·0024	98

TABLE 9.5 (continued)

Source of gas	Dust or mist	Particle size microns	Loading (gr./ft³)		Average efficiency of collection %
			inlet	exit	
Pulp and Paper Industry					
Lime kiln	Lime dust	0·1-50	5-10	0·05-0·15	99
Lime kiln	Soda fume	0·1-2	2-5	0·01-0·05	99
Black Liquor Recovery Boiler	Salt cake	—	4-6	0·4-0·6	90
Miscellaneous					
Pickling tanks	Hydrogen chloride fumes	—	0·011	0·001	90
Boiler flue gas	Fly ash	0·1-3	1-2	0·05-0·08	98
Sodium disposal incinerator	Sodium oxide fumes	0·3-0·1	0·5-1	0·02	98

The efficiencies shown above are average values for a particular plant or group of installations operating under a specific set of conditions.

Details of industrial installations can be found in the literature, and a number of references for particular applications are listed in Table 9.4. Table 9.5 gives the efficiency found with venturi scrubbers in plant installations. The draft producing venturi scrubber has been used in the paint industry for varnish kettle fume scrubbing.[518]

To cover the throat of a large venturi scrubber with liquid presented a number of problems. In an early design several sprays were distributed

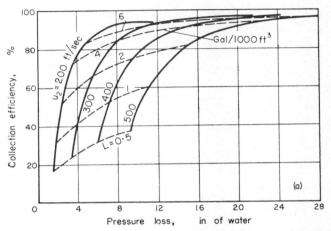

(a) Pease–Anthony ventury scrubber performance for solid particles (salt cake fume from Kraft Mill).[241]

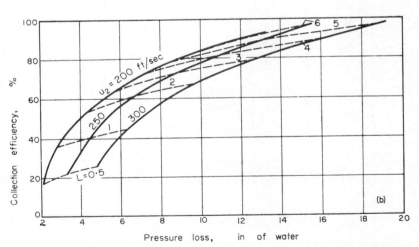

(b) Pease–Anthony venturi scrubber performance for mist droplets (sulphuric acid mist).[241]

FIG. 9.28. Liquid consumption and pressure losses for venturi scrubbers.

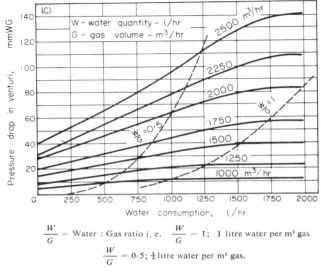

$\dfrac{W}{G}$ = Water : Gas ratio i. e. $\dfrac{W}{G}$ = 1; 1 litre water per m³ gas

$\dfrac{W}{G}$ = 0·5; ½ litre water per m³ gas.

(c) Waagner–Biro venturi scrubber pressure drop/water consumption curves.[359]

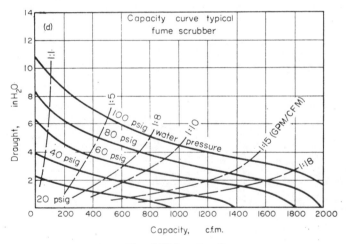

FIG. 9.28 (continued)

(d) Schutte–Korting draught producing venturi scrubber performance draught capacity.[518]

within the throat, but the high velocities rapidly eroded the nozzles and pipes. Present practice is to use a narrow, rectangular throat, with sprays from both sides. If the gas volumes handled vary, the throat can be constructed in such a way that the cross-section can be altered by moving one side. When a cone spray is used and is to cover the whole orifice, this is difficult for a large tube, and a number of small tubes in parallel are used (Figs. 9.24 b and 9.25 c). The capacity of the draft producing venturi is fairly high, and it is only used on small plants, so one or sometimes two units in parallel are adequate.

Water consumption and pressure drop data have been published and are shown in graphical form in Fig. 9.28. Curves (a) and (b) are for Pease–Anthony scrubbers with solid particles (salt cake fume) and mist droplets (sulphuric acid mist), while sections (c) and (d) show the data for the Waagner–Biro and Draft Producing venturi respectively.

In an attempt to reduce the high pressure losses which occur in the high efficiency venturi scrubbers, a design called the Solivore, which emphasises the condensation on the particles as droplets, has been developed (Fig. 9.29 a). The dust enters at the top of the chamber, where it is saturated with a fine spray which also precipitates the coarse particles. The saturated gases then enter the venturi section, where, with the velocity rise, the pressure falls, and more drops evaporate. Further on the gases are slowed down, the pressure increases again, and condensation then takes place on the particles, which agglomerate readily and are deposited by a coarse spray. In a single section the pressure drop is only 1 in. W.G., while for a four stage unit (Fig. 9.29 b) the pressure drop is less than 6 in. W.G.

The efficiency of this unit is high. For example, electric furnace fume concentration was reduced from 2·38 to 0·02 gr./ft^3, representing an efficiency of 99·1 per cent. Although this scrubber has low direct energy requirements for the gases, efficient collection needs fine atomization of the liquid, and this requires further energy in the form of compressed air or water pumps, so the net energy gain in this unit may not be so high as it appears, as well as the fact that the water requirements are rather high.

9.9. FOAM SCRUBBERS

The collection of fine particles and gases requires a large collecting surface area. As an alternative to spray droplets, foam has been suggested as being a suitable collecting agent. The simplest type of equipment, which appears to be widely used in the Soviet Union[16] is of the sieve tray pattern.

The development seems to be largely based on the work of Pozin et al.[375] who have found that the efficiency of collection depends not only on the physical properties of the dust but also on the operating conditions which determine the height of the mobile foam layers on the plates, and have developed empirical equations by dimensional analysis that can be used in the design of foam scrubbers. The efficiency, η of this scrubber for dust which is easily wetted can be calculated from

$$\eta = 0.89 \left(\frac{Ul}{g(h_c - h_b)^2}\right)^{0.005} \left(\frac{\varrho_s d^2 U}{g\mu D'}\right)^{0.04} \tag{9.5}$$

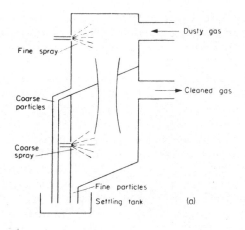

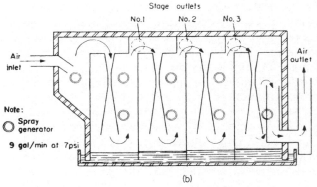

FIG. 9.29. Condensation venturi scrubber:[277]
(a) Single stage.
(b) Four stage experimental "Solivore" collector.

while if the dust is not easily wetted

$$\eta = 0.89 \left(\frac{Ul}{g(h_c - h_b)^2} \right)^{0.005} \left(\frac{\varrho_s d^2 U}{g\mu D'} \right)^{0.235} \tag{9.6}$$

where U = free space velocity of the gases (m/sec)
  l = liquid flow rate on the tray
  h_c = height of overflow orifice (m)
  h_b = height of baffle (m)
  g = gravity acceleration (9·81 m/sec²)
  ϱ_s = density of dust (kg/m³)
  d = diameter of dust (m)
  μ = viscosity of liquid (kg · sec/m²)
  D' = diameter of holes in sieve tray (m).

It should be noted that all units are in the m. k. s. system, and that the formula holds well for foam heights between 4 and 20 cm, which are common practice. It was found experimentally that apatite and nepheline dust, with an average particle size of 20–25 microns and a concentration of 2 g/m³, was effectively collected with foam heights of 6–10 cm and completely removed by 20 cm of foam.

9.10. CORRELATION OF SCRUBBER EFFICIENCY

It has been mentioned several times in the preceding sections, particularly with reference to the efficiency of venturi scrubbers, that for the same dusts higher efficiencies require greater power consumption, or for finer dusts, the same efficiency needs more power.

These ideas have been correlated on a quantitative basis, particularly by Semrau.[299, 431, 432, 433] The total pressure loss for the scrubber, P_T, is made up of two parts, the pressure loss of the gas passing through, P_G and of the spray liquid during atomization, P_L. Semrau has given formulae which give approximate values for P_G and P_L based on power consumption (in h.p. or kW) per unit volume of gas (either 1000 ft³/min or 1000 m³/hr) in the appropriate units. There are

$$P_G = 0.157\, \Delta p \quad \text{h.p.}/(1000\ \text{ft}^3/\text{min}) \tag{9.7a}$$

where Δp = pressure loss across the unit in in. W.G. or

$$P_G = 2.724 \times 10^{-3}\, \Delta h \quad \text{kWh}/1000\ \text{m}^3 \tag{9.7b}$$

where Δh = pressure loss across the unit in mm W.G., and

$$P_L = 0.583\, \Delta p_L (Q_L/Q_G) \quad \text{h.p.}/(1000\ \text{ft}^3/\text{min}) \tag{9.8a}$$

where Δp_L = pressure loss in liquid – water (lb/in.²)
Q_L = liquid rate (gal/min)
Q_G = gas rate (ft³/min)
or $\qquad P_L = 28.15\, \Delta p_{\text{atm}}\, Q'_L/Q'_G$ (kWh/1000 m³) $\qquad$ (9.8 b)
where Δp_{atm} = pressure in nozzle (atm)
Q'_L = liquid rate (m³/hr)
Q'_G = gas rate (m³/hr).

The efficiency of a collector is correlated by a dimensionless transfer unit N_t which is defined in terms of the collection efficiency η by

$$N_t = \ln\left(1/(1 - \eta)\right) \tag{9.9}$$

which gives comparatively low values of transfer units for efficiencies better than 99 per cent. A table of comparative values is given (Table 9.6).

Semrau has plotted the transfer units against total power consumption P_T for a series of scrubbers and dusts, and a linear relation, independent of the type of scrubber, on a log–log plot has been obtained in each case (Fig. 9.30). It was possible to express this relation as

$$N_t = \alpha P_T^{\beta}.\qquad(9.10)$$

where α and β are characteristic parameters for the dust being collected. These parameters are given in Table 9.7. The efficiency of collection can

TABLE 9.6. SCRUBBER TRANSFER UNITS
AND PER CENT EFFICIENCIES

Number of transfer units	Collection efficiency %
0·5	39·35
1·0	63·21
2·0	86·47
4·0	98·17
6·0	99·752
10·0	99·9955

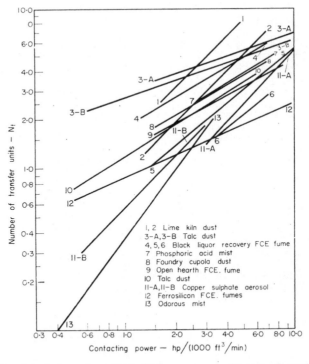

1, 2 Lime kiln dust
3-A, 3-B Talc dust
4, 5, 6 Black liquor recovery FCE fume
7 Phosphoric acid mist
8 Foundry cupola dust
9 Open hearth FCE. fume
10 Talc dust
11-A, 11-B Copper sulphate aerosol
12 Ferrosilicon FCE. fumes
13 Odorous mist

FIG. 9.30. Correlation of scrubber efficiency, measured in transfer units, with contacting power for a series of aerosols, independent of type of scrubber.[431]

thus be expressed in terms of total power used and the characteristics for the dust being collected, and independently of the actual *type* of scrubber being used.

TABLE 9.7. SCRUBBER EFFICIENCY CORRELATION PARAMETERS[431]

Curve in Fig. 9.30	Aerosol	Scrubber	Correlation parameter	
			α	β
	Lime kiln dust and fume (Kraft mud kiln)			
1.	Raw gas (lime dust and soda fume)	Venturi and cyclonic spray	1·47	1·05
2.	Pre-washed gas (soda fume)	Venturi, pipe line and cyclonic spray	0·915	1·05
3.A.	Talc dust	Venturi	2·97	0·362
3.B.		Orifice and pipe line	2·70	0·362
4.	Black liquor recovery furnace fume. Cold scrubbing water humid gases	Venturi and cyclonic spray	1·75	0·620
5.	Hot fume solution for scrubbing (humid gases)	Venturi, pipeline and cyclonic spray	0·740	0·861
6.	Hot black liquor for scrubbing (dry gases)	Venturi evaporator	0·522	0·861
7.	Phosphoric acid mist	Venturi	1·33	0·647
8.	Foundry cupola dust	Venturi	1·35	0·621
9.	Open hearth steel furnace fume	Venturi	1·26	0·569
10.	Talc dust	Cyclone	1·16	0·655
11.A.	Copper sulphate	Solivore (A) with mechanical spray generator	0·390	1·14
11.B.		(B) with hydraulic nozzles	0·562	1·06
12.	Ferrosilicon furnace fume	Venturi and cyclonic spray	0·870	0·459
13.	Odorous mist	Venturi	0·363	1·41

CHAPTER 10

ELECTROSTATIC PRECIPITATION

10.1. INTRODUCTION

In the process commonly called electrostatic precipitation, small droplets and particles are first charged by gas ions produced by the electrical breakdown in the gases surrounding a high tension electrode, and then drift towards earthed collector electrodes. On arrival at the earthed collector, the particles adhere and are discharged to earth potential. When a layer of particles has formed, these are shaken off by "rapping" and fall into a hopper. Because the system is not quite static, as the charges carried by the particles and gas ions produce a small current, many workers prefer to call this type of plant electro-precipitators or electro-filters. In this book, however, the conventional term "electrostatic precipitator" will be used.

Electrostatic precipitators are applied wherever very large volumes of gases have to be cleaned and there is no explosion risk. The plants are invariably used for fly ash collection in modern base-load pulverized-fuel-fired power station boilers and for the collection of dusts in the cement industry. Precipitators are also employed for large scale fume collection systems in the metallurgical industry; for the collection of particles and mist droplets (tar, phosphoric acid, sulphuric acid) in the chemical and allied industries; for dust removal in air conditioning systems; in fact for fine particle and mist collection problems where large gas volumes are involved.

That small fibres were attracted by a piece of amber after it had been rubbed was known to the Greek philosophers about 600 B.C., and the names of Coulomb and Benjamin Franklin are associated with early studies on the inverse square law for electrostatic forces and the corona discharge, respectively. The first demonstration of electrostatic precipitation is attributed to Hohlfeld, who in 1824 showed that a fog was cleared from a glass jar which contained an electrically charged point. Similar demonstrations by other workers were published later in the nineteenth century, an example being the precipitation of tobacco smoke in a glass cylinder 18 in. long and 9 in. dia. by Guitard about 26 years after Hohlfeld's paper.

The successful commercial application of the principle of electrostatic precipitation, however, dates to the first years of the twentieth century and is associated with the names of Lodge in England, Cottrell in the United

States and Moeller in Germany. Lodge had been experimenting with electrostatic precipitation since 1880, and indicated the commercial possibilities of the method in a paper published in *Nature* in 1883.[314] Together with two others, Walker and Hutchings, he installed the first commercial electrostatic precipitator at a lead smelter in Bagillt, North Wales. The design is shown in Fig. 10.1, and illustrates the discharge points installed in a duct, as well as the two Wimshurst machines, each 5 in. dia., which supplied the high voltage, and which were driven by 1 horse-power steam engines.

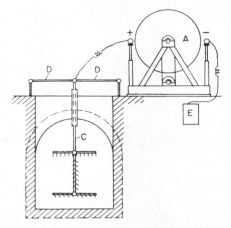

Fig. 10.1. Illustration from the first United States patent on electrostatic precipitation.

A. O. Walker, U.S. Pat. No. 342 548 (1886).[533]

Unfortunately the plant was unsuccessful, for which there were two main reasons;[422,533] the primitive method of producing the high voltage power, and the fact that lead smelter fume is very fine and has a high resistivity, making it one of the most difficult fumes to collect. Had the fume consisted of conducting particles or droplets, such as sulphuric acid mist which was used by Cottrell in his first investigations, then electrostatic precipitation would undoubtedly have come into commercial use 25 years earlier.

The development of alternating current technology and electrical machinery made new sources of high voltage direct current available from combinations of transformers and synchronous mechanical rectifiers or mercury arc rectifiers. Lodge patented the latter for the purpose of electrostatic precipitation in 1903, while Cottrell experimented with the mechanical rectifier when he found that the discharge from a spark coil proved inadequate for a corona discharge from more than just one or two points in a spark chamber. Cottrell also found that a cotton covered wire gave a continuous glow, indicating corona formation, over the whole of its surface, and developed the *pubescent* discharge electrode of non-conducting fibrous material covering the conductor (Fig. 10.2). The combination of alternating current transformer, mechanical rectifier and pubescent electrode led to a successful precipitator, able to remove sulphuric acid mist on a laboratory scale with flows of several cubic feet per minute.[101, 102, 103] Cottrell and his colleagues, notably W. A. Schmidt, who was responsible for many of the later improvements, applied the electrostatic precipitator

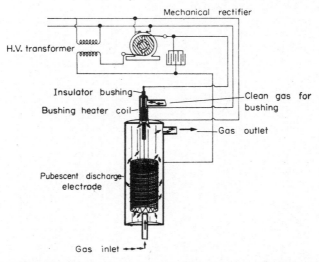

Fig. 10.2. Illustration from Cottrell's first electrostatic precipitation patent—
U.S. Pat. No. 895729 (1908).

The construction of the electrode, and the purge gas stream to prevent the insulation shorting is clearly marked.[533]

on an industrial scale: first at a powder works at Pinole (near Berkeley) and then at the Selby smelter where there was an acute air pollution problem. At Selby the precipitator operated on the gases from the parting kettles for precious metal recovery, and collected 2 gal/min of sulphuric acid from 5000 ft³. Other features of Cottrell's patent which are shown in Fig. 10.2 are the heating and ventilating system provided for keeping the high voltage insulation dry. Cottrell used a negative corona because he found that this could carry higher currents than the positive corona.

The next plant was installed at the lead smelter at Balaclala, where 250,000 ft³/min of lead and zinc fume laden gases were to be treated. As Lodge *et al.* had found, this was a difficult problem. However, the newer techniques of high voltage direct current production enabled the plant to operate at efficiencies between 80 and 90 per cent.[330] Many of the features found in modern electrostatic precipitators were developed by W. A. Schmidt when he installed the precipitator at the Riverside Portland Cement Company (Southern California) in 1912.[421] This plant handled 1,000,000 ft³/min at 400–500 °C. Fine wire discharge electrodes operating at 45 kV were used here for the first time, and the plant was still in operation 45 years later.

The development of electrostatic precipitators has been very largely empirical, and over one thousand patents cover all aspects of precipitator construction. The theory of precipitation has lagged far behind its practical application. Thus a theoretical expression for collection efficiency in the absence of turbulence was derived by Deutsch in 1922[126] and a modified theory was presented by Williams and Jackson[544] to allow for turbulent remixing at a rate controlled by the gas stream turbulence in 1962.

Equations describing the bombardment and diffusion processes of particle charging were suggested by Pauthenier and Moreau-Hanot[363] in 1932 for the former process and by Arendt and Kallmann[20] (1925) and White[528] (1951) for the latter process. A detailed model of the precipitation process of particles in the presence of others has not yet been attempted. However, the extensive studies of electrostatic precipitation published in the past fifteen years enable the calculations based on the fundamental processes to be correlated with experimental behaviour. It is therefore becoming possible in some cases either to design the units from first principles or to extrapolate the sparse experimental data to plants with larger capacity.

The basic processes which occur in electrostatic precipitators are discussed in detail in this chapter. These are the formation of the corona or ionized zone around the high tension wire, which may be positively or negatively charged; the charging and drift of the particles; particle deposition and discharge and the possibility of particle re-entrainment. This is followed by details of some aspects of the construction of modern electrostatic precipitators.

10.2. CORONA FORMATION

When an electrical potential is established between two parallel plates, the field between the plates is uniform, and its magnitude can be expressed in terms of the voltage gradient between the plates (V/cm). When this voltage gradient is increased to a critical value—about 30 kV/cm in ambient air—electrical breakdown occurs and a spark flashes between the plates. However, if a non-uniform field is produced, for example between a sharply curved surface such as a point or a fine wire, and an enclosing tube or a plate, then electrical breakdown can occur near the curved surface, producing a glow discharge or "corona", without sparkover. The corona is of great importance in other industrial applications beside precipitation of particles, as, for example, it accounts for much of the power losses in high voltage power transmission lines, and so has been studied extensively. Detailed accounts of electrical breakdown in gases and corona can be found in specialized references such as Cobine's *Gaseous Conductors*[95] or Craggs and Meek's *Electrical Breakdown in Gases*.[106]

Because an a.c. corona produces oscillating motions in charged particles, and a d.c. corona produces a steady force driving particles towards the passive collector electrode, conventional precipitation requires a unipolar discharge. The negative corona is more stable than the positive corona, which tends to be sporadic and cause sparkover at lower voltages than for the negatively charged conductors (Fig. 10.3), and so these are generally used for industrial application. The negative corona however does give rise to higher ozone concentrations, and so is not used for air conditioning plant.

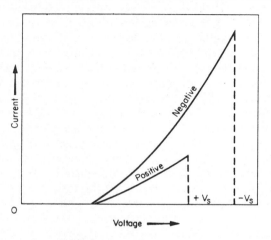

Fig. 10.3. Representative current–voltage characteristics for positive and negative corona in air.[529]

The corona on a positive wire has the appearance of a bluish-white sheath covering the entire wire, while the corona on a negative wire is concentrated in reddish tufts along the wire. On a polished conductor these tufts are spaced more or less regularly, their number increasing with the current. The uniform spacing of the beads can be explained by the mutual space charge repulsion of the beads. On an unpolished wire, or a wire provided with barbs or other discharge points, the discharge tufts concentrate on imperfections in the wire surface, or on the special points.

The *mechanism of negative corona* formation is as follows: The gases normally, when no current flows, contain some ionized gas molecules, about $1000/cm^3$, formed by cosmic rays. With current flowing, more ionized molecules are formed from the ultra-violet radiation from the corona glow. The positive gas ions and photons formed in this way are accelerated towards the negative conductor and release electrons from the surface of the conductor. These electrons, moving through the strong field near the conductor generate new electrons and positive ions by molecular impacts. The electrons then swarm outside this region, slowing to a speed less than that necessary for ionization by collision, and attach themselves to gas molecules, forming gas ions. These gas ions then move towards the passive electrode with a speed proportional to their charge and the intensity of the electric field.

The space outside the corona is therefore filled with a dense cloud of unipolar ions, which in practice is of the order of 5×10^7 ions/cm^3, and it is in this zone that the majority of the dust particles acquire their negative charge. The dust particles passing through the corona zone are likely to become positively charged because of the predominance of positive gas ions and high mobility of electrons in this zone, and are then precipitated on the discharge electrode. The ionic mobility of the gas ions and the dust concentration outside the corona zone are the major factors affecting the voltage–current characteristics of the precipitator.

The mobilities of the ions and electrons depend on the gas and on the presence of particles. Pure nitrogen, for example, absorbs only a few of the electrons. The current is mainly transferred by these electrons, which have a high mobility, and so the corona current rises very steeply. On the other hand electro-negative gases such as oxygen or methyl chloride absorb electrons very easily, and the gas ions, with much lower mobilities, become the current carriers and the current is much lower (Fig. 10.4.). Similarly dust particles or mist droplets when present in large concentrations can act as

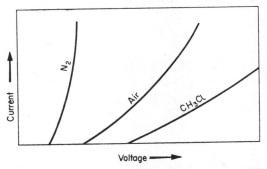

Fig. 10.4. Variations in corona current–voltage characteristics for the negative corona in typical gases (nitrogen, air, methyl chloride).[529]

absorbers of electrons and gas ions, and also reduce the corona current. This is called corona quenching or corona suppression. When it occurs (for example with very fine fumes) it is common practice to use precipitators with several stages in series.

The corona current–voltage characteristic for air (without particles) is about half way between oxygen and nitrogen, and the ionic mobility of the gas ions is of the order of $1 \cdot 8$ cm/sec per V/cm (540 cm/sec per e.s.u/cm). In a typical gas mixture such as flue gases, the speed of the negative ions is of the order of 30 m/sec (100 ft/sec).

The *mechanism of positive corona* formation differs markedly from the negative corona, and accounts for the different properties such as lower flash-over voltage, and lower ozone formation. The electrons in the gas move towards the corona region near the discharge wire where electron avalanches form to maintain the corona region. The positive gas ions formed by these electron avalanches move slowly away from the wire, at much lower speeds than the electrons in the negative corona region, and consequently fewer ionizing collisions occur in their movement to the passive electrode. At the low field strengths near this electrode they gain little acceleration so few electrons are emitted by cathode bombardment and most of the current is carried by the positively charged gas ions. Because fewer ionizing collisions occur in the high intensity corona region, the formation of ozone and oxides of nitrogen is much less than in the case of the negative corona.

10.3. FIELD STRENGTH AND CORONA CURRENT

The strength of an electric field E (V/cm), at any point is defined as the potential gradient at that point. If the applied voltage or potential difference between two concentric electrodes, such as a wire and tube system, radius R_1 and R_2 respectively, is $\mathscr{V}$, then:

$$\mathscr{V} = \int_{R_1}^{R_2} E \, dr \qquad (10.1)$$

Before the corona has been formed a negligible number of gas ions are present, and in the absence of any ionic current the field strength at radius r is given by the integrated form of equation (10.1).

$$\mathscr{V} = Er \ln R_2/R_1 \qquad (10.2)$$

or

$$E = \frac{C_0}{r} \qquad (10.3)$$

where

$$C_0 = \mathscr{V}/\ln (R_2/R_1) \qquad (10.4)$$

which is a function of the applied voltage and the geometrical dimensions of the system.

It can be seen from equation (10.3) that the field strength has its maximum value for the lowest r; that is at the surface of the wire, at radius R_1. For the corona to start it is necessary for electrical breakdown to occur at the wire, and so this maximum field strength value must be greater than the critical value for electrical breakdown in the gas. This has been found experimentally to require approximately equal electrical field strengths for both positive and negative corona. For air in coaxial cylinders the critical field strength, E_c is:

$$E_c = 31 \frac{m\varrho}{\varrho_s} \left(1 + \frac{0 \cdot 308}{\sqrt{[(\varrho/\varrho_s)R_1]}}\right) \text{kV/cm} \qquad (10.5)$$

while for parallel wires

$$E_c = 30 \frac{m\varrho}{\varrho_s} \left(1 + \frac{0 \cdot 301}{\sqrt{[\varrho R_1/\varrho_s]}}\right) \text{kV/cm} \qquad (10.6)$$

where R_1 = radius of the wire

$\dfrac{\varrho}{\varrho_s}$ = relative air density

= 1 at 760 mm Hg (Torr) pressure, 25 °C

= $(0 \cdot 392 P)/T$ (for other conditions)

where P = atmospheric pressure in mm Hg

T = absolute temperature, °K

while m is an irregularity factor which is 1 for polished wires, 0·82 for a general corona on stranded wires, or 0·92 for roughened and weathered wires.

The applied voltage required for starting the corona can be found by substituting equation (10.6) in (10.2):

$$\mathscr{V}_c = 31 \frac{m\varrho}{\varrho_s} \left(1 + \frac{0 \cdot 308}{\sqrt{[\varrho R_1/\varrho_s]}}\right) R_1 \ln R_2/R_1 \qquad (10.7)$$

where $\mathscr{V}_c$ = the corona starting voltage (kV).

After the corona has started, the presence of an ionic space charge modifies the field strength in the precipitator, and the dust particles present in the precipitator during operation introduce further complications. Allowances can, however, be made for these.[95, 316, 404, 495, 546]

In the presence of the ionic space charge, the field strength distribution is given by Poisson's equation for coaxial cylinders.[96]

$$\frac{1}{r} \frac{d}{dr} (Er) = 4\pi\sigma \qquad (10.8)$$

where σ is the space charge, per unit volume (cm³). When a gas, but no particles are present, this is determined by i, the ionic current per unit length of conductor. In this case, the ionic current is:

$$i = 2\pi r \sigma u_i E \quad \text{(A/cm)} \qquad (10.9)$$

where u_i = ionic mobility in a unit field (cm²/sec V)

and $u_i \times E$ = ionic velocity (cm/sec)

Transforming equation (10.9) and substituting in equation (10.8) gives

$$\frac{dE}{dr} + \frac{E}{r} - \frac{2i}{u_i rE} = 0 \tag{10.10}$$

This can be integrated, using as boundary conditions $r = R_1$, when $E = E_c$ the critical field strength for starting the corona. Then:

$$E = \sqrt{\left[\left(\frac{R_1 E_c}{r}\right)^2 + \frac{2i}{u_i}\left(1 - \left\{\frac{R_1}{r}\right\}^2\right)\right]} \tag{10.11}$$

From equation (10.3), C_0 can be substituted for $R_1 E_c$, and for zero ionic current, equation (10.11) reduces to equation (10.3). The other important case is for a large current i and when $R_2 \gg R_1$. Then:

$$E = \sqrt{\left(\frac{2i}{u_i}\right)} \tag{10.12}$$

which gives an equation for constant field strength in the region of a precipitator tube some distance from the corona wire, which can be used for approximate precipitator calculations *(wire in tube case)*. This equation has been confirmed experimentally by the measurements of Pauthenier and Moreau-Hanot.[364]

In the case of the *wire and plate* type precipitator Troost[495] has shown experimentally that

$$E = \sqrt{\left(\frac{8iL}{u_i W}\right)} \tag{10.13}$$

where L = distance between wire and plate

W = distance between successive wires.

Where the wires are spaced approximately the same distance apart as the plates ($W = 2L$):

$$E = \left(\frac{4i}{u_i}\right). \tag{10.14}$$

The ion mobility can be calculated from the kinetic theory of gases:[546]

$$u_i = \frac{e}{\varrho \bar{u} \pi \sigma_{AB}^2} f(\mathscr{M}) \quad (\text{cm}^2/\text{V}) \tag{10.15}$$

e = charge on an ion (Coulombs)

ϱ = gas density = PM'/kT (ideal gas law)

P = gas pressure

$\bar{u}$ = mean gas molecular velocity

$$= \sqrt{\left(\frac{8kT}{\pi M'}\right)} \quad \text{or} \quad \sqrt{\left(\frac{8RT}{\pi M}\right)}$$

M = molecular weight

M' = weight of a molecule

k = Boltzmann's constant

T = absolute temperature

σ_{AB} = sum of radii of charge carrier and gas molecule

$f(\mathcal{M})$ = function of $\mathcal{M}$ where $\mathcal{M} = m/(M' + m)$

m = weight of a charge carrier (i.e. charged ions).

The values of $f(\mathcal{M})$ in some typical cases are listed in Table 10.1.

TABLE 10.1. VALUES OF $f(\mathcal{M})$ FOR VARIOUS μ IN EQUATION (10.15)[546]

Gas–ion system	$\mathcal{M}$	$f(\mathcal{M})$
Free electrons in nitrogen	2×10^{-5}	284·3
Monomolecular ions	0·5	1·38
Normal gas ions	0·9	0·837
Coarse particles	1·0	0·75

By substituting for the gas density and mean molecular velocity, equation (10.15) can be re-written to demonstrate the dependence of the ionic mobility on the gas type, the pressure and absolute temperature and on whether the charge is being carried by gas ions or electrons:

$$u_i = \frac{e\, f(\mathcal{M})}{\sigma_{AB}^2 P} \sqrt{\left(\frac{kT}{8\pi M'}\right)} \tag{10.16}$$

When particles as well as gas ions are present in the space between the high tension wire and the earthed electrode, the space charge in equation (10.8) must be modified to allow for these also:

$$\frac{1}{r}\frac{d}{dr}(Er) = \begin{pmatrix} \text{charge on} \\ \text{gas ions} \end{pmatrix} + \begin{pmatrix} \text{charge on} \\ \text{particles} \end{pmatrix} \tag{10.17a}$$

If the charge on the particles is assumed to be the limiting charge received by bombardment charging (equation 10.30) this equation is:

$$\frac{1}{r}\frac{d}{dr}(Er) = \frac{2i}{u_i rE} + 4\pi \left\{ \frac{3\epsilon}{\epsilon + 2} E \sum \frac{d^2}{4} \right\} \tag{10.17b}$$

Here d is the diameter of the particles, and the surface area of all the particles in a unit volume, A, is given by $\pi \sum d^2$. Substituting A and integrating equation (10.17) gives:

$$E^2 = \frac{K}{r^2} \exp\left(\frac{6\epsilon Ar}{\epsilon + 2}\right) - \frac{i}{u_i}\left[\frac{2(\epsilon + 2)}{3\epsilon Ar} + \left(\frac{\epsilon + 2}{3\epsilon Ar}\right)^2\right] \tag{10.18}$$

where ϵ = dielectric constant of the particles

K = constant of integration.

This constant has been shown to be[364]

$$K = C_o^2 + \frac{i}{u_i}\left(\frac{\epsilon + 2}{3\epsilon A}\right)^2 \tag{10.19}$$

where C_0 has been defined in equation (10.4).

The field strength, considering both the dust and the space charge present, is now:

$$E = \left[\left\{\frac{C_o^2}{r^2} + \frac{i}{u_i}\left(\frac{\epsilon + 2}{3\epsilon A}\right)^2\right\}\exp\left(\frac{6\epsilon Ar}{\epsilon + 2}\right) - \frac{i}{u_i}\left\{\frac{2(\epsilon + 2)}{3\epsilon Ar} - \left(\frac{\epsilon + 2}{3\epsilon Ar}\right)^2\right\}\right]^{1/2} \tag{10.20}$$

When $3\epsilon A/(\epsilon + 2)$ is small (much less than unity) the exponential term in equation (10.20) can be expanded and the equation simplified:

$$E = \left[\frac{2i}{u_i}\left(1 + \frac{2\epsilon Ar}{\epsilon + 2}\right) + \frac{C_o^2}{r^2}\right]^{1/2} \tag{10.21}$$

When there is no dust present, this equation reduces to equation (10.11), while for large radii, i.e. small C_o^2/r^2, this term can be neglected, and then equation (10.21) simplifies further to:

$$E = \left[\frac{2i}{u_i}\left(1 + \frac{2\epsilon Ar}{\epsilon + 2}\right)\right]^{1/2} \tag{10.22}$$

It has been suggested[364] that for the dust burden normally encountered, the term in the parentheses can be expanded as a series, and all terms other than those of the first order neglected. Then, for a wire in tube precipitator, equation (10.22) reduces to:

$$E = \sqrt{\left(\frac{2i}{u_i}\right)} \cdot \left(1 + \frac{\epsilon Ar}{\epsilon + 2}\right) \tag{10.23a}$$

By analogy a similar equation can be written for a plate type precipitator:

$$E = \sqrt{\left(\frac{8iL}{u_i W}\right)} \cdot \left(1 + \frac{\epsilon Ar}{\epsilon + 2}\right) \tag{10.23b}$$

Equation (10.23) shows that the field strength is a function of the ionic current i, the ion mobility, u_i, and is greater when particles are present, being also dependent on their aggregate surface area A.

Lowe and Lucas[316] calculated the strength across a 5 in. radius tubular precipitator with an applied voltage of 40 kV in the following cases:

(i) Zero dust burden and zero ionic current (equation 10.2)

(ii) Zero dust burden, and an ionic current of 25 μA/ft of discharge conductor

(iii) A dust burden, assumed to be equivalent to fly ash with a concentration of 18 gr./m³ and an effective surface area of 0·083 cm²/cm³ gas, and an ionic current of 25 μA/ft of discharge conductor.

The calculated field strengths are plotted in Fig. 10.5.

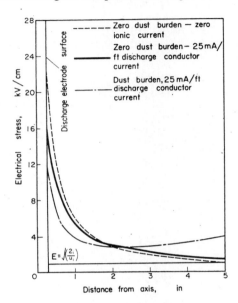

FIG. 10.5. Field strengths across a precipitator tube at different conditions (calculated).[316]

The *corona current i* in a precipitator is a function of the applied voltage $\mathscr{V}$, the ion mobility u_i and the precipitator dimensions. For a wire in tube type unit, with low currents, Townsend[494] and others obtained the following equation by integration of equation (10.11).

$$i = \frac{2u_i}{R_2^2 \ln(R_2/R_1)} \, \mathscr{V}(\mathscr{V} - \mathscr{V}_c) \tag{10.24}$$

This equation has been modified by Fazel and Parsons[546] to allow for the width of the corona on the discharge electrode, S, the outer edge of which is the critical field strength E_c:

$$i = \frac{2u_i}{R_2^2 \ln(R_2/R_1 + S)} \, \mathscr{V}(\mathscr{V} - \mathscr{V}_c) \tag{10.25}$$

Here it is assumed that the width of the corona annular layer increases with the potential $(\mathscr{V} - \mathscr{V}_c)$. More satisfactory are empirical relations, such as that suggested by Schaffers:[546]

$$i = \frac{u_i}{2} \left[\frac{\mathscr{V} - \mathscr{V}_c}{R_2 \ln (R_2/R_1 + S)} \right]^x \qquad (10.26)$$

where $x = 2$ when $R_2/R_1 > 1000$

$\qquad = \log_{10} (R_2/R_1 + S)$ when $R_2/R_1 < 1000$

as long as x remains less than 2, otherwise this should be used as the limiting value. The width of the corona layer is assumed in this equation to be constant at 0·03 cm.

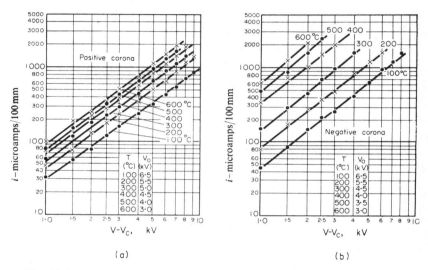

Fig. 10.6. Dependence of ionic current on potential at various temperatures.[546]

(a) Positive corona.

(b) Negative corona.

Another empirical relation between corona current and voltage is given by Koller and Fremont:[271]

$$i = \beta \mathscr{V}^{\alpha} \qquad (10.27)$$

where α and β are constants for the particular gas which were found by Koller and Fremont to be $\alpha = 4·2$ for air and $\alpha = 2·8$ for methyl chloride. This is higher than that found by other workers w. o obtained $\alpha = 1·6$ for air.

Generally, the corona current can be expressed as the relation:

$$i = \beta(\mathscr{V} - \mathscr{V}_c)^x \qquad (10.28)$$

where β is an empirical constant which is a function of the ion mobility and the precipitator geometry and the type of dust, while x depends on gas composition and has a value between 1 and 2.

This last empirical relation (10.28) has been extensively investigated by Winkel and Schütz[546] using a tube precipitator, 35 mm dia., 100 mm long, and with a 0·3 mm nichrome wire discharge electrode. Temperatures up to 600 °C were used, and the experimental values obtained for V_c, β and x in equation (10.28), which are listed in Table 10.2. The experimental points are also shown in Fig. 10.6.

If the value of β varied as the square root of the absolute temperature, which is to be expected from equation (10.16) for the ionic mobility u_i, then the ratio $\beta/\sqrt{T}$ would be approximately constant. The upwards trend with temperature of this ratio, shown in the last column of Table 10.2 indicates that the model for ionic mobility is an over-simplified one, and much further work is required for a more comprehensive theory to be established.

TABLE 10.2. VALUES OF x, β AND $\beta/\sqrt{T}$ FOR CORONA
CURRENT RELATION AT VARIOUS TEMPERATURES*[546]

Air—negative corona

$T°C$	$\mathscr{V}_c(kV)$	x	β	$\beta/\sqrt{T}$
100	6·5	1·72	4·5	0·234
200	5·5	1·62	8·5	0·390
300	4·5	1·76	14·5	0·605
400	4·0	1·62	34·0	1·31
500	3·5	1·75	48·0	1·72
600	3·0	1·84	62·0	2·10

Air—positive corona

$T°C$	$\mathscr{V}_c(kv)$	x	β	$\beta/\sqrt{T}$
100	6·5	1·52	3·0	0·155
200	5·5	1·56	4·3	0·197
300	4·5	1·58	5·3	0·220
400	4·0	1·60	6·8	0·260
500	3·5	1·55	7·8	0·280
600	3·0	1·61	9·0	0·304

Air with water vapour—positive and negative corona,
405 g/Nm³—Dewpoint 72°C

$T°C$	$\mathscr{V}_c$	x	β	$\beta/\sqrt{T}$
200	5·0	1·65	2·1	0·097
300	4·5	1·67	3·2	0·133
400	4·0	1·60	5·0	0·192

* Results of other experimental investigations of corona characteristics are given in Table 10.3.

TABLE 10.3. EXPERIMENTAL CORONA CHARACTERISTICS (SPROULL)[454]
Parallel plate type precipitator with plates 4 in. apart and an 0·11 in. wire, 1 ft long stretched midway

Gas	Temp. °C	Polarity					
		negative			positive		
		thresh-old voltage kV	spark-over voltage kV	current at spark-over mA	thresh-old voltage kV	spark-over voltage kV	current at spark-over mA
Air	20	20	54	2·8	20	28	0·2
	225	9	35	3·1	8	22·5	2·1
Air +20% steam	225	4	45	3·0	5	31	2·6
+35% steam	225	4	46	2·2	4	48	2·2
Air +1% carbon tetra-chloride	20	24	62	2·3	26	63	2·2
Carbon dioxide	20	21	49	1·2	29	49	0·7
Methane	20	2·5	29	17·0	25	21	0·2
Water (steam)	225	9	67	5·2	9	>40	>1·0

(i) Steady (not pulsating) d.c. was used.

(ii) Data for water (steam) was obtained with less accurate apparatus, and the power supply could not reach sparkover with positive polarity.

10.4. PARTICLE CHARGING

As particles or droplets move into the field of a precipitator they acquire an electrostatic charge by two mechanisms, bombardment charging and diffusion charging. The gas ions, and also electrons in the case of a negative corona, move normally across the gas stream carrying the particles under the influence of the electric field, and charge the particles with which they collide. This is called *bombardment charging*. In addition the gas ions (and electrons where present) land on the particles because of their thermal motion, and this is *diffusion charging*.

Although the two mechanisms act at the same time, a theory combining the two has not yet been developed, and it is usual to consider each mechanism separately. The error due to this is not very great, because the bombardment charging mechanism is of primary importance for particles greater than 1 micron, while diffusion charging is more important for particles smaller than 0·2 micron. Because these small particles normally only represent a small fraction of the dust entering a precipitator, they are neglected in most precipitation theories. When these small particles are a large proportion of the dust and fume load, a number of equations (e.g. 10.17 b; 10.37–10.42) have to be modified.

In bombardment charging the magnitude of the electric field, the aggregate surface area of the particles and their dielectric properties play a major part in the process, while in ion diffusion charging the number of ions, their mobility, which is a function of temperature, and the time available for the process are the most important factors. The theoretical calculations of the charge acquired by the particles make the following assumptions:

(i) The particles are spherical.

(ii) Interparticle distances are large compared to the particle diameters.

(iii) The ion concentration and electric field is initially considered to be uniform.

(iv) There is no effect on the charging process on one particle by the fields of other charged particles.

Bombardment charging has been studied by Rohmann[399] and Pauthenier and Moreau-Hanot.[363] It is assumed that the gas ions move along the lines of force between the high tension electrode and the passive electrode. Some of the gas ions will be intercepted by the uncharged particles, and their charge will be deposited. The particles are now charged, and the lines of force will distort, and some of the gas ions will be repulsed by the charged particle, thus reducing the rate of charging. After a time the charge on the particle will reach a limiting value.

The charge on a particle, q (coulombs), which is a product of the electronic charge e and the number of these charges n, can be found from the equation by Pauthenier.[316]

$$ne = q = \frac{3\epsilon}{\epsilon + 2} \frac{d^2}{4} \frac{Et}{t + \tau} \text{ coulombs} \qquad (10.29)$$

where t = time of charging

τ = time constant = $1/\pi N_i e u_i$

ϵ = dielectric constant of particle

N_i = ion concentration per unit volume

$N_i e$ = space charge density.

The limiting charge, which is also the maximum, can be found by allowing t to approach infinity.

$$q = \lim_{t \to \infty} \frac{3\epsilon}{\epsilon + 2} \frac{d^2}{4} \frac{E}{1 + \tau/t}$$

$$= \frac{3\epsilon}{\epsilon + 2} \frac{d^2}{4} E \tag{10.30a}$$

$$\doteqdot \frac{3\epsilon}{\epsilon + 2} \frac{d^2}{4} \sqrt{\left(\frac{2i}{u_i}\right)} \tag{10.30b}$$

Lucas and Lowe[316] have pointed out that 91 per cent of the limiting charge is attained in 10τ sec., which in the case of a tubular precipitator 10 in. dia., with a 0·3 in. dia. corona wire, operating at 40 kV and a current of $40\,\mu\text{A/ft}$ is 0·2 sec. If the current is reduced to $10\,\mu\text{A/ft}$, the 91 per cent value is reached in 1 sec.

The influence of particle size, field strength, and to a lesser extent, the dielectric constant and the charge on a particle is indicated by the terms in equation (10.30). For particles consisting of a material with insulating properties, where $\epsilon = 1$ the ratio $3\epsilon/(\epsilon + 2)$ is also 1, while for a good conductor, where ϵ has a high value, the ratio approaches 3. The influence of temperature on the dielectric constant function is negligible.[546] However, the temperature effect on the rate of charging is appreciable, and at constant discharge current, where it is inversely proportional to the ionic mobility, it is also proportional to the inverse of the square root of the absolute temperature (equation 10.16).

Diffusion charging has been studied in detail by Arendt and Kallmann[20], and White,[528] and is primarily a function of the thermal movement of the gas ions. The formula developed by Arendt and Kallmann is limited because it applies only to those particles that already possess some charge. Also, because of the particular differential form, it can only be integrated numerically. The equation is

$$\frac{dn}{dt}\left(1 + \frac{d^2\sqrt{u^2}}{16nke}\right) = \frac{\pi}{4} d^2\sqrt{(u^2)}\, N_i \exp\left(-\frac{2ne^2}{dkT}\right) \tag{10.31}$$

where $\sqrt{(u^2)}$ = root mean square molecular velocity
$$= \sqrt{(3kT/M')}$$

White's approach to the diffusion charging process is simpler. It is shown that the density of a gas in a potential field is not uniform, but varies according to

$$N = N_i \exp\left(\mathscr{V}/kT\right) \tag{10.32}$$

Where $\mathscr{V}$ is the potential energy.

In the case of gas ions near a suspended particle, with charge, ne, the potential energy of an ion of the same polarity at a distance r from the centre of the particle is $\mathscr{V} = -ne^2/r$.

TABLE 10.4. NUMBERS OF CHARGES ACQUIRED BY PARTICLE[316]

Particle dia. microns	Ion bombardment				Ion diffusion			
	period of exposure (sec)				period of exposure (sec)			
	0·01	0·1	1	∞	0·01	0·1	1	10
0·2	0·7	2	2·4	2·5	3	7	11	15
2·0	72	200	244	250	70	110	150	190
20·0	7,200	20,000	24,400	25,000	1,100	1,500	1,900	2,300

The ion density near the particle is then:

$$N = N_i \exp\left(-2ne^2/dkT\right)$$

From the kinetic theory, the number of ions which strike the surface of the particle each unit of time is $\pi d^2 N \sqrt{(u^2)}/4$. If it is assumed that all ions which reach the particle attach themselves, the ion current to the particle (i.e. the rate of charging) will be given by:

$$\frac{dn}{dt} = \frac{\pi d^2 N_i \sqrt{(u^2)}}{4} \exp\left(-\frac{2ne^2}{dkT}\right) \tag{10.34}$$

Integrating this equation, using the uncharged particle at zero time as a boundary condition, gives the total charge as:

$$q = ne = \frac{dkT}{2e} \ln\left(1 + \frac{\pi d \sqrt{(u^2)} N_i e^2}{2kT} t\right). \tag{10.35}$$

From equations (10.29) and (10.35) Lowe and Lucas[316] calculated the charges (n) acquired by particles with bombardment or ion diffusion charging. The calculations were based on a tubular precipitator with the following conditions:

Tube diameter: 10 in.
Discharge wire diameter: 0·3 in.
Temperature $(T) = 300°K(27°C, 80·6°F)$.
Ions per unit volume $(N_i) = 5 \times 10^7$ ions/cm³.
Field Strength $(E) = 2$ kV/cm.
Dielectric Constant function $(3\epsilon/(\epsilon + 2)) = 1·8$.
Electronic charge $(e) = 4·8 \times 10^{-10}$ e.s.u.
Corona current $(i) = 40$ μA/ft.

For approximate calculations, Heinrich and Anderson[212] recommend the equation by Ladenburg[280, 281]

$$ne = d \times 10^6 \tag{10.36}$$

as adequate for practical precipitators.

10.5. PARTICLE DRIFT

As soon as the dust particles acquire some charge they will be influenced by the field in the precipitator. Most of the particles will migrate towards the passive collector electrodes away from the discharge electrode with the same polarity as the particles, while a few particles very close or within the corona zone are charged with gas ions of the opposite polarity to that of the corona and collect on the discharge electrode. The overall picture is a very complex one, as the electric field decreases away from the corona and the particles become more fully charged as they move through the precipitator. Near the passive electrode the concentration of the charged particles will be high, and interparticle interferences will occur, as well as the effect of the partially discharged layer of particles on the collector electrode.

The calculation of particle drift velocity which is used to predict precipitator size and efficiency is of necessity based on a much simpler model and the following assumptions are made:

(i) The particle is considered fully charged during the whole of its residence in the precipitating field.

(ii) The flow within the precipitator is assumed to be turbulent, giving a uniform distribution of particles through the precipitator cross-section.

(iii) Particles moving towards the electrode normal to the gas stream encounter fluid resistance in the viscous flow regime and Stokes law can be applied.

(iv) There are no repulsion effects considered between the particles which are charged with the same polarity.

(v) There are no hindered settling effects in the concentrated dust near the wall.

(vi) The effect of the movement of the gas ions, sometimes called the electric wind, is neglected.

(vii) The velocity of the gas stream through the precipitator does not affect the migration velocity of the ions.

(viii) The particle moves at its terminal velocity.

The migration or drift velocity, which is the velocity of the particles normal to the gas stream based on these eight assumptions can hardly be realistic, but it has been found to give reasonable estimates of the cross stream drift velocity in many cases while in others it tends to be conservative. This is ascribed to the effects of turbulence in the gas stream, the favourable direction of the electric wind, and the gas resistance which is lower than predicted for viscous flow. On the other hand, hindered settling and the residual charge on the deposited particles tend to resist rapid precipitation.

The force F on a particle, with charge q, in a field of strength E directed towards the passive electrode is:

$$F = qE \tag{10.37}$$

and the resistance of the gas, assuming the particle is moving with its terminal velocity is:

$$F' = \frac{C_D}{C} A \tfrac{1}{2}\varrho\omega^2 \tag{10.38}$$

where ω = migration velocity of the particles.
Combining equations (10.37) and (10.38) give the migration velocity as:

$$\omega = \sqrt{\left(\frac{2qCE}{C_D A\varrho}\right)} \tag{10.39}$$

The direct solution of this equation is not usually attempted without substituting $24/\mathrm{Re}$ for C_D (Stokes' Law) assuming the particles are spheres, and assuming that they have been fully charged by bombardment (equation 10.30) in a field of strength E':
Then

$$F = \frac{3\in}{\in + 2} E'E \frac{d^2}{4} \tag{10.40}$$

and

$$F' = 3\pi\mu d\omega/C \tag{10.38a}$$

These two equations can be combined to give the drift velocity:

$$\omega = \frac{\in CE'Ed}{(\in + 2)\, 4\pi\mu} \tag{10.41}$$

Where the precipitator has only a single zone for both charging and precipitating E and E' are the same, and (10.41) simplifies to

$$\omega = \frac{\in CE^2d}{4\pi(\in + 2)\mu} \tag{10.42}$$

When the particles are of a conducting material with large dielectric constant:

$$\omega = 0{\cdot}08CE^2d/\mu \tag{10.43}$$

For a particle with low dielectric constant, where the ratio $3\epsilon/(\epsilon + 2)$ is taken as $1 \cdot 75$:

$$\omega = 0 \cdot 046 C E^2 d / \mu \tag{10.44}$$

If the particles are small, and Ladenburg's approximate charging by diffusion equation (10.36) is used:

$$\omega \doteq \frac{CeE \times 10^5}{\mu} \tag{10.45}$$

This formula indicates that the terminal migration velocity for very small particles (less than 0·2 microns) is approximately constant and independent of particle size.

In section 10.8 the migration velocity calculated from the formulae in this section are compared with the effective migration velocities (e. m. v.) ω' obtained from experimental precipitator efficiencies and the specific collecting surface which, in turn, is a function of the precipitator dimensions and gas volume throughput.

10.6. COLLECTION EFFICIENCY OF PRECIPITATORS

If there were no particle re-entrainment in a precipitator, it would be possible, in theory, to construct a precipitator which would collect all the particles entering the unit. The dimensions of this precipitator can be calculated from the drift velocity, ω, which is assumed constant, the average velocity of the gas stream, the diameter of the discharge wire, its potential

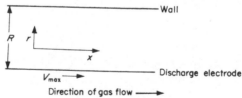

Fig. 10.7. Direction of gas flow in relation to the dimensions of a precipitator.

and current, and the relative diameters of tubes or distances between the plates acting as the passive electrode.

To consider first a tubular precipitator, radius R, with centrally placed discharge electrode. If the flow in the tube is streamline, (unlikely in an industrial precipitator, but readily possible in special research units used for gas sampling), then the streamline flow pattern will be approximately parabolic, and the average velocity, v_{av}, can be shown to be one half of the maximum velocity v_{max}. Then, at a time t, the velocity at a radius r (Fig. 10.7) will be

$$\frac{dx}{dt} = v_{max}\left(1 - \frac{r^2}{R^2}\right) \qquad (10.46a)$$

$$= 2v_{av}\left(1 - \frac{r^2}{R^2}\right) \qquad (10.46b)$$

The drift velocity at radius r will be ω

$$\text{and } \omega = \frac{dr}{dt}$$

The equation for the particle path will be

$$\frac{dx}{dr} = \frac{dx}{dt} \cdot \frac{dt}{dr} = \frac{2v_{av}}{\omega}(1 - r^2/R^2) \qquad (10.47)$$

If the drift velocity is assumed to be approximately constant across the cross-section of the precipitator, the equation (10.47) can be integrated to give:

$$x = \frac{2Rv_{av}}{\omega}\left\{\frac{r}{R} - \frac{1}{3}\left(\frac{r}{R}\right)^3\right\} + \text{constant} \qquad (10.48)$$

The constant of integration is zero, because when $r = 0$, $x = 0$ for a particle starting at the centre of the tube (or between the plates). When a particle starts at the axis, it has to traverse the distance R before collection. So for all particles to be collected the length of the precipitator has to be greater than

$$x = \frac{4}{3}\frac{Rv_{av}}{\omega} \qquad (10.49)$$

If the flow in the tube is turbulent, piston flow is assumed, and the minimum length for 100 per cent collection is equal to the distance travelled by the gas stream while the particle starting from the centre of the tube reaches the wall at constant drift velocity ω. Thus:

$$x = vR/\omega \qquad (10.50)$$

Similar equations for the length of a precipitator of plate and wire or plate and plate type can be calculated,[404] and are listed in Table 10.5.

In practice re-entrainment occurs, and it was found experimentally[13] that the efficiency of a precipitator was an exponential function of the gas stream residence time in the precipitator field. Deutsch[126] derived an equation of this form based on the assumptions that the dust is uniformly distributed at the beginning, that the uncollected dust remains uniformly

TABLE 10.5. THEORETICAL LENGTH OF PRECIPITATOR FOR COMPLETE REMOVAL
OF DUST, ASSUMING CONSTANT DRIFT VELOCITY

Electrode system	Flow pattern	Precipitator length
Tube type	Streamline	$4v_{av} R/3 \omega$
	Turbulent	$v_{av}R/\omega$
Plate electrodes	Streamline	$v_{av}L^*/\omega$
(discharge and passive)	Turbulent	$v_{av}L^*/\omega$
Wire (active) and plate	Streamline	$v_{av}L\dagger/\omega$
(passive) electrodes	Turbulent	$v_{av}L\dagger/\omega$

L^* = distance between charged and passive plate.
$L\dagger$ = distance between charged wire and passive plate.

distributed, and that the drift velocity is effectively constant. Then the efficiency η is found from

$$\eta = 1 - \exp\left(\frac{-2\omega x}{Rv_{av}}\right) \text{ (tube precipitator)} \qquad (10.51\,a)$$

$$= 1 - \exp\left(\frac{-\omega x}{Lv_{av}}\right) \text{ (plate precipitator)} \qquad (10.51\,b)$$

$$= 1 - \exp\left(\frac{-\omega \mathscr{A}}{Q}\right) \text{ (either type)} \qquad (10.51\,c)$$

where $\mathscr{A}$ = precipitator collecting plate area

Q = gas flow.

These are the most common equations used for predicting the efficiency of a precipitator. When a migration velocity—called the effective migration velocity, ω'—is calculated from a measured precipitator efficiency, equation (10.51 c) is expressed as:

$$\eta = 1 - \exp(-\omega'\mathscr{S}) \qquad (10.52)$$

where $\mathscr{S}$ is the specific collecting surface per unit volume gas flow.

An equation identical with the Deutsch equation has been derived on a more general basis by White[531] who considered the probability ($\mathscr{P}$) of capture of a particle within a precipitator. For a particle to be collected during its residence time Δt, it must be within a distance $\omega \Delta t$ of the passive electrode. Thus, for a particle in a tubular electrode, the probability of collection is equal to the ratio of outer annulus, width $\omega \Delta t$, and the cross sectional area of the tube:

$$\mathscr{P} = \frac{\omega \Delta t \times 2\pi R}{\pi R^2} = 2\omega \Delta t/R \qquad (10.53)$$

The possibility of avoiding capture $(1 - \mathscr{P})$ in n sections of a precipitator is given by

$$(1 - \mathscr{P})^n = (1 - 2\omega \, \Delta t/R)^n$$

$$= (1 - 2\omega t/Rn)^n \qquad (10.54)$$

For large n, the possibility of escaping (which is $(1 - \eta)$) is then given by $e^{-2\omega t/R}$, and expressing this in terms of the average gas velocity v_{av} and the length of the precipitator $x(t = x/v_{av})$, the efficiency is found to be given by an equation identical with (10.51 a).

A modification of this equation, which will account for efficiency in capturing particles with a range of diameters, d_1, to d_2, has also been given by White

$$1 - \eta = \exp\left(-\frac{\mathscr{A}EE'}{2\pi\mu Q}\right) + \frac{\mathscr{A}EE'}{2\pi\mu Q} \int_{d_1}^{d_2} \left\{ f(d) \exp.\left(-\frac{\mathscr{A}EE'd}{4\pi\mu Q}\right)\right\} dd$$

$$(10.55)$$

where $f(d)$ is the function expressing the cumulative size distribution of the particles. Because the cumulative size distribution is usually logarithmic, equation (10.55) can be conveniently solved by plotting the experimental particle size distribution on log-probability graph paper, combining this with the function $\mathscr{A}EE'/2\pi\mu Q$, and then integrating numerically.

A modification of the Deutsch equation, a major assumption of which was the perfect distribution of the unprecipitated dust, has been introduced by Williams and Jackson.[544] Their theory assumes that the re-mixing of the unprecipitated particles is a function of the eddy diffusion in the turbulent core of the gas stream, their other assumptions being the same as those used by Deutsch. Essentially, the differential equation for diffusion is used (equation 3.1) with additional terms for the superimposed particle drift due to the electrostatic force. The equation is transformed using two dimensionless parameters, τ expressing the path length in the precipitator (x) in terms of the distance between wire and plate (L), and φ the drift velocity (ω), in terms of the stream velocity (v_{av}):

$$\tau = \frac{x}{L} \left[4(N + 1)^2 \frac{\mathscr{D}}{v_{av}L} \right] \doteqdot 7\cdot41 \, \frac{x}{L} \qquad (10.56\,a)$$

$$\varphi = \frac{\omega}{v_{av}} \left[2(N + 1) \frac{\mathscr{D}}{v_{av}L} \right]^{-1} \doteqdot 5\cdot67 \, \frac{\omega}{v_{av}} \qquad (10.56\,b)$$

where N = No. of points in the precipitator at which calculation is carried out

$\mathscr{D}$ = eddy diffusivity.

At the velocities commonly used for precipitation, the eddy diffusivity is directly proportional to the stream velocity, and so the ratio $\mathscr{D}/v_{av} L$ is 0·0042 for a Fanning friction factor of 0·0035*. The equation was solved numerically at 20 points through the precipitator ($N = 20$) using a digital computer, and the solution obtained graphs the precipitator efficiency in terms of the parameters τ and φ (Appendix IV). The constants in equation (10.56) are based on this. Excellent agreement between experimental and predicted efficiencies were obtained for a pilot plant precipitator.

10.7. SECONDARY FACTORS IN PARTICLE COLLECTION—DUST RESISTIVITY

The previous sections have discussed the removal of particles and droplets from gas streams with electrostatic forces. The practical efficiency of a precipitator, however, depends on a number of secondary factors governed by the behaviour of the dust on arrival at the collection electrodes, and its removal from the electrodes. These factors are a function of the type of dust, its physical properties — particle size and resistivity — and, to a certain extent, of the overall gas velocity in the precipitator. They are allowed for in the effective migration velocity (e.m.v.) which is calculated from the measured efficiency of a precipitator (equation 10.52) and the specific collecting surface area (projected) per unit volume flow $\mathscr{S}$. The most important of these factors is the particle resistivity, which determines whether or not electrostatic precipitation can be applied to a particular dust removal problem. When particles or droplets arrive at the collecting electrode, they are partially discharged by the electrode, and adhere to it by a combination of forces — molecular adhesive forces of the London–van der Waals type, surface tension forces from the moisture present and electrostatic forces. The extent of the electrostatic adhesion depends on the rate at which the charge leaks away from the particles to the earthed collector, which depends on the resistivity of the dust, and which, in turn, depends on the conductivity of the dust particles, and of any moisture present.

Liquid droplets and some metallic and carbon particles are very good conductors, while the particles from most industrial smelting plant consist of metallic oxides which are excellent insulators when dry. In industrial type fumes traces of impurities are always present as well as moisture. So, if the temperature is sufficiently low, enough moisture will be there to form a conducting film.

The resistivity of dusts handled by electrostatic precipitators covers a range from 10^{-3} ohm · cm for carbon black to 10^{14} ohm · cm for dry lime rock dust at 200°F.[456] For most effective operation the dust resistivity should lie in the range from 10^4 to 5×10^{10} ohm · cm. When particles have

* $\mathscr{D} = 0·071\, v_{av}L\, \sqrt{\text{(Fanning friction factor)}}$

low resistivity as in the case of carbon black, they are rapidly discharged on meeting the earthed electrode. Because the molecular and surface tension forces are inadequate to hold the carbon black particles on the collector electrode, they are re-entrained in the gas stream. Carbon par-

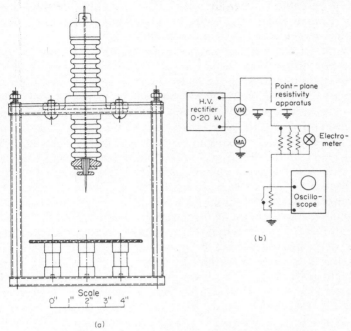

(a)

FIG. 10.8. Point-plate cell for measuring dust resistivity:[532]

(a) Diagram of cell.

(b) Schematic circuit diagram.

One type of laboratory cell is shown. The cell is mounted in an electrically heated and thermostated oven capable of reaching temperatures of 600 – 700°F. A particle layer several millimeters thick is generally used. The layer may be placed on the plate electrode manually or else precipitated on by means of a d.c. corona from the high-tension point. The high tension disk electrode is lowered on the dust layer for the actual resistivity measurement.

In another type of cell, humidity as well as temperature may be controlled, with humidity values ranging from bone dry up to 30 or 40 per cent by volume. The higher humidities are possible, of course, only for temperatures above the dew point.

The schematic electric circuit used with these cells is shown. The electrometer is sensitive to 10^{-12} amp., permitting measurement of resistivities as high as 10^{15} ohm-cm. Field measurements of particle resistivities in plant flues may be made by use of a compact, light-weight apparatus similar in principle to that used in the laboratory. The cell may be shielded against direct gas impact where high gas velocities are met. In another arrangement gas may be withdrawn from the flue through a side chamber and resistivity measured under controlled lower gas velocities.

Experiment shows that the resistivity depends somewhat on the compactness of the particle layer and also on the applied voltage. The compactness effect normally may introduce an uncertainty factor of about two in the measured resistivity. Applied voltage is limited by breakdown or sparking through the layer. The breakdown strengths of particle layers usually range from a few hundred volts per centimeter to 10 or 20 kV/cm, with the latter being more common. Since the current through a particle layer usually increases somewhat faster than the applied voltage, the measured resistivity will be lower at higher voltages; therefore resistivity measurements generally are made at voltages near breakdown or at least at values corresponding to a field strength of a few kilovolts per centimetre.

ticles in flue gas tend to "hop" or "creep" through the precipitator when the electrodes are flat plates and means of preventing re-entrainment are not provided. In the case of air cleaning precipitators for occupied spaces it is usual to cover the collector plates with a sticky, soluble oil to prevent re-entrainment. The dust quantities collected from the atmosphere are small and barely cover the plates before the oil is washed off and replaced at intervals of one to six weeks.

When the resistivity of the particles is very high (greater than 5×10^{10} ohm · cm), the rate of discharge from the collected particle layer is very small, and a charge builds up on the collected particles until electrical breakdown of the gases occurs, first in the spaces between the particles, and then on the surface of the dust layer. This is called "back ionization" or "back corona".

Some ions of opposite polarity to that of the charge on the dust are formed and these migrate back towards the discharge electrode. They reduce the charge in the charging zone and neutralize the charge on the charged particles. To overcome this problem the charge on the dust layer has to be given more time to leak away. This can be done by temporarily reducing the precipitator current, and so, temporarily, the precipitator efficiency.

When the resistivity of the deposited dust is in the range of 10^4 to 10^{10} ohm · cm these problems are avoided. Considerable measurements of the resistivity of deposited dusts have been carried out to see conditions under which their resistances lie within this range.[532, 453, 456] A laboratory cell (point-plate type) of the type shown in Fig. 10.8 mounted in a thermostat oven, is used for these. The electrical circuit includes an electrometer sensitive to 12^{-12} A, which allows the measurement of resistivities as high as 10^{15} ohm · cm. It is necessary to carry out the resistivity measurements near the breakdown voltage (or at least at field strengths of the order of several kV/cm), because the measured resistivity is lower at these high voltages, and these are conditions similar to those within an actual precipitator. A number of curves showing the experimentally measured dust resistivity for industrial dusts with various moisture contents is shown in Figs. 10.9 a–h. It is seen that in all of these, a high moisture content lowers the resistivity, particularly at temperatures below 200 °F, when conduction through the moisture enclosing the particles takes place. The curves reach a maximum between 200–350 °F, and then fall off again as conduction through the particles themselves, either by electronic or ionic processes, takes over. At about 500–600 °F the effect of moisture becomes negligible. In some semi-conductors such as lead sulphide the conduction is electronic, while in others such as lead chloride, it is ionic. In all cases the resistance falls off rapidly with rising temperature.

The resistivity decrease has the form:[456]

$$r = a \, e^{b/T} \tag{10.57}$$

where a and b are constants which have to be determined experimentally.

An exception to this behaviour, even at ambient temperatures, is sulphur in the powdered form. Sulphur is hydrophobic and remains a perfect insulator.

Besides the conditioning of gases with water to bring the deposited dust into the right resistivity range chemical conditioning agents are also used. The most common of these are sulphur trioxide and sulphur dioxide which occur naturally in flue gas: sulphur trioxide injection has been used for difficult cement and fly ash problems,[530] which occur when coal with a low sulphur content (0·1–0·6 per cent) is used as a fuel. For example, a concentration of 0·5 per cent sulphur dioxide was used in cement dust precipitation at 220°C, and the e.m.v. was increased from 3·5 to 5 cm/sec, as the dust resistivity was reduced to 10^{11} from a much higher value.[453] Tests indicate that when sulphur trioxide injection is used, this gas is almost wholly absorbed by the collected dust and does not create a secondary air pollution problem.[263] One of the best examples of chemical gas conditioning is the injection of 20 ppm ammonia into the gas stream entering a precipitator and carrying powdered aluminium silicate catalyst from petroleum cracking. This reduced resistivity from 5×10^{11} to 10^{10} ohm · cm, and improved precipitator efficiency from 96 to 99·8 per cent.[532]

Sproull and Nakada[456] suggest an equation for estimating the potential build up across the dust layer, considering this as a condenser, and assuming that an equilibrium is established between the arrival of new charged dust particles and the leaking away of the charge to earth.

$$\mathscr{V}_d = rx\varphi \left(1 - \frac{r\epsilon}{36 \times 10^{11}\pi t}\right) \tag{10.58}$$

where $\mathscr{V}_d$ = potential difference across dust (V)

r = resistivity (ohm · cm)

φ = current density (A/cm^2)

ϵ = dielectric constant (dimensionless)

x = thickness of dust layer (cm).

When r is not very high (less than 10^{13}) equation (10.58) simplifies to:

$$\mathscr{V}_d = rx\varphi \tag{10.59}$$

The actual attractive force F of the particle towards the passive electrode can be found from[316]

$$F = d^2(K\mathscr{V}_d ir - \mathscr{V}_d^2/32) \tag{10.60}$$

where K = constant.

The first term in parentheses represents the attractive force based on the charge on the particle, and the second term the induced potential repulsive force. When dust resistivity is low, the repulsive force may be larger

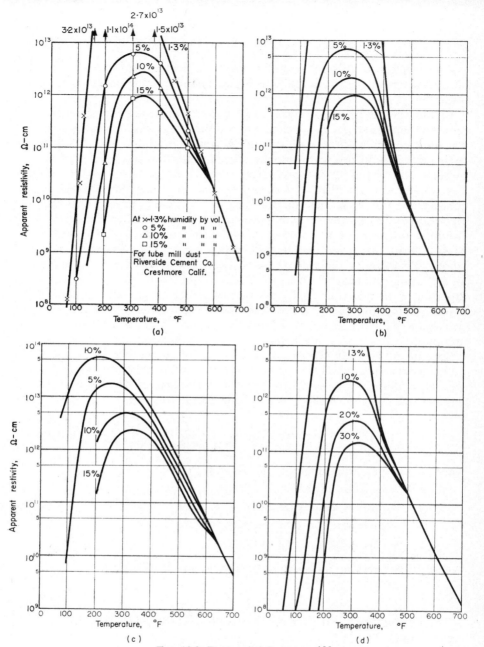

FIG. 10.9. Dust resistivity curves.[456]

(a) Apparent resistivity of powdered lime rock used in making Portland cement (various moisture concentrations: 1·3, 5, 10, 15%).

(b) Apparent resistivity of lead fume from a sintering plant, which contains about 3% zinc, otherwise mainly lead sulphate (various moisture concentrations: 1·3, 5, 10, 15%).

(c) Apparent resistivity of lead fume from a lead blast furnace, which contains about 13% zinc (various moisture concentrations: 1·0, 5, 10, 15%).

(d) Apparent resistivity of lead fume from a slag treatment plant, which contains about 20% zinc, otherwise chiefly lead sulphate (various moisture concentrations: 1·3, 10, 20, 30%).

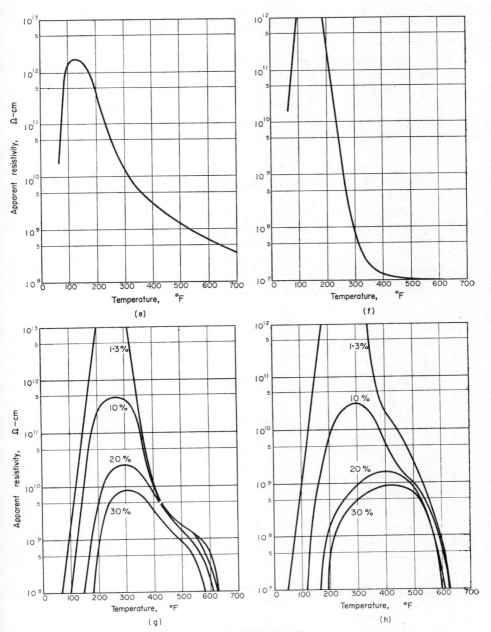

FIG. 10.9 (*continued*)

(e) Apparent resistivity of zinc fume from a slag fuming plant, with about 40%
zinc (moisture concentration: 1·3%).

(f) Apparent resistivity of zinc fume from a melting plant, which contains about
50% zinc (moisture concentration: 1·3%).

(g) Apparent resistivity of fume from an open hearth furnace. The furnace
handles large quantities of scrap (moisture concentrations: 1·3, 10, 20, 30%).

(h) Apparent resistivity of fume from an open hearth furnace different to (g)
(moisture concentrations: 1·3, 10, 20, 30%).

than the attractive force. There are still the molecular and surface tension forces holding the particle. If the surface tension forces are negligible, as is the case at high temperatures generally, the molecular forces alone retain the particle, and these vary directly with the diameter d of the particle. Hence large particles may be more likely to leave the electrode than small ones (the repulsive force varying with $(\mathscr{V}_d d)^2)^{316}$. Strict confirmation of these relations is not available.

10.8. EFFECTIVE MIGRATION VELOCITY (e. m. v.)

The apparent migration velocity of particles in a precipitator, calculated from the collector surface area of the precipitator, the gas flow, and the measured collection efficiency (equation 10.52) is called the effective migration velocity. It incorporates the effects of such factors as particle resistivity and entrainment losses during rapping.

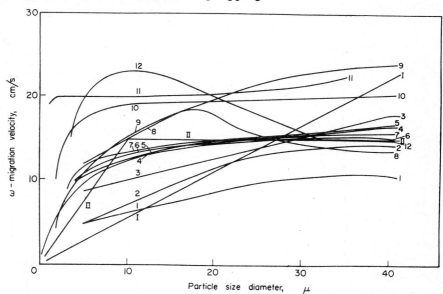

FIG. 10.10. Effective migration velocities as a function of particle size for boiler flue dust, catalyst dust, cement dust and coal dust.[209]

| I | Theoretical curve based on $E = \sqrt{4i/U_i} = 1·3 \text{ kV/cm}$. |
| II | Assumed average curve for average conditions. |

1)		7	= boiler flue dust precipitator.
2) = boiler flue dust precipitator.		8	= boiler flue dust precipitator (vertical).
3)		9)	
4	= catalyst dust precipitator.	10) = boiler flue dust precipitator	
5	= cement kiln dust precipitator.	11	= coal dust precipitator.
6	= boiler flue dust precipitator.	12	= boiler flue dust precipitator (vertical).

Early workers, such as Mierdel,[339] found that the e.m.v. values obtained for cement and brown coal dust agreed with the migration velocity calculated from equation (10.42). Similarly the extensive experimental work on fly ash,[495] flue dust, catalyst dust and cement dust,[209] by later authors give reasonable agreement between theoretical and experimental migration velocities, particularly for particles larger than 20 microns. However, these values were all obtained over a limited range of gas stream velocities of

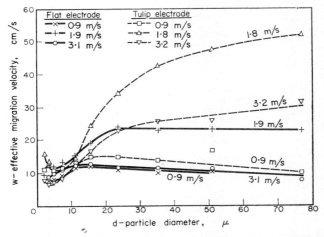

FIG. 10.11. Relation between effective migration velocity and particle diameter for different gas velocities with flat and tulip electrodes in a pilot plant.[112]

$3\frac{1}{2}$–6 ft/sec. Heinrich[209] who studied the effect of particle size on e.m.v. (Fig. 10.10) found that theory gives much lower velocities than those obtained experimentally for particles below 15 microns.

Although the theoretical equations (10.41) and (10.42) indicate that the migration velocity should be independent of the gas stream velocity, experiments have shown that this has in fact considerable bearing on the e.m.v.[84, 112, 209, 210]

Thus Dalmon[112] found a maximum e.m.v. for gas stream velocities of 6–7 ft/sec, while Busby and Darby[84] found a maximum at 15–18 ft/sec. Even Kalaschnikow in 1934[251] observed a slight maximum although he attributed this to experimental error. Dalmon investigated the relation between e.m.v. and gas stream velocity for different electrode types (tulip and flat plate) and the complex relation found is shown in Fig. 10.11 for pilot plants and in Fig. 10.12 for commercial plant (chute and hexagonal tube electrodes).

To overcome the velocity dependence problem in practical design calculations, Koglin[266] suggested an empirical modification of the e.m.v., which he successfully applied to pocket plate type collector electrodes. The modified e.m.v., which is also the maximum, ω'_{max} can be calculated from an experimental e.m.v. at a particular gas stream velocity v (m/sec)

$$\omega'_{max} = (50\omega' + v^2)/200v^2 \text{ (m/sec)} \qquad (10.60)$$

The efficiency of a precipitator at any velocity, v can then be found from

$$\eta_T = 1 - \exp\left[\frac{-(\sqrt{(200\omega'_{max})} - v)x}{50L}\right] \qquad (10.61)$$

where x = length of field (metres)

L = distance between wire and plate (metres).

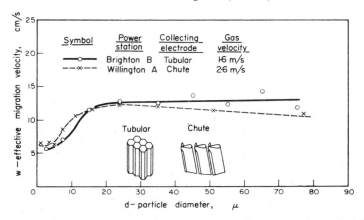

FIG. 10.12. Relation between effective migration velocity and particle diameter with tubular and chute electrodes in commercial sized plant.[112]

The most economical gas stream velocity for operating the precipitator occurs at the maximum e.m.v. The gas stream velocity is then

$$v = \sqrt{(50\omega'_{max})} \quad \text{m/sec}$$

The effect of gas temperature on the e.m.v. is complex as it consists of the following aspects:

(i) The temperature dependence of corona and the sparkover characteristics of the system.

(ii) The temperature dependence of gas viscosity.

(iii) The effect of temperature on the resistivity of the deposited dust.

From the discussion of corona and sparkover characteristics it was seen (section 10.3) that lower field strengths must be used at higher temperatures, and this results in lower migration velocities. The viscosity of all gases increases with temperature, and this also reduces the speed of particle migration. The temperature dependence of dust resistivity is not simple, but at high temperatures it has been shown that this generally decreases ex-

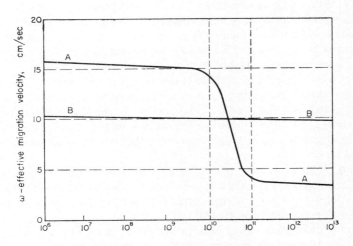

FIG. 10.13. Relation between effective migration velocity and apparent resistivity in a single stage (curve AA) and double stage (curve BB) precipitator collecting lime rock test dust.[453]

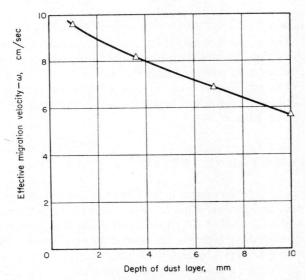

FIG. 10.14. Changes in effective migration velocity with depth of deposited dust layer on flat electrodes (fly ash).[67]

ponentially with rising temperature.[456] The combination of these temperature dependent terms to give a comprehensive method of predicting the effect of temperature on the e.m.v. has not been attempted at this stage, so experiments have to be carried out when attempts are made to increase the temperature in precipitators.[436]

The effect of increased dust resistivity is also not readily predictable. For example, Sproull[453] found that the e.m.v. of a cement test dust in a single stage precipitator fell from 14·8 to 3·5 cm/sec as the dust resistivity increased from 10^{10} to 10^{11} ohm · cm (curve AA in Fig. 10.13), while in a two stage precipitator an approximately constant e.m.v. of 10 cm/sec was maintained (curve BB).

The depth of a layer of high resistivity dust also affects the e.m.v. Brandt[67] found that a 1 mm fly ash layer on the passive electrode resulted in an e.m.v. of 9·8 cm/sec, but this decreased to 5·8 cm/sec when the layer had increased to 10 mm (Fig. 10.14).

The effect of changes in the specific power input on the e.m.v. is that, for a given *size distribution*, (30 per cent less than 10 microns) a 50 per cent rise in e.m.v. results from doubling the specific power input (mA/1000 ft^2).[209] For individual particle sizes the migration velocity for each increases in direct proportion with the power input. The migration velocity tends to remain constant with constant power input, regardless of whether this is achieved by high current and low potential or high potential with low current.

Results of tests were correlated by Heinrich[209] for a large number of power stations. These had dry bottom pulverized coal fired boilers and precipitators with 4 mm squared, fluted, or barbed wire discharge electrode and pocket or chute type passive electrodes 12–13 in. apart. Good correlations were obtained between e.m.v. and specific current or power input, but very little correlation was found to exist between e.m.v. and the applied high tension voltage.

10.9. REMOVAL OF DEPOSITED MATTER

When mist droplets are deposited on the passive electrode of a precipitator, these run together forming larger droplets, which in turn run down the plates or tubes and are collected. Often mist precipitators are irrigated with additional liquid streams to increase the rate of droplet removal from the plates. When solid particles are deposited, these can also be washed or scraped off the electrodes, but most frequently they are dislodged from the electrodes by *rapping* with hammers or vibrators.

Vertical flow irrigated electrostatic precipitators (Fig. 10.15) are widely used in the chemical industry for precipitation of acid and tar mists. They have to be constructed from corrosion resistant materials for these duties, which increases their initial cost. Water consumption is usually fairly high with these units. When used for hot gases, they will be cooled by the precipitator and a cold gas plume will be emitted. This cold plume settles in the immediate surroundings of the plant without dispersing, and may cause difficult or harmful conditions if insoluble toxic or obnoxious gases are present in the gases.

A new type of horizontal irrigated precipitator has been described by Parkington and Laurie-Walker[362] which has small plate spacings and continuously irrigated passive electrodes. This results in a more compact design, and greater effective field strength at lower operating voltages (15 kV) than with the conventional design (operating voltages 45–60 kV).

A special case of a precipitator with many of the characteristics of the irrigated precipitator is the two stage, positive corona, air cleaning precipitator used for cleaning air for air-conditioning applications. The plates in this precipitator are covered with a soluble oil to which the dust sticks, and which are washed down at intervals between 2 and 8 weeks to remove the accumulated dust, and are then recoated with clean oil.

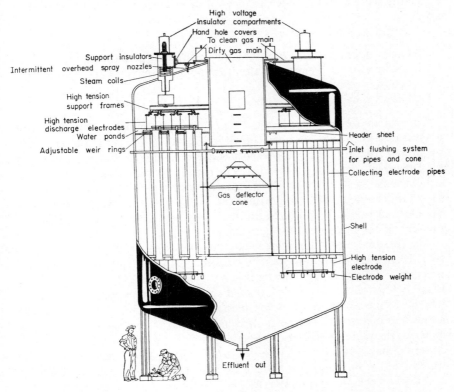

Fig. 10.15. Vertical gas flow tube type irrigated precipitator.[524]

If a dry precipitator is washed down during shut down periods, great care must be taken to remove all the water from the plates before passing dirty gases through the plant. The residual liquid tends to form a crust with the particles, and this may be difficult to remove without further shut down and washing.

Removing the accumulated dust by scraping the electrodes during operation has only been applied where the electrodes are of a semi-conducting material such as concrete reinforced with conducting rods. These electrodes are used where there is a tendency to discharge at a potential below that required for efficient precipitation. The resistance in the electrode tends to suppress the discharging of the dust and stabilize the field. The dust is scraped off by dragging scraper chains across the electrode, usually with the gas stream shut off to avoid re-entrainment.

Continuous brushing of electrodes has been applied on a very small scale, where precipitators have a continuous belt of electrodes, operating at comparatively low voltages, and where a brush is installed in the base of the unit.[435] In an industrial scale precipitator where there are large passive collecting plate areas, this design has not proved economic, and rapping is used.

The rapping devices are of three types:

(i) Cam operated drop hammers or spring loaded hammers.
(ii) Magnetic or pneumatic impulse rappers, controlled by timing switches.
(iii) Electromagnetic vibrators.

The plates are usually rapped by devices in categories (i) or (ii), and diagrams illustrating these are shown in Fig. 10.16. Modern practice tends to favour the impulse rappers because these are more easily adjusted for changing operating conditions. The high tension electrodes are rapped either mechanically or with electromagnetic vibrators. Care must be taken to ensure the electrical insulation of the high tension rapping system from the earthed casing of the precipitator. A typical mechanical rapping arrangement for high tension electrodes is shown in Fig. 10.17.

The passive electrode plates can be rapped in either an "in-line" (Fig. 10.16b) or "cross-rapping" arrangement. In the "in-line" two section precipitator shown, the plates are individually suspended from a supporting beam, while their lower ends hang between rails. A complete wall section, which in this case consists of five plates, is displaced in the same plane to allow a projection to strike a rigid platform. In a common alternative method, the plates, similarly suspended, are hit directly by a hammer. The energy consumed by either method is the same, being governed by the weights of the hammers (or the plates) and the distance these are lifted.

A fairly recent development is a cross-rapping arrangement, which shakes rather than shears the dust layer from the plates. This system also has the advantage that the acceleration of the vibrations of the plates in cross rapping is much larger than in "in-line" rapping, making it more efficient.[67, 210] The plates have a fundamental frequency of vibration depending on the type and position of the suspension, which may be a pin (Fig. 10.16b) or springs, and the point where the plates are struck by the

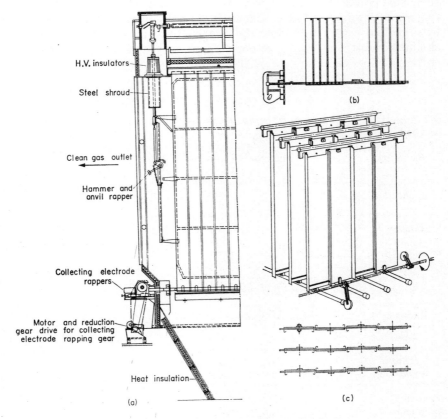

H.V. insulators

Steel shroud

Clean gas outlet

Hammer and anvil rapper

Collecting electrode rappers

Motor and reduction gear drive for collecting electrode rapping gear

Heat insulation

(a)

(b)

(c)

FIG. 10.16. Various plate rapping mechanisms:
(a) Hammer and anvil rappers — in line.[222]
(b) In line impulse rappers (two sections).[311]
(c) Cross rapping, using hammers.[210]

hammer. The striking of the plates superimposes harmonics on the fundamental frequency which lead to varying accelerations in the plate which shake off the dust. These accelerations have been measured in some cases[67] and these are listed in Table 10.6.

On the basis of this work it can be concluded that vibration of the plates has not been as successful as striking them with hammers because of the relatively small accelerations obtained when using a vibrator (see column 4, Table 10.6A). In many cases also the even vibrations may tend to compact the dust on the plates instead of shaking it off.

Rapping may be either continuous or intermittent, and the timing of the intermittent rapping is determined by the amount of dust being collected. It is usual practice to allow $\frac{1}{4}$–$\frac{1}{2}$ in. (6–12 mm) of material to collect before rapping. If the quantities collected are too small, the agglomerates will not be sufficiently large to fall into the hopper, but will re-entrain. If the accumulated dust is too thick, re-entrainment may take place, and dust resistivity factors can also cause difficulties.

TABLE 10.6. ACCELERATION (IN g) ON RAPPED PLATES[67]

(A) Single plate — 7·5 m high, 77 cm wide and 1·5 mm thick, suspended by a pin and held between rails.

Exited by:	Hammerblow 2·6 kilo (force)-meter			Vibrator 67 Hz cross vibration
Point of application	Right-angle stroke at base of plate	Right-angle stroke at centre of plate	In line-stroke at base of plate	
Maximum	9,300	65,000	550	590
Minimum	540	500	64	101
Mean	2,950	4,000	215	290

(B) Groups of plates — 2 groups of 5 plates each $3\frac{1}{4}$ m tall, 47 cm wide, 3 mm thick.

Exited by:	Hammerblow 2·6 kilo (force)-meter				Vibrator 67 Hz		
Suspension	*Pin*				*Springs*		
Point of application	Cross base	Cross centre	In-line base	In-line top	Cross base	In-line base	In-line top
Maximum	2,300	232	14,000	92	191	97	91
Minimum	28	50	16	6	46	79	26
Mean	133	108	58	37	91	90	63

As different sections of precipitators accumulate dust at different rates, the rappers should be in independently controlled sections, so that the optimum dust layer accumulates in each section before rapping.

It has been found in practice that intermittent rapping tends to give higher precipitator collection efficiencies than continuous rapping.[157, 311] Little[311] found that the maximum efficiency of $95\frac{1}{2}$ per cent for a fly ash precipitator was obtained by rapping at intervals of 90–120 min, isolating the section being rapped during cleaning, compared with 93 per cent with continuous rapping. Longer rapping intervals than 120 min tended to give reduced efficiencies. By grading the intensity of rapping better performance has been obtained.[8] For example, moderate impacts can be used initially during rapping to loosen the dust layer, and then larger blows, increasing in intensity, for shaking off the finer dusts.

Practical rapping cycles for optimum precipitator performance have to be established experimentally in the individual cases, and depend on such factors as electrode types, temperature and humidity. Dalmon and Lowe,[112]

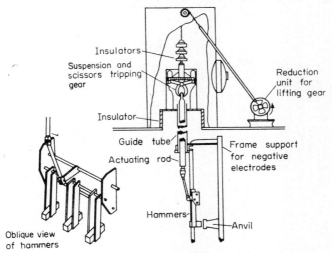

Insulators

Suspension and scissors tripping gear

Reduction unit for lifting gear

Insulator

Guide tube

Actuating rod

Frame support for negative electrodes

Hammers

Anvil

Oblique view of hammers

FIG. 10.17. High-tension discharge wire rappers.[311]

for example, found in full scale plant with flat electrodes, maximum efficiency was obtained with 20–30 min intervals between rapping but a similar plant with tulip electrodes (section 10.10) gave better performances with 45 min rapping intervals. These periods are shorter than those found by Little, but are still considerably longer than the 4–10 min rapping cycles frequently used in industrial plant. When vibrators are used, it has been found that 3–4 sec vibration periods remove nearly all the deposited dust, and no further dust is shaken off after 6 sec.[408]

10.10. ELECTROSTATIC PRECIPITATOR ELECTRODES AND OTHER STRUCTURAL FEATURES

The main structural features of electrostatic precipitators are the high tension electrodes suspended on an insulated framework, the passive electrodes which are earthed to the shell, and the enclosing shell. Provision must be made for dust removal from the plates and the collecting hoppers, for thermal insulation if the gases are hot and the temperature is to be maintained; and for housing for the electrical equipment associated with the installation. Care must be taken to ensure that no corrosion takes place in the precipitator, and that in the case of direct short circuiting the system fails "safe".

The type of precipitator used depends on the duty. In industrial units the air flow is either horizontal or vertically upwards. Downward vertical flow

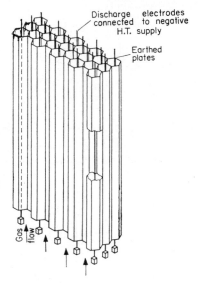

FIG. 10.18. Hexagonal tube type precipitator.

is not used because during rapping the falling dust would re-entrain in the gas stream leaving the precipitator. The vertical tube type of plant is used generally for smaller gas flows than horizontal flow plant, and in the case of special mist precipitation problems. For dry dusts, a hexagonal tube pattern (Fig. 10.18) is used because this gives the largest collecting surface possible with no space to be blocked off between the tubes. The tubes have to be rapped as a group to dislodge the dust.

Circular tubes can be easily equipped with weirs around the top to give an even liquid flow down the walls (Fig. 10.15). Irrigated tubes do not require rapping, and so can have lower mechanical strength. They can therefore be made of a soft, corrosion resistant material such as lead, which is an important factor when precipitating dilute sulphuric acid mists and other corrosive mists.

The discharge wires in vertical precipitators can be either fine round wires, wires with small barbs or wires with a square or star shaped cross-section. Because the discharge wires are often more than 20 ft long, round wire which is thin enough to give a stable corona may not be sufficiently strong, particularly as it will be subjected to vibrations during rapping. Heavier gauge square or star sectioned wires, with the sharp edges giving stable coronas, are used. Barbed wire has been favoured in some precipitators, a recent application being for the precipitation of iron oxide fume from oxygen steel making.[208]

The wires are generally hung from an insulated frame and are individually weighted. They are loosely retained near the bottom in a guide assembly, thus allowing for individual wire expansion, preventing buckling of the wires when there is an uneven temperature rise. For example, a 20 ft stainless steel discharge wire electrode expands 1·4 in. when being heated from ambient temperatures (60°F) to an operating temperature of 700°F. The wire shapes, sizes and materials used in some typical industrial applications are listed in Table 10.7.

TABLE 10.7. DISCHARGE WIRES USED IN ELECTROSTATIC PRECIPITATORS[282]

Application	Electrode wire shape	Materials of construction	Wire size (effective) in.	Operating temperature °F
Acid mist	Star	Lead with monel wire core	$\frac{3}{8}$	110
Cement dust	Barbed	Mild steel	$\frac{3}{4}$	700
Open heart fume	Barbed	Mild steel	$\frac{3}{4}$	550
Fly ash	Square	Mild steel	$\frac{3}{16}$	290
Environmental air	Round	Tungsten	0.005	70

Great care must be taken during installation of the wires to avoid damaging them, otherwise frequent breakages are likely to occur when the precipitator is operating.[208]

Two stage precipitation can be achieved in a vertical tube precipitator by having the precipitating section high voltage electrode in the form of a heavy wire or a tube, without corona formation at the upper end, and the charging section with a fine wire on which a corona forms, attached to the bottom of the precipitating high voltage electrode (Fig. 10.19).

Vertical flow plate electrodes can be either simple flat plates, a design used in fuel gas de-tarring plant (Fig. 10.20b), or, when dust loads are very high, "tulip" electrodes.[157] These are made of bent steel strips welded on to two sides of a frame (Fig. 10.20a), so that when rapping occurs the dust falls down the space between the plates, reducing re-entrainment.

Horizontal flow precipitators (Fig. 10.21) are more frequently applied on a large scale and in cases where high dust resistivity makes collection difficult in a single stage unit. Thus, in the case of a zinc oxide fume precipitator, where a particularly high fume resistivity is encountered, a four zone precipitator has been successfully used. In the first zone, where there is high charge density, particle charging and agglomeration takes place, and currents of only 2·5 mA are passed, while in the subsequent zones more even fields with different field strengths are used, with the currents increasing to 25 mA in the second zone, 32 mA in the third zone and 52 mA in the fourth zone. In this last zone 95 per cent of the dust was precipitated, while the overall efficiency was about 99 per cent.[212] The rapping in the different

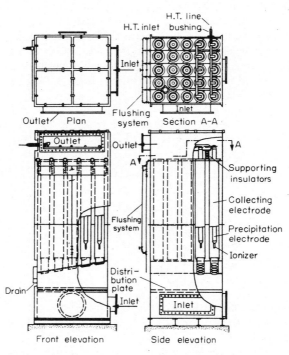

FIG. 10.19. Two-stage discharge electrode vertical flow tube precipitator.[298]

zones must here be timed for different intervals to give most effective deposition.

In the first zone the discharge electrodes are often long steel barbs cut from steel strip, while the electrodes in the precipitating zones consist of star shaped wires which are more closely spaced. The discharge electrodes are suspended from a metal framework, which sometimes consists of tubes, and it is this framework which is rapped to remove deposited material from the wires. The framework is, in turn, suspended on insulators, usually of porcelain, and rated for the voltage of the precipitator. Care must be taken to avoid dust and moisture settling on the insulators, causing short circuits. The chief method is to blow clean air over the insulators to prevent

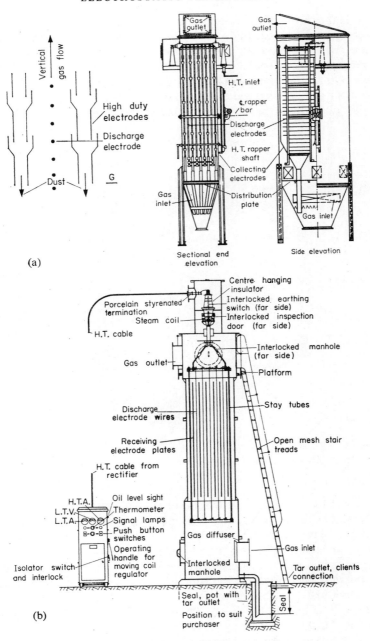

FIG. 10.20. Vertical flow plate type precipitators:
(a) Tulip-type heavy-duty dust precipitators.[298]
(b) Flat plate detarrer for mist collection.[212]

fouling. If the inside of the precipitator is at pressures above atmospheric, clean compressed air is used, while for precipitators at sub-atmospheric pressures, clean external air can be drawn in over the insulators. In many cases heating coils surround the insulators to raise their temperature above the dew point and prevent the deposition of moisture.

Shapes of passive electrodes in horizontal flow precipitators are numerous. Flat plates have the best electrical characteristics and induce the least

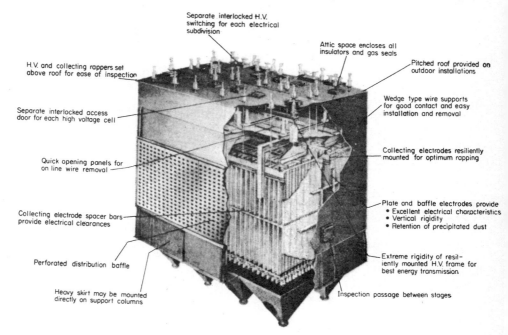

FIG. 10.21. Large, two-stage, horizontal flow precipitator, showing main features of construction.[2]

turbulence in the gas stream. However, re-entrainment tends to occur more easily from flat plates than other sections, and also, to avoid buckling of the plates a heavy gauge material has to be used for construction. Profile electrodes are therefore often found to be more economical and to give better performance. The shapes used are narrow sections rolled together with comparatively small projections (Fig. 10.22a): "C" section channels rolled individually and bolted together,[416] (Fig. 10.22b) triangular baffles welded on[536] (Fig. 10.22c), chute electrodes (Fig. 10.22d),[212] or similar sections not shown here. The profiled electrodes provide low velocity areas at the plate surface downstream from the projections or inside the "C" of a "C" electrode, from which the dust is less readily entrained. Rod curtains and zigzag plates (Figs. 10.22e and f) are also used. Pocket electrodes (Fig. 10.22g)

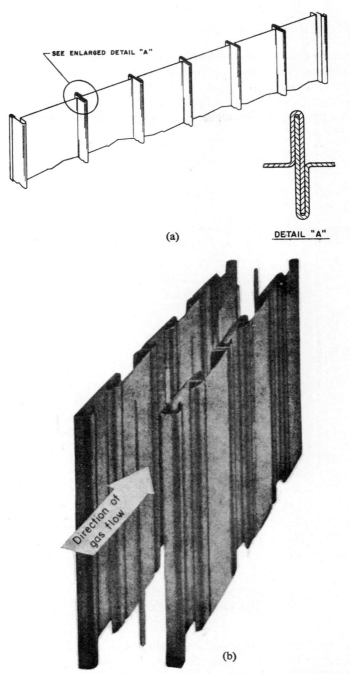

(a)

DETAIL "A"

(b)

FIG. 10.22. Passive electrodes used in horizontal flow precipitators:
(a) Rolled together plates with small projections.[2]
(b) C electrodes, bolted together.[222]

where catch pockets are provided on the outside of the plates and the dust falls down the dead space between the plates (as with "tulip" electrodes), are useful for heavy dust burdens. The suspension of these plates has been discussed in the section on rapping. A recent development[425] is the "hole electrode plate", where the gas stream passes through holes in the passive

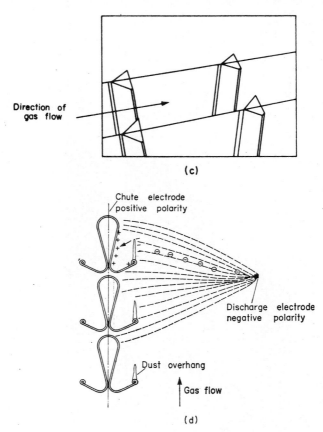

Fig. 10.22 (*continued*)

(c) Triangular baffle electrodes.[536]
(d) Chute electrodes.[212]

collector instead of moving parallel to the electrode, which forces the particles closer to the collecting electrode and enhances their chance of collection. These electrodes can be set on a rotating disk and the dust removed by brushes or doctor blades instead of the conventional rapping technique (Fig. 10.23).

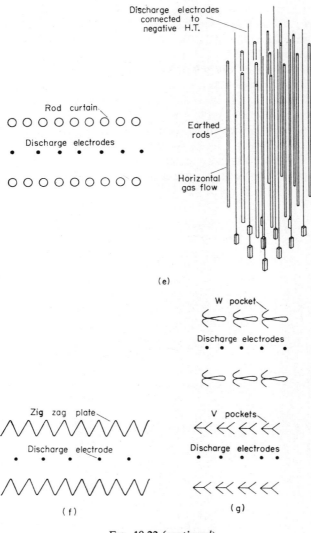

FIG. 10.22 (*continued*)

(e) Rod–curtain electrodes.[529]
(f) Zigzag electrodes.[524]
(g) Pocket electrodes.[524]

The gas flow distribution in precipitators is controlled by flow distributors, dampers and deflector plates. These are required to reduce the gas stream velocity and distribute the dirty gases evenly across the precipitator. Perforated baffles are frequently used for this. The damper system sometimes operates a by-pass for the gases during rapping to reduce losses by entrainment. Air and water models of precipitators are used to determine the shape and positions of baffles and dampers to give the best possible flow distribution.[455, 547]

The construction of the shell for a precipitator depends on whether plates or tubes are used and on operating conditions. If the unit is pressurized, a cylindrical shell is most suitable. Tubular electrodes can be readily arranged in a cylindrical shell, but when plate electrodes are used, a rectangular housing is preferred. Only when operating at particularly high (or low) pressures will plates be housed in a cylindrical shell. Rectangular or cylindrical shells are normally fitted with hoppers for collecting the dust. The hoppers should be large, because fine fumes are not compacted on

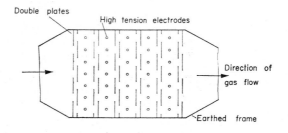

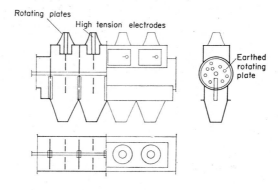

FIG. 10.23. Hole electrode plate precipitator.[425]

collection and tend to occupy far more space than is indicated by the bulk density of the material.

The precipitator shells can be built of brickwork, reinforced concrete or steel, the choice of the material depending largely on the operating conditions (temperature and corrosion) and the local availability of the materials. Steel shells have the advantage that the plant can be pre-fabricated in the shop, with many of the attachments in position, before removal to the site. Concrete shells are to be avoided when operating temperatures exceed 500°F. For high temperature operation, where lowering of the temperature may be undesirable, the plant has to be thermally insulated. Metal doors and other metallic conductors have to be arranged so that heat conduction through these is minimized. Construction of experimental precipitators to operate up to 1500°F has been discussed by Shale and Moore.[436]

In all cases access doors and staircases have to be provided. Special locks have to be fitted so that no access can be gained to the plant without switching off the high tension and discharging the electrodes.

The standard electrostatic precipitator for cleaning environmental air is a two stage unit with positive corona (Fig. 10.24). The ionizing stage has thin (0·005 in.) tungsten wires, charged to 13 kV, and the precipitating section consists of aluminium plates, spaced $\frac{5}{16}$ in. apart, which are in alternation charged to 6 kV or earthed. The gas flow rate in the precipitator varies between 6 and 8·2 ft/sec, and efficiencies considerably better than 95 per cent are usually achieved. Complete plants are made up of cells, each handling about 1400 ft³/min, and for very small units (1 or 2 cells) either vertical or horizontal flow can be used. Large flow rates, frequently over 150,000 ft³/min are readily handled in multicell horizontal flow plants.

As the accumulated dust is removed from the plates by washing them down at intervals of upwards of a week to several months, depending on the dust burden, drainage must be provided as well as ready access for personnel. Some sort of protection from coarse particles and insects for the plant is often necessary, as these can cause frequent short circuits if many are present.

Stringent requirements for such applications as nuclear powered submarines have led to the development of environmental air cleaning precipitators operating at much higher velocities (33·5 ft/sec) and at efficiencies of the order of 99·8 per cent.[537] The units consisted of a plate charging section followed by horizontal hexagonal tubes with $\frac{1}{2}$ in. cylindrical high tension tube electrodes as a precipitating section. The charging section used a potential of 38 kV, and 20 kV was used in the precipitation section. A full scale unit with shorter (3 ft) precipitating field tubes used velocities of 25 ft/sec. Other operating conditions were tried. For example, a single stage plant, using velocities of 100 ft/sec, reduced the efficiency to 91 per cent and gave relatively high ozone concentrations (1·43 ppm) at currents of 121 mA. Reducing the current to 27 mA, reduced the ozone concentration to 0·32 ppm and the efficiency to 80 per cent. Lower velocities (50 ft/sec) gave efficiencies of 98 and 96 per cent with similar corona currents.

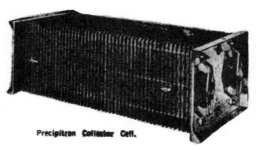

Precipitron Collector Cell.

Frame showing built-in Ionizer.

Fig. 10.24. Environmental air cleaning positive corona precipitator.[525]

This work indicates that if high ozone concentrations of the order of 1 ppm can be tolerated, high throughput precipitators of much smaller dimensions than those at present in use for environmental air can be constructed.

10.11. ELECTRIC POWER SUPPLY FOR PRECIPITATORS

A reliable high voltage d.c. supply is essential for electrostatic precipitators where negative potentials up to 90 kV are used for industrial plant and positive potentials up to 13 kV for environmental air cleaning. The current supplied to industrial precipitators varies according to the size and duty, between 30 and 500 mA, and so transformers and rectifiers with capacities up to 40 kVA are required. Because the migration velocity is a function of the charging and precipitating field strengths, the largest voltage possible without arcing should be applied. The arcing potential however varies with the type of gas — its composition and the humidity and temperature conditions — the dust concentration and the physical dimensions of the precipitator. These are affected by the dust layers deposited on the electrode, and by rapping. Arcing should be avoided not only because it lowers the effective potential in the precipitator, but also because it loosens the deposited dust, assisting re-entrainment, and tends to melt the discharge electrode wire. When arcing does occur, the applied potential must be reduced to zero in the minimum time to extinguish the arc. The field intensity falls off, reducing the migration velocity, and in turn, the efficiency of the precipitator. Voltage control systems are therefore usually included in all industrial precipitator installations.

The power supply to a precipitator consists of three sections: the voltage control system, the transformer which steps up the line voltage (usually 415 V) to the precipitator potential, and the rectifier which converts a.c. to d.c. In some small older installations the voltage control may be manual, but automatic voltage control is universal practice with all large modern installations. It has been shown[534] that automatic voltage control gave a 60 per cent increase in corona power in one plant. A low tension variator may be used for this, as it can be either an automatically stepped or continuously variable transformer. A typical installation has a 16 step transformer which supplies power from 230–380 V in 10 V steps, and is fed with 415 V 50 cycle single or two phase mains power. The automatic control is based on current-sensitive relays which maintain the voltage in the precipitator either just below flashover or at the maximum rating of the variator-step up transformer set. Alternative methods use transducers to monitor the number of flashovers during a short time interval. White[535] suggests that 10–100 sparks/min per high tension section is the range for optimum efficiency in industrial precipitators.

The transformers are of the usual types, fin cooled for operation at temperatures up to 113 °F, and with additional water cooling if the transformer is to operate in warmer conditions. If selenium rectifiers are used, these are included in the units with the transformers at ratings up to 40 kVA.[426] The

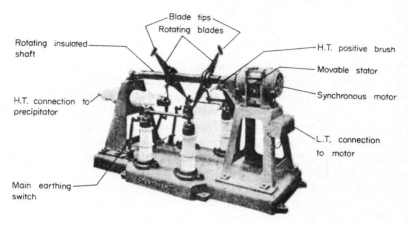

FIG. 10.25. Mechanical rectifier.[478]

transformer output voltages used are 30, 60, 75 or 90 kV, the two central values, 60 and 75 kV, being the most usual. Three types of rectifiers are used:

(a) Mechanical rectifier.
(b) Solid state rectifier (selenium, copper oxide or more recently silicon).
(c) Electronic valve rectifier.

Mechanical rectifiers (Fig. 10.25) were used in the first commercial precipitators installed by Cottrell and remained popular till 1945 because of their low cost, rugged construction, and the fact that their performance is not affected by fluctuations in process conditions. However, oxides of nitrogen are produced at the contacts, so these require frequent maintenance, and a well ventilated housing has to be provided. Suppressors to reduce radio and television interference must be fitted. A circuit incorporating a mechanical rectifier plant is shown in Fig. 10.26.

The most common rectifiers in use at present are those of the solid state type, generally selenium rectifiers. These are slightly more costly to install than the mechanical type, but they do not require special shielded and ventilated housing as they do not produce radio or UHF receiver interference, or nitric oxide gases. The early solid state rectifiers used copper oxide, and present trends are to the use of silicon rectifiers.

High vacuum hot cathode diodes with a life of 25,000–30,000 hr have been developed in the United States and this has led to their wide use in that country. The circuit (Fig. 10.27) is a special four tube one which gives a full wave voltage wave form. In industrial installations is is often possible to mount the tubes on sockets on the transformer bushings. Electron tube rectifiers are also used for positive corona air cleaning precipitators.

In industrial units either half wave or full wave rectification is used from either one or more phases. The half wave pattern allows sparks to extinguish in less than one cycle, leading to smooth precipitator operation. With

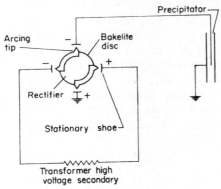

FIG. 10.26. Circuit including mechanical rectifier.[524]

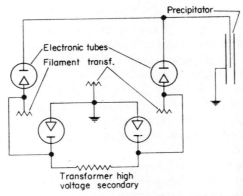

FIG. 10.27. Circuit including diodes as rectifiers.[524]

the full wave form there is a greater tendency for the sparks to develop into high current arcs and operation tends to be rougher.

White[529] has developed a method of pulse energization which gives a peak voltage several kilovolts higher and greater corona current than is possible with conventional rectification. The equipment is similar to that developed for microwave radar, and consists of a line pulser in which energy is accumulated in a high voltage capacitator, and is then discharged rapidly into the load. The pulse time is of the order of some hundreds of microseconds, repeated with a frequency of several hundred pulses a second. The pulse output may be commutated to several precipitator sections. This mode of operation results in 50–60 per cent more efficient collection, halving the losses from the plant.

If a precipitator is built in sections, because these have different power requirements, it is best to have a separate power supply for each. It may also be necessary in the case of very large installations where sections in parallel are separately rapped, to have separate supplies to these sections to give the highest efficiency. For a tube precipitator it has been suggested that a bank of 900 tubes is the maximum to run off a single supply.[362]

The difference in elevation between power supply and the insulators on the high tension electrode should be kept to a minimum, not only because of the very high cost of the high voltage cable, but also because the insulation impregnation compound tends to migrate to the lower level, and leads to insulation failure. The best arrangement is to mount the precipitator voltage control, transformer and rectifier unit on top of the precipitator and connect the high tension electrodes with busbars.

10.12. PRACTICAL PRECIPITATOR OPERATING DATA

Gas Velocities. The average gas velocity used in a precipitator should be the one which gives maximum efficiency and also maximum effective migration velocity. For fly ash this appears to be about 6–7 ft/sec,[112] just below the fly ash entrainment velocity. For carbon black, the entrainment velocity can be as low as 2 ft/sec, while for cement dust it is 12 ft/sec. Mist re-entrainment velocities are even higher; 15–18 ft/sec. Practical precipitator flow rates are normally kept well below these values to about 3 to 6 ft/sec, although experimental fly ash precipitators have used velocities in the region of 30–40 ft/sec.[157]

Power Consumption and Efficiency. The efficiencies, inlet and exit concentrations of a number of industrial precipitators have been listed by Heinrich and Anderson,[212] and are given in Table 10.8. In some instances in this table gas velocities have been added from other sources. Power consumption in environmental air cleaning positive corona precipitators is somewhat greater per unit volume of gas treated than in negative corona precipitators.

Pressure Loss. The pressure loss in electrostatic precipitation is very low, much lower than for other industrial gas cleaning methods. It is generally of the order of $\frac{1}{2}$ in. W.G. and rarely exceeds 1 in. W.G. except when experimental high velocity plants are being tested.

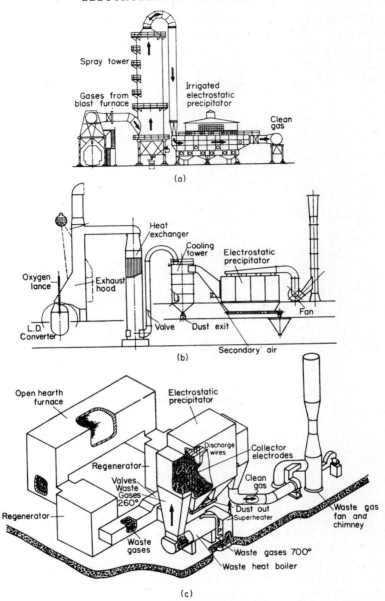

FIG. 10.28. Electrostatic precipitators in the metallurgical industry:[192]

(a) Spray tower and precipitator in series on blast furnace gases.
(b) Waste heat boiler, ring scrubber and precipitator in series on a Linz–Donau-
    witz convertor plant.
(c) Checkerwork brick regenerator, waste heat boiler and precipitator in series
    on an open hearth furnace.

In the case of environmental air cleaning precipitators, the pressure drop is 0·003 in. W.G. at 6 ft/sec and increases to 0·004 in. W.G. at 8·2 ft/sec. This is so low that additional gas resistance has to be added to give uniform flow over the cell bank. Aluminium mesh filters, with a pressure drop of 0·1 in. W.G. are normally used *after* the electrostatic precipitator, and

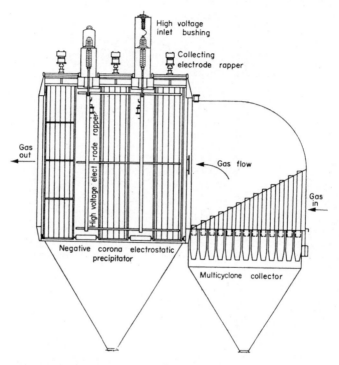

FIG. 10.29. Electrostatic precipitator in series with multiple cyclones on boiler flue gases.[524]

this has the additional purpose of preventing water droplets from the washing cycle being carried past the plant.

Combination of Electrostatic Precipitators with other Gas Cleaners. Electrostatic precipitators are often combined with mechanical or other collectors in cases where gases have exceptionally high dust concentrations or need conditioning, or both. For example, blast furnace gases are often passed through a spray tower before entering the precipitator (Fig. 10.28 a), while low density waste gases are cooled in a waste heat boiler and scrubbed in a ring scrubber (Fig. 10.28 b). Open hearth furnace gases are also passed through waste heat boilers, having given up some of their heat to the chequerwork brick regenerator, and are then cleaned in electrostatic

TABLE 10.8. TYPICAL PERFORMANCE DATA FOR ELECTROSTATIC PRECIPITATORS[212]

Type of plant	Gas flow ft³/min at temperature	Dust concentrations gr/ft³ at operating temp.		Collecting efficiency %	Power consumption kW/100,000 ft³/min
		inlet	outlet		
1. Power Stations:					
Pulverized fuel fired boilers	161,850	5·72	0·071	98·67	19·6
Pulverized fuel fired boilers	144,231	4·76	0·027	99·43	22·3
Refuse burning boilers	50,000	7·3	0·252	96·6	23·8
Lignite stoker fired boilers	235,300	0·7–0·874	0·00743–0·01616	98·15	20·4
Lignite pulverized fuel fired boiler (hammer mills)	942,000	2·015	0·0698	96·5	6·8
2. Coal Industry:					
Lignite rotary type steam dryer	17,050	15·32	0·1225	99·25	5·1
Lignite rotary type steam dryer	15,300	7·96	0·0394	99·40	4·76
Lignite plate type steam dryer	14,700	3·42	0·0272	99·20	4·25
Combustion gas lignite dryer	24,700	6·25	0·0481	99·50	8·5
Lignite mill dryer	23,580	10·93	0·1445	98·67	13·6
Lignite conveying system de-dusting	12,050	23·8	0·121	99·40	3·4
Bituminous coal tube type steam dryer	25,300	7·09	0·0355	99·50	11·9
Bituminous coal conveying system de-dusting	6,480	9·75	0·0656	99·30	49·3
Bituminous coal–coke grinding plant	2,825	6·02	0·0245	99·59	51·0
3. Coal Gas Industry:					
Peat gas producer	2,650	2·32	0·00351	99·85	119·0
Cracking plant for natural gas	5,120	0·0976	0·000875	99·20	204·0
Producer gas from lignite briquettes	7·650	16·4	0·0875	99·47	110·5
Producer gas from semi-bituminous lignite	28,250	12·47	0·0437	99·7	102·0
Shale-gas cleaning plant	20,000	17·4	0·0026	99·9	153·0
Coke oven town gas cleaning	1,825	10·5	0·00437	99·9	153·0
Coke oven town gas cleaning	1,350	7·35	0·00131	99·9	272·0

TABLE 10.8 *(continued)*

Type of plant	Gas flow ft³/min at temperature	Dust concentrations gr/ft³ at operating temp.		Collecting efficiency %	Power consumption kW/100,000 ft³/min
		inlet	outlet		
Coke oven gas cleaning	8,230	12·17	0·0342	99·8	127·5
Oil carburetted water gas cleaning	7,360	2·06	0·0171	99·2	238·0
Tar carburetted water gas cleaning	2,358	4·37	0·0219	99·5	306·0
4. Paper Industry:					
Pyrites roaster 25 ton/day	5,570	1·398	0·0205	98·5	115·7
Pyrites roaster 36 ton/day	8,230	1·79	0·0157	99·1	93·5
Acid mist from sulphur burning furnace 7·5 ton/day	1,470	2·99	0·0179	99·4	136
Sulphuric acid mist following cooler tower	2,530	5·33	0·0267	99·5	161·5 (4–5)*
Sulphuric acid mist following cooler tower	2,940	3·29	0·0306	99·1	132·5 (4–5)*
Black liquor burning plant	78,000	1·234	0·058	95·3	45
5. Cement Industry:					
Rotary kiln dry process 520 ton/day	80,000	9·0	0·084	99·06	15·3 (1·5–3·3†)
Lepol rotary kiln dry process 470 ton/day	74,750	2·75	0·032	98·85	5·1 (2·6–3·3†)
Rotary kiln wet process 350 ton/day	85,400	9·26	0·029	99·68	14·5 (4–5†)
Rotary kiln with calciner, wet process 350 ton/day	85,400	4·82	0·105	98·2	17 (1·5–3†)
Vertical kiln	73,600	0·78	0·021	97·3	15·3
Raw material dryer	21,200	21·3	0·052	99·75	79·9
Cement mill	14,100	22·3	0·037	99·8	76·4
Packing machine	8·840	16·4	0·048	99·7	79·9
6. Chemical Industry:					
Pyrites roaster 29 ton/day	6,480	0·95	0·0162	98·3	136
Pyrites roaster 35 ton/day	7,660	0·525	0·00157	99·7	163
Blende roaster	9,140	2·23	0·0328	98·5	87
Arsenic and sulphuric acid mist removal	8,250	1·18	0·0000022	99·99	145

* Lineal velocity through the precipitator: data from R. L. Cotham. Paper No. 29. *Clean Air Conference*, Sydney, 1962.

† Lineal velocity through precipitator: data from G. Funke, *Zement, Kalk, Gips.* **12**, 189 (1959).

TABLE 10.8 *(continued)*

Type of plant	Gas flow ft³/min at temperature	Dust concentrations gr/ft³ at operating temp.		Collecting efficiency %	Power consumption kW/100,000 ft³/min
		inlet	outlet		
Tail gas for sulphuric acid concentration	12,380	5·38	0·022	99·6	61
Elemental sulphur fume from hydrogen sulphide combustion plant	2,530	11·2	0·0875	99·2	289
7. Mineral Earths and Salts Processing:					
Bauxite dryer 180 ton/day	11,800	6·73	0·021	99·69	19·4
Bauxite calcining and processing kiln 220 ton/day	25,900	2·185	0·026	98·8	30·6
Alumina calciner with multicyclone pre-cleaner 45 ton/day	8,950	129·5	0·013	99·99	78·8
Potassium chloride dryer	17,100	3·5	0·035	99·0	32·3
Fullers earth dryer	17,650	1·88	0·00875	99·54	35·7
8. Non-Ferrous Metallurgical Industry:					
Vertical blast furnace: lead ore	5,880	5·25	0·0289	99·5	37·4
Vertical blast furnace: lead ore	9,410	2·76	0·0656	97·5	32·3
Rotary kiln processing: zinc ores	4,710	17·25	0·193	98·90	34·0
Rotary kiln processing: zinc ores	7,360	5·74	0·0267	99·53	27·2
Vertical blast furnace tin ores	5,700	2·145	0·0149	99·29	30·6
Vertical blast furnace: tin ores	2,120	2·98	0·0425	98·70	40·8
Vertical blast furnace: antimony ores	3,650	1·64	0·00307	99·80	71·4
Copper converters	8,530	1·97	0·0591	97·00	11·9
Rotary kiln for nickel bearing iron ores	26,500	12·03	0·0285	99·76	45·9

precipitators having been conditioned by water sprays, before being emitted to the atmosphere (Fig. 10.28 c).

For flue gases, power stations frequently use centrifugal collectors of the multicellular cyclone type (straight through or reverse flow patterns) (Fig. 10.29) before final cleaning with the electrostatic precipitators. This combination however cannot always be used with success. For example, in the collection of fly ash from boilers burning New South Wales coal, which has exceptionally high resistivity, the combined unit gave lower efficiencies than the precipitator alone. This is explained by the mechanical collector removing the coarse particles which appear to assist agglomeration in the precipitator. The removal of the coarse fraction also results in a fine dust adhering to the electrodes and being much more difficult to remove by rapping.[263] In the case of carbon black, it is not possible to collect all of the carbon in the precipitator because of its low resistivity, but the precipitator does act as an agglomerator. The precipitator is followed by low velocity cyclones, and then bag filters or venturi scrubbers are used to achieve the final cleaning.

CHAPTER 11

SUNDRY METHODS AND MECHANISMS IN PARTICLE COLLECTION

11.1. INTRODUCTION

Some properties of particles which may at times be important to their collection, have not been discussed to any extent in the previous chapters. They should, however, be included because mechanisms such as agglomeration occur in all clouds of particles, while others, such as thermal precipitation, may be the basis of new developments in gas cleaning. Increasing the rate of agglomeration by sound waves has been used to make agglomerates of very small particles which can then be collected by conventional means. Although this method has been proved technically, it has had only limited commercial success.

Thermal precipitation of particles occurs whenever a cold body is placed in dust laden gases. Although the phenomenon of thermal precipitation was known in the last century, and a satisfactory quantitative theory was developed over thirty years ago, the effect has not yet been used for commercial gas cleaning plant.

This chapter outlines the theories of agglomeration and thermal precipitation, and indicates the extent of their commercial exploitation. Other aspects of particle mechanics, such as the movement of charged particles in magnetic fields are mentioned briefly because these may lead to future developments in particle separation techniques.

11.2. AGGLOMERATION OF PARTICLES BY BROWNIAN MOTION

A simple theory of agglomeration of particles has been developed by Smoluchowski,[450] which indicates that the rate of decrease of the number of particles is approximately equal to the square of the number present. This has been generally confirmed by experiment.[540, 496]

A space contains a number of particles, c, randomly distributed, and a sphere of influence, diameter d', is considered to exist within this space. Whenever a particle moves within this sphere of influence it will become part of it, and so a dust free region will exist immediately around the sphere.

Because of the dust free region, a concentration gradient will exist between the sphere and the bulk of the particles in the space, and particles will diffuse to the sphere with a diffusivity $\mathscr{D}$. If Ficks' law (equation 3.1) is applied, then the particles removed will be a function of the surface of the sphere (area $2\pi d'$) in unit time, the number removed is $2\pi d'\mathscr{D}c$. Now all the particles present can be considered as centres of spheres of influence for removal of particles, so the rate of removal is

$$-\frac{dc}{dt} = \frac{c}{2} \cdot 2\pi d'\mathscr{D}c = \pi d'\mathscr{D}c^2 \qquad (11.1)$$

The diffusivity of the two colliding particles consists of the sum of their individual diffusivities, $\mathscr{D}_1$ and $\mathscr{D}_2$. $\mathscr{D}$ must be replaced by this sum; and similarly the diameter d' must be replaced by $(d_1' + d_2')/2$ where d_1' and d_2' are the diameters of the spheres of influence of the two particles. Substituting these in equation (11.1)

$$-\frac{dc}{dt} = \frac{\pi}{2} (\mathscr{D}_1 + \mathscr{D}_2)(d_1' + d_2') c^2 \qquad (11.2)$$

The diffusivity $\mathscr{D}$, was found by Einstein (section 7.4) to be

$$\mathscr{D} = CkT/3\pi\mu d \qquad (7.16)$$

This equation was derived by assuming Stokes' law and incorporating the Cunningham Correction for slip, C. Substituting equation (7.16) for the diffusivities $\mathscr{D}_1$ and $\mathscr{D}_2$ for particles with diameters d_1 and d_2,

$$-\frac{dc}{dt} = \frac{CkT}{3\pi\mu} \left(\frac{1}{d_1} + \frac{1}{d_2} \right) \frac{\pi}{2} (d_1' + d_2') c^2$$

$$= \frac{CkT}{6\mu} \left(\frac{1}{d_1} + \frac{1}{d_2} \right) (d_1' + d_2') c^2 \qquad (11.3)$$

If the particles' spheres of influence are such that they join on touching, then d_1' and d_2' are identical with the particle diameters. If, however, other forces exist between the particles, such as electrostatic or thermal forces, then the spheres of influence may be greater (or smaller) than the actual particle dimensions. It is convenient to express the particle's sphere of influence as the product of the actual particle dimension d and an influence factor S, where S is the ratio of the diameter of the influence sphere divided by the actual particle diameter. Equation (11.3) can then be modified

$$-\frac{dc}{dt} = \frac{CkTS}{6\mu} \frac{(d_1 + d_2)^2}{d_1 d_2} c^2 \qquad (11.4)$$

If the particles are all the same size, i.e. the aerosol is monodisperse, then $d_1 = d_2 = d_3 = \cdots = d_n$, and equation (11.4) simplifies to

$$-\frac{dc}{dt} = \frac{2CkTS}{3\mu} c^2 \qquad (11.5)$$

So, except for the particle size occurring as a first order correction factor in the Cunningham Correction C, the rate of agglomeration of a monodisperse aerosol is independent of particle size. Equation (11.5) can be integrated, assuming constant conditions and a constant Cunningham correction factor:

$$\frac{1}{c} = \frac{1}{c_0} + \frac{2}{3} \frac{CkTS}{\mu} t \qquad (11.6)$$

where c_0 = concentration of particles at time t_0.

TABLE 11.1. COAGULATION CONSTANTS OF VARIOUS AEROSOLS[173, 185]
(air at ambient conditions—760 mm Hg, 25°C)

Substance	$\varkappa \times 10^9$ cm^3/sec
Ferric oxide	0·66
Magnesium oxide	0·83
Cadmium oxide	0·80
Stearic acid	0·51
Oleic acid	0·51
Resin	0·49
Paraffin oil	0·50
p-Xylene-azo-β-naphthol	0·63
Ammonium chloride (ambient)	0·51
Ammonium chloride (46% relative humidity)	0·43
Zinc oxide formed in arc	1·9
Silica powders in electric field	2·8–3·7
Theoretical value	0·51

The group $2CkTS/3\mu$ is called the coagulation constant $\varkappa$, and this has been experimentally found in a number of cases (Table 11.1). The theoretical value for the coagulation constant under the same conditions (air at 1 atm, 25°C) and assuming that $S = 2$, is $0·51 \times 10^{-9}$ cm^3/sec, which is in excellent agreement with the cases of stearic and oleic acid aerosols, which are virtually monodisperse and have no electric charge. Differences in the values for other aerosols, which were always larger than the theoretical one, are explained by the following:

(a) The aerosol was not monodisperse, which can account for small increases in $\varkappa$.
(b) Electrostatic charges were present on the particles which can account for large increases in $\varkappa$.

(c) The presence of humidity tends to decrease the rate of coagulation, until at very high humidities (relative humidity greater than 60 per cent) this trend is reversed.

It is observed in mixtures of small and larger smoke particles, that the fine particles tend to disappear as they agglomerate with the larger ones. This is indicated by the term incorporating particle size in equation (11.4). The changes in rates of agglomeration can be calculated from the ratio $(d_1 + d_2)^2/d_1d_2$, which is unity for a monodisperse aerosol. When the particles are in two distinct groups, and the ratio of their diameters is large, e.g. $d_1:d_2 :: 1:50$, then the effect on the rate of coagulation is large (Table 11.2 A). When the particles are of a range of sizes, which is the practical case, then the effect is much smaller. Values in Table 11.2 B have been calculated on the assumption that the particles occur in groups of equal sizes in ratios from 1:1 to 1:8 (1–8 times the diameter).

TABLE 11.2. EFFECT OF POLYDISPERSIVITY ON
THE COAGULATION CONSTANT[540]

A

Size of particle colliding with unit size particle	$\dfrac{(d_1 + d_2)^2}{4d_1d_2}$
1	1·00
2	1·13
5	1·80
10	3·02
25	6·76
50	12·74
100	25·5

B

Diameter ratio range	$\dfrac{(d_1 + d_2)^2}{4d_1d_2}$
1 : 1	1·0
1 : 1 to 2 : 1	1·06
1 : 1 to 5 : 1	1·19
1 : 1 to 8 : 1	1·27

If the particles are small (below about 0·5 microns) the first order correction introduced by the Cunningham correction factor becomes appreciable and is written most simply as

$$C = 1 + 2A\lambda/d \qquad (4.21)$$

where λ = mean free path of the gas molecules and,

$$A = 1 \cdot 257 + 0 \cdot 400 \exp\left(-\frac{1 \cdot 1d}{2\lambda}\right)$$

which may be considered approximately constant in a first order correction. This can be introduced in the integrated form of the rate equation:

$$\frac{1}{c} = \frac{1}{c_0} + \frac{4kT}{3\mu}\left(1 + \frac{2\lambda A}{d}\right)t \qquad (11.7)$$

From this it is seen that the coagulation "constant" $\varkappa$ is not a constant, but decreases as the coagulation proceeds and the value of C falls off and approaches unity. Experimentally this has only been found, as would be expected, for very small particles.

A secondary factor which influences the coagulation constant $\varkappa$ and tends to give slightly greater values than are calculated from the classical Smoluchowski equation is the presence of van der Waals' forces between the particles. The correction introduced by these forces however is only of the order of a few per cent (at most, 10 per cent),[183] and so can be neglected for most gas cleaning plant calculations.

The effect of charges on the aerosol particles is very complex, and experimental evidence is conflicting. If all particles carry the same charge, this tends to slow coagulation, while bi-polar charges, which were present on the particles in the powerful electric field introduced by Gillespie,[173] speed up agglomeration. If calculations including electric charges on particles have to be considered, they may be found elsewhere.[184] The effect of temperature, pressure and viscosity on the rate of agglomeration can be calculated from the changes in the temperature, viscosity and Cunningham correction term (which is a complex function of pressure, temperature and viscosity effects on the mean free path of gas molecules) on the coagulation constant $\varkappa$, i.e. $(4CkT/3\mu)$ (where $S = 2$).

11.3. INCREASING AGGLOMERATION RATES BY STIRRING

The rate of particle agglomeration can be increased by stirring the gas to introduce turbulence, thus increasing the collision rate. For spherical particles, diameter d, in a fluid in laminar flow with a velocity gradient dy/dx normal to the streamlines, the rate of agglomeration is

$$-\frac{dc}{dt} = \frac{4}{3} d^3c^2 \frac{dy}{dx} \qquad (11.8)$$

When a cloud of particles is fanned, it has been shown that the losses are due to the combined effect of Brownian coagulation, and losses to the surfaces of the fan and the enclosing vessel,[172]

$$-\frac{dc}{dt} = \varkappa c^2 + \beta c = -\left(\frac{dc}{dt}\right)_c - \left(\frac{dc}{dt}\right)_l \qquad (11.9)$$

where β is a "loss constant", and the subscripts c and l stand for "coagulation" and "loss" terms.

Experimentally it has been shown that the value of $\varkappa$ varies about 50 per cent with time, but the values of β increase lineally with time. It is therefore necessary to determine these experimentally if it is intended to use the stirring of an aerosol as a method of agglomeration.

In general of course, the increasing rate of stirring not only increases turbulence, but presents new surfaces to the aerosol to which the particles can stick, and once there, form part of the surface. Since aerosol particles are removed each time they contact the blades of a fan, faster fan rotation will achieve a more rapid rate of removal.

A similar argument can be applied to passing a gas through a packed bed where the passages in the bed present a tortuous path to the gas, and so produce increased turbulence in the gas, as well as new surfaces, as the gas winds its way through.

11.4. ACCELERATED FLOCCULATION BY SOUND

Perhaps the most effective way of rapidly agglomerating particles and droplets to larger units, which are then capable of being collected by conventional mechanical collectors, such as cyclones, is by passing the cloud of particles or mist through a column in which the gas is subjected to standing sound waves. When a cloud in a narrow tube has low intensity sound waves passed through it, which give a simple standing wave pattern, the smoke first takes on a banded appearance, as the particles start to migrate to the antinodal regions. Flocculation then becomes visible, and the smoke appears granular. The flocs grow larger and collect on the walls, or become suspended at the antinodal planes, representing wafer-like layers, in some ways similar to the piles of dust formed at the antinode in the classical Kundt tube.[413]

The mechanism of sonic flocculation is not fully understood, but is probably a combination of three factors:[412]

(i) Co-vibration of the particles with the vibrating gas called orthokinetic coagulation.[66]
(ii) Sonic radiation pressure.[261]
(iii) Hydrodynamic attractive and repulsive forces between neighbouring particles.

Orthokinetic coagulation: When standing sound waves pass through a gas containing a cloud of particles, the particles, depending on their size and the frequency of vibration, may vibrate with the gas if the sound frequency is low, and tend to lag when the frequency is increased. When the frequency is very high, the larger particles remain almost stationary while the smaller ones follow the vibrations. An equation giving the degree of participation of a spherical particle in the gas vibrations was first deduced by König.[272]

$$\frac{u_g}{u_p} = \left[\frac{1 + 3b + 9b^2/2 + 9b^3/2 + 9b^4/4}{a^2 + 3ab + 9b^2/2 + 9b^3/2 + 9b^4/4} \right]^{1/2} \tag{11.10}$$

where u_g = velocity amplitude of the gas

u_p = velocity amplitude of the particle

a = $\frac{1}{3}(1 + 2\varrho_p/\varrho)$

b = $2/d.\sqrt{(\mu\tau/\varrho\pi)}$

ϱ_p = particle density, ϱ = gas density

τ = period of vibration.

This equation is not readily soluble, and a simpler one has been deduced by Brandt, Freund and Hiedemann[66] which has been shown to give virtually the same result.[414] This theory neglects the buoyancy effect of the gas on the particle, and it assumes that Stokes' law can be applied to the relative motion of the particle through the gas. This last assumption is justifiable when the particle Reynolds number is less than 0·2 (section 4.1). Appropriate particle velocities to which this can be applied in air are listed in Table 11.3.

TABLE 11.3. PARTICLE VELOCITIES AND CUNNINGHAM
CORRECTION FACTORS FOR PARTICLE Re = 0·2[66]

Particle diameter microns	Cunningham correction	Velocity in air at Re = 0·2 cm/sec
1	1·3	600
2	1·15	300
4	—	150
10	—	60

Because the velocity of an air segment at the antinode is about 250 cm/sec at frequencies of 10 kilocycles/sec, the assumption of Stokes' law is a reasonable one for particles smaller than 3 microns at this or lower frequencies. For higher frequencies the assumption can be justified for smaller particles.

The ratio of the amplitude of particle vibration X_p to the amplitude of vibration of the gas X_g, has been found[66] to be with the stated assumptions:

$$\frac{X_p}{X_g} = \frac{1}{\left\{\left[\dfrac{\pi d^2 v \varrho_p}{9\mu C}\right]^2 + 1\right\}^{1/2}} \tag{11.11}$$

where v = frequency

C = Cunningham correction.

For constant particle density (ϱ_p) and gas viscosity, $(\pi\varrho_p/9\mu)$ is a constant, and also the Cunningham correction can be considered approximately constant, so that (11.11) simplifies to

$$\frac{X_p}{X_g} \doteq \frac{1}{(kd^4 v^2 + 1)^{1/2}} \tag{11.12}$$

where $k = \pi\varrho_p/9\mu C$.

Equation (11.12) can also be deduced from König's formula (11.10) when certain restrictions are placed on it.[66]

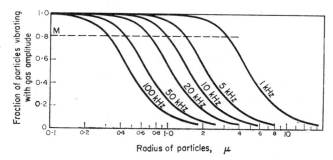

FIG. 11.1. Fraction of particles of unit density of various radii vibrating with gas at sound intensities between 1 and 100 kHz (kc/s) amplitude. The broken line at 0·8 (80%) indicates the size above which nearly all particles are considered to vibrate with the gas.[66]

For particles of unit density vibrating in air, the relative amplitude has been plotted (Fig. 11.1) for frequencies varying from 1–100 kilocycles/sec. For the highest frequencies (50 and 100 kilocycles/sec) the curves can only be taken as approximations, as the assumptions regarding the Stokes' law region no longer hold.

Figure 11.1 shows how, until a certain particle size, the aerosol particles swing along with the vibrations in the gas. This size can be called the critical particle size for the particular frequency, while a critical frequency for a particular particle size can be similarly calculated. The critical particle size is indicated by the point where the curves enter the steep gradient after their initial shallow decrease, which occurs at approximately the 80 per cent value for X_p/X_g, shown by the broken line in Fig. 11.1. Substituting 0·8 for X_p/X_g in equation (11.12) gives the critical particle diameter d_c as approximately

$$d_c^2 v \doteqdot 4 \times 10^{-4} \text{ cm}^2/\text{sec} \qquad (11.13)$$

or more generally, from equation (11.11)

$$\left[\frac{d_c^2 \varrho_p v}{C\mu} \right]_{\text{critical}} \doteqdot 2 \cdot 16 \qquad (11.14)$$

Equations (11.13) and (11.14) indicate that, as a first approximation, a unique relation exists between the critical particle size and the frequency of vibration of the gas, which for particles less than 7 microns occurs in the frequencies greater than 1 kilocycles/sec and extends into the ultrasonic region. These equations enable the critical frequency or particle sizes to be readily calculated.

From the movement of a particle it becomes possible to calculate the volume in which the particle will collide with other particles and coagulate with them (the aggregation zone). The amplitude of the gas vibration can be calculated from

$$X_g = \mathscr{A} \sin (2\pi a/\lambda) \qquad (11.15)$$

where $\mathscr{A}$ = amplitude at the antinode (maximum)

λ = wavelength

a = distance from the node

and substituting equation (11.15) in (11.11) gives

$$X_p = \frac{\mathscr{A} \sin (2\pi a/\lambda)}{\left\{ \left(\frac{\pi d^2 v \varrho_p}{9\mu c} \right)^2 + 1 \right\}^{1/2}} \qquad (11.16)$$

The volume swept by a vibrating particle can be calculated, neglecting the ends of the cylinder (Fig. 11.2a), as $\pi(d + d')^2 X_p/4$. The particle also moves towards the antinode owing to radiation pressure, and after time t, having moved distance L, will have a new amplitude X_p'. The swept volume during this period will be (Fig. 11.2b).

$$V_a = (X_p + X_p')(d + d') \left[L + \frac{\pi}{4} (d + d') \right] \qquad (11.17)$$

If the time has been sufficient to reach the antinode, the value of X_p will have reached the maximum possible:

$$X_{p_{\max}} = \frac{\mathscr{A}}{\left\{ \left(\frac{\pi d^2 v \varrho_p}{9\mu C} \right)^2 + 1 \right\}^{1/2}} \qquad (11.18)$$

and the swept volume will be

$$V_{a_{max}} = (X_p + X'_{p_{max}})(d + d') \left[\lambda - a + \frac{\pi}{4} (d + d') \right] \qquad (11.19)$$

The efficiency of flocculation can be calculated from the ratio V_a/V where V is the total volume of the chamber enclosing the cloud, basing the values of X_p on the critical particle size for the frequency of vibration.

The speed of the particle in moving towards the antinode can be estimated from a consideration of the *radiation pressure* of the vibrating gas.[261,414]

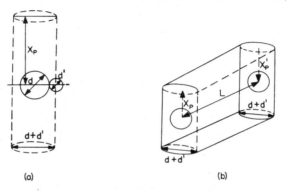

(a)   (b)

FIG. 11.2. (a) Volume swept by particle vibrating at one point.
(b) Total volume swept by vibrating particle as it approaches the antinode.

When the diameter of a sphere is small compared to the wavelength λ, then the force can be found approximately from

$$F_r = \frac{5}{12} \frac{\pi^2 d^3}{\lambda} \bar{E} \sin (2\pi a/\lambda) \qquad (11.20)$$

when F_r = radiation pressure (dynes)
$\bar{E}$ = energy intensity (ergs/cm³).

This will be a maximum when $a = \lambda/4$, i.e. half way between node and antinode and will be

$$F_{r_{max}} = \frac{5}{12} \frac{\pi d^3}{\lambda} \bar{E} \qquad (11.21)$$

This force will be opposed by the resistance of the gas, which is assumed to be in the Stokes' law region. The velocity of the particle towards the antinode is given by

$$\frac{dl}{dt} = F_{r_{max}} \frac{C \sin (2\pi a/\lambda)}{3\pi\mu d} \qquad (11.22)$$

which has been solved to give

$$l = \frac{\lambda C}{2\pi} \text{ artan } \left(\tan \frac{2\pi a}{\lambda} e^{Bt} \right) \tag{11.23}$$

where

$$B = \frac{5}{9} \frac{\pi^2 d^2 \overline{E}}{\lambda^2 \mu} \tag{11.23a}$$

At both the node and antinode the velocity due to radiation pressure is zero. An order of magnitude calculation can be done using $2\pi a/\lambda = \pi/6$ as the initial point and $2\pi a/\lambda = \pi/3$ as the final point; then $t = (\ln 3)/B$ and for a 2 micron particle at 20 °C in air, with a frequency of 10 kilocycles/sec, $t = 1{\cdot}07 \times 10^4/\overline{E}$. So if the energy intensity is approximately 1000 ergs/cm^3, then t is approximately 10 sec. Calculations showing the time taken for a particle to move to within a short distance (particle radius) of the antinode will indicate the desirable residence time for particles in the sonic field.

When spheres are at rest in a vibrating medium, they will attract one another when their line of centres is normal to the direction of the vibrations, and will repel one another if their line of centres is parallel to the vibrations. These *hydrodynamic forces* were used by König[272] to explain the stirations observed at antinodes in the Kundt tube.

For two spheres, diameters d and d', distance l apart from one another, the attractive force F_h along the connecting line at right angles to the direction of vibration is given by:

$$F_h = \frac{3\pi\varrho}{128} d^3 d'^3 \frac{(\Delta v)^2}{l^4} \tag{11.24}$$

where Δv is the relative velocity amplitude of the spheres. When the two particles are the same size ($d = d'$) equation (11.24) reduces to

$$F_h = \frac{3\pi\varrho}{128} \cdot d^6 \frac{(\Delta v)^2}{l^4} \tag{11.24a}$$

If the resistance of the gas opposing the particles coming together follows Stokes' law, the velocity of the spheres towards one another will be

$$\frac{dl}{dt} = \frac{128 \mu l^4}{\varrho d^5 (\Delta v)^2} \tag{11.25}$$

and the time taken for the particles to come from a distance l to touch one another (d) can be found by integrating (11.25).

$$t = \frac{(\Delta v)^2 \varrho}{384\mu} \left(d^2 - \frac{d^5}{l^3} \right) \tag{11.26}$$

Calculations[66] show that at low frequencies (up to about 50 kilocycles/sec) the hydrodynamic force between particles does not contribute markedly to their coagulation. However, at ultra high frequencies (of the order of several hundred kilocycles/sec), when orthokinetic flocculation is negligible, hydrodynamic forces become the major contributor to agglomeration.

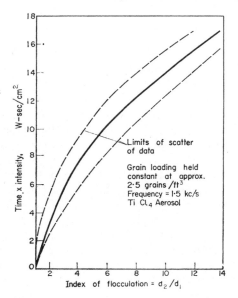

FIG. 11.3. Correlation of data on flocculation and sound intensity.[349]

The exact interrelation of these mechanisms of sonic agglomeration has not been found, but the above equations help to present an order of magnitude as to the effectiveness of sound waves of a certain frequency and intensity in agglomerating a cloud of particles or droplets.

The application of sound waves to aerosol collection depends on a number of factors:[63, 349] the sound frequency and intensity, the aerosol concentration and turbulence, and the exposure time. It has been shown (equations 11.13 and 11.14) how the vibration of particles depends on the sound frequency. A smoke or mist cloud contains a mixture of particle sizes, so in practice a wide range of frequencies greater than a few kilocycles/sec is suitable. In industrial plant the sound generators usually operate in the range 1–4 kilocycles/sec[114] because at higher frequencies it becomes more difficult to produce the required sound intensity. The acoustic power or sound intensity requirements of sonic agglomeration systems are very high. The threshold value for noticeable flocculation is 130–140 decibels (db) (130 db = 10^{-3} watt/cm^2) while values over 150 db are necessary for industrial plants.[349]

The particle concentration should not be less than 1–2 g/Nm³ for particles in the 1–10 micron range, and concentrations of 5 g/Nm³ have been found most suitable. When concentrations become very high (say 200 g/Nm³) sonic energy will be lost because of increasing attenuation of the sound in the aerosol.[114] In some cases it is helpful to add water mist to the aerosol.[63]* It has also been shown that turbulent flow introduced by the acoustic field enhances agglomeration.

The length of the exposure of the aerosol to the sound waves has been shown by the theory to have a significant effect on the degree of flocculation achieved. The index of agglomeration I, which is the ratio of the final to the initial mean particle diameters has been found experimentally to be a function of the product of exposure time and field intensity watts/cm² (Fig. 11.3). Industrial practice uses contact times of about 4 sec, which may be reduced to 2 sec when intensities greater than 165 db are used.[63]

Sound Generators. High powered sound waves can be produced by one of four methods:

(a) The vibration of piezoelectric crystals and ceramics (quartz, tourmaline or Rochelle salt, Barium titanate ceramics).
(b) The sound caused by the vibration of a cylinder.
(c) Whistles (static generators).
(d) Sirens (dynamic generators).

The first two types of sound generators are largely for laboratory use. Piezoelectric crystals are used for high frequency sounds, but will not produce the high sound intensities required for plant-size generators. The sound waves generated by a vibrating metal rod were used in the classical Kundt tube, and these two devices for producing intense high frequency sound can be useful, particularly on a limited scale.

An electromagnetic sound generator described by St. Clair[411] (Fig. 11.4a) consists of a solid duralium cylinder with a supporting web and a driving ring machined from the same piece. The driving ring projects into the radial gap of a pot magnet, and acts as a one turn secondary of a transformer, of which the primary is the field coil of the magnet. An input of 200 watt into the coil from an amplifier produced a high intensity sound of 10–20 kilocycles/sec.

A second vibrating rod type generator is the air driven stem jet whistle (Fig. 11.4b) which consists of a cylindrical rod in the axis of a nozzle resonator system. This device will produce high intensity sound levels (160 db) and frequencies between 9 and 15 kilocycles/sec with low nozzle pressures (30 lb/in.²).

Whistles fall into two main categories. In the first an air jet impinges on a resonating cavity, while in the second the air is introduced tangentially

* See also J. Olaf, *Staub*, **22**, 513 (1962).

into a circular tube, creating a vortex and then escaping axially, producing a loud sound.

The original impingement jet type whistles were developed by Galton (1883), and later modified by Hartmann, and are usually called Hartmann whistles (Fig. 11.4c). They have been used for frequencies from 10 to 100 kilocycles/sec, and in their original (Hartmann) form have efficiency of about 4 per cent. The dimensions suggested by Hartmann were to have

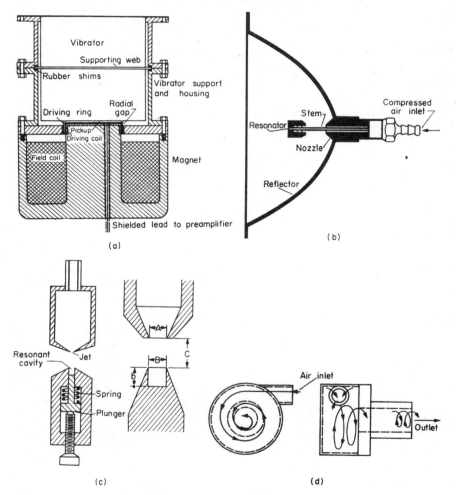

FIG. 11.4. Sound generators (other than sirens).
(a) Electromagnetic sound generator.[411]
(b) Stem jet whistle.[63]
(c) Hartmann whistle.[63]
(d) Vortex whistle.[63]

the same jet diameter A as opening diameter B and depth of resonating cavity b.

The intensity of sound $\mathscr{I}_0$ from a Hartmann whistle can be calculated from[197]

$$\mathscr{I}_0 = 3 \cdot 0 B^2 \sqrt{(P - 0 \cdot 9)} \text{ watt} \qquad (11.27)$$

where B = 2–6 mm

P = gauge pressure = 2·07–3·44 atm

$A = B = b$ in all cases.

A modified Hartmann whistle[62] with efficiencies twice that of the original pattern has been made by increasing the relative width of the resonating aperture to a diameter more than 30 per cent greater than the jet width $(B/A \geq 1 \cdot 3)$. In addition, placing the nozzle in a secondary resonance chamber has increased the overall efficiency of the whistles up to 20 per cent.

Vortex whistles (Fig. 11.4d) have been studied by Vonnegut[507, 508] who gave the following approximate formula for the frequency of the emitted sound.

$$\nu = \alpha \left(\frac{U_s}{\pi D} \right) \sqrt{\left(\frac{P_1 - P_2}{P_2} \right)} \qquad (11.28)$$

where α = constant (< 1) which accounts for friction losses

U_s = velocity of sound

D = tube diameter

P_1 = inlet pressure

P_2 = exhaust pressure.

Frequencies obtained experimentally with the vortex whistle were about 15 kilocycles/sec.

Dynamic sound generators (sirens) have higher efficiencies of energy conversion into sound energy from other forms of energy than other types of sound generators. In the form used industrially, particularly in the United States, the siren was developed by Allen and Rudnik[10] (Fig. 11.5a). It consists essentially of a high speed rotor, which has ports in the annulus with matching ports in a stator, which interrupt the flow of a gas (usually air) through the stator ports.

In Allen and Rudnik's original design, the rotor had 100 ports evenly spaced around a 6 in. disc, and the adjacent rotor and stator surfaces were very closely fitted. The rotor speed was 8000–20,000 rev/min. The conversion efficiency in the Allen–Rudnik pattern was 17–34 per cent, with frequencies of 3–19 kilocycles/sec and power outputs between 80 and 176 watts.

More recent designs use rotor speeds up to 50,000 rev/min and efficiencies up to 50 per cent have been reported. If a comparatively pure sound is required, the stator ports should be circular and the rotor ports rectangular.

The major problem with sirens is the maintenance of the high speed rotor. Deposits on the rotor produce poor balance, bearings tend to overheat, and the frequency of the sound cannot be varied except by changing the number of openings, or by changing the rotor speed. Recent developments[324] have led to a modified siren, which has intensities as high as 170 db in the zone close to the siren, and is coupled directly to a centrifugal extraction fan which removes the agglomerates (Fig. 11.5b).

For sirens the sound intensity $\mathscr{I}_0$ can be found from[324]

$$\mathscr{I}_0 = \frac{\varrho U_s}{2} (2\pi v \mathscr{A})^2 \qquad (11.29)$$

$\mathscr{A}$ = amplitude of vibrations.

A number of design equations for sonic agglomerating systems have been suggested by Inoue and agree satisfactorily with experiment.[63] The average sound intensity in the agglomeration chamber, $\mathscr{I}$, can be found from

$$\mathscr{I} = \beta \mathscr{I}_0 / \text{cross-sectional area of chamber} \qquad (11.29\,\text{a})$$

$$= \frac{4\beta \mathscr{I}_0}{\pi D^2} \text{ (for cylindrical chamber with diameter } D)$$

where β is a constant characteristic for the plant so that $0 \cdot 07 < \beta \eta_A < 0 \cdot 16$ where η_A is the acoustic efficiency of the generator. Boucher[63] has suggested that $\eta_A \beta$ is closer to $0 \cdot 07$ than $0 \cdot 16$.

The index of agglomeration I can be found from

$$I = \exp \frac{t}{3} \sqrt{\left(\frac{4\beta \mathscr{I}_0}{\pi D^2}\right)} \qquad (11.30)$$

where t is the contact time (sec).

The ideal tower height H (cm) for the agglomerator can be estimated from

$$H = 3v \ln I \sqrt{\left(\frac{\pi D^2}{4\beta \mathscr{I}_0}\right)} \text{ cm} \qquad (11.31)$$

where v = mean linear velocity of aerosol (cm/sec) (usually about 100 cm/sec).

The design of a sonic agglomeration plant is extremely simple. The source of the high intensity sound is placed at one end of an agglomeration chamber through which the gases to be cleaned are passed, and the agglomerated particles or droplets are then collected by a cyclone. Two typical arrangements are shown in Fig. 11.6. In the first arrangement, the gases

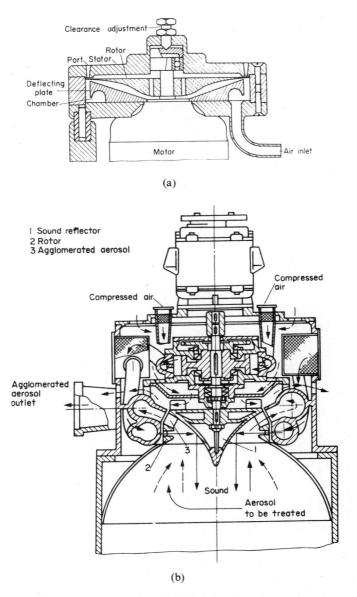

(a)

(b)

FIG. 11.5. Sound generators (sirens).
(a) Allen–Rudnik siren.[10]
(b) C.I.O.P. siren.[63]

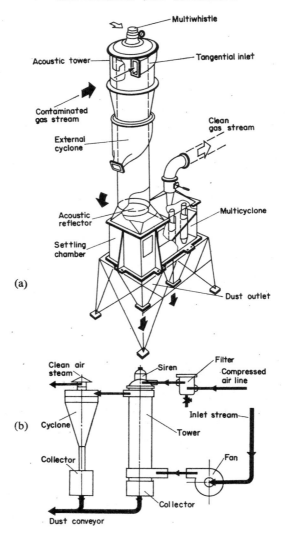

Fig. 11.6. Arrangement of sonic agglomeration–collection systems:
(a) Gases move away from source of sound.[63]
(b) Gases move towards source of sound.[63]

move towards the source of the sound, while in the second, after passing
through a preliminary cyclone, the gases move away from the sound.

Gas velocities of 100 cm/sec (3·3 ft/sec) have been suggested as suitable,
and from this velocity the tower diameter required to handle the gas volume
can be found.

Sonic agglomeration has been used successfully on a number of difficult collection problems.

Sulphuric acid mist[114] has been agglomerated successfully, and inlet concentrations of 3·5 g/Nm³ have been reduced to exhaust concentrations varying between 0·14 and 0·018 g/Nm³, i.e. efficiencies of 96–99·5 per cent, depending on the mist residence time between 0·6 and 3·0 sec (see Fig. 11.7).[114] The plant consisted of a long column where the gases were exposed to the sound waves, followed by multicyclones.[352]

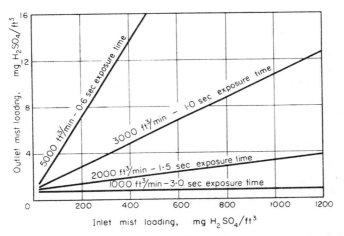

FIG. 11.7. Effect of inlet mist loading and exposure time to sound on the outlet mist loading in a plant collecting sulphuric acid mist.[114]

Carbon Black[470] has been successfully agglomerated in a sound field of 155 db with a frequency of 3–4 kilocycles/sec. When the concentration of the carbon black was 8–10 g/Nm³, and the residence time 4½ sec, and an efficiency of 82 per cent was achieved. When the concentration was less than 5 g/Nm³ the efficiency decreased. The introduction of a water mist improved collection at low concentrations.

Sonic agglomeration has been tried on fume collection for several metallurgical operations:[63] ferro-alloy furnaces,[234] ferro-manganese blast furnace gas,[73] zinc oxide fumes from copper recovery furnaces[63] (average efficiency 78 per cent) and lead oxide fumes (95–98 per cent efficiency, with 15 kilocycles/sec siren).

The operating and maintenance costs of sonic agglomeration–collection systems are rather high, although installation costs tend to be about 15 per cent lower than for electrostatic precipitators of similar capacity.[424] The efficiency of sonic agglomeration is virtually independent of temperature, and the technique could find application in high temperature precipitation. When the fumes are corrosive it is easily possible to construct the agglomerator shell from corrosion resistant materials, while a sound whistle can be very robust. Thus sonic agglomeration is applicable when highly corrosive conditions are likely to occur. Further improvements in sound generation efficiency may lead to considerable industrial applications of sonic agglomeration techniques.

11.5. COLLECTION BY BEDS
OF FLUIDIZED SOLIDS

The use of fluidized beds, where solid particles are held in turbulent suspension in a gas stream, would appear an obvious application for particle and mist collection, because the turbulent movement of the particles in the bed tends to favour agglomeration and impaction of the droplets with the particles in the bed. However, only a limited amount of experimental work has been carried out.[337,427] This has indicated that efficiencies over 90 per cent would not be obtained and so the equipment would be inadequate for commercial plant.

The experimental studies covered the collection of sulphuric acid mist droplets, 2–14 microns dia., with fluid beds of glass beads, silica (both non porous), alumina and silica gel (both porous); dioctyl phthalate droplets, essentially 0·6–1·1 microns dia. with fluid beds of alumina; and ammonium nitrate dust, 0·25–2·5 microns dia., with fluid beds of glass beads.

It was found in all cases that the collection efficiency was independent of the inlet concentration. As would be expected, for the larger droplets (2 to 14 microns) inertial impaction appeared to be the predominant collection mechanism, efficiency improving with increasing superficial gas velocity. For the smaller dioctyl phthalate droplets, diffusion collection predominated, as was shown by the opposite trend of a decreasing efficiency with increasing superficial gas velocity. The work with ammonium nitrate was very limited and no definite trends were discerned.

For particles in the micron ranges (averaging 8 microns) Meissner and Mickley[337] found that an empirical equation of the form

$$-\ln c_2/c_1 = 0 \cdot 142 u_s W^n \qquad (11.32)$$

where c_1 = inlet concentration (lbs/10^6 ft^3)

c_2 = outlet concentration (lbs/10^6 ft^3)

u_s = superficial gas velocity (ft/sec)

W = Wt. of bed per unit cross-sectional area (lbs/ft^2)

n = empirical constant (0·16–0·34)

could be fitted to their limited experimental data. Here the exponent n was specific for the bed particle mixture.

For sub-micron sized particles, the limited work indicated that an equation of the form

$$-\ln c_2/c_1 \propto u_s^{0.78} \tag{11.33}$$

could be fitted to the experiments[427] but no bed weight effect was noticed, and other empirical constants were not suggested, although collection efficiencies close to 90 per cent were found in some runs.

11.6. THERMAL PRECIPITATION

The force that drives particles away from hotter towards colder regions was observed first by Tyndall[499] and later by Lord Rayleigh[389] as the dust free region or "dark space" which surrounds a hot body placed in a smoke cloud. Aitken[3] was able to show that this dust free space extended completely around the hot body and was caused neither by gravity, evaporation from the surface, electrostatic forces nor centrifugal forces, but by a purely thermal force which exists in regions of unequal temperature, driving particles away from hot and towards cold surfaces.

The reason for the thermal force is partially explained by the theories that have been put forward to predict the magnitude of the force, and seems to depend on whether the particle is considerably smaller or larger than the mean free path of the gas molecules.

When the particles are smaller than the mean free path (λ) of the gas molecules, the suggested relation by Einstein[133] and Cawood,[90] which was later modified by Waldmann,[510] appears to agree reasonably well with experimental findings. The equation is based on the thermal force being applied by the translational motion of the gas molecules which are conducting the heat from the hot to the cold region, and which tend to bombard the side of the particle facing the hot region with greater force than the side facing the cold.

Einstein,[133] and later Cawood[90] deduced the thermal force on the small particle as the resultant force of the differential bombardment by the gas molecules, using the kinetic theory of gases. This gave:

$$F_t = -\frac{1}{2} \lambda P \frac{\pi d^2}{4} \cdot \frac{dT}{dx} \tag{11.34}$$

where P = gas pressure

λ = mean free path of gas molecules

$\dfrac{dT}{dx}$ = thermal gradient in the gas ($\Delta T/\Delta x$)

ΔT = temperature fall through distance Δx

and the negative sign indicates that the force is in the opposite direction to the rise in temperature.

Substituting equations (3.3) and (4.21a) for λ in equation (11.34) gives:

$$F_t = -\frac{\pi}{8} \frac{P\mu d^2}{\varrho} \Big/ \!\sqrt{\left(\frac{\pi M}{2RT}\right)} \cdot \frac{dT}{dx} \qquad (11.35)$$

A more sophisticated calculation with the same basic ideas by Waldmann[510] which introduces the translational part of the thermal conductivity of the gas $\varkappa_{g_{tr}}$ gives:

$$F_t = -\frac{4}{15} d^2 \varkappa_{g_{tr}} \Big/ \!\sqrt{\left(\frac{\pi M}{2RT}\right)} \cdot \frac{dT}{dx} \qquad (11.36)$$

where $\varkappa_{g_{tr}} = 2 \cdot 5 c_v \mu$

$\qquad\qquad = (15/4)(R/M)\mu$ (Eucken's Theory)

c_v = specific heat at constant volume.

Substituting (11.37) in (11.36):

$$F_t = -d^2\mu \Big/ \!\sqrt{\left(\frac{\pi R}{2MT}\right)} \cdot \frac{dT}{dx} \qquad (11.38)$$

The resistance by the gas to the movement of these small particles can be found from Epstein's equation[140] for fluid resistance

$$F = \frac{4}{3} \pi d^2 P \Big/ \!\sqrt{\left(\frac{M}{2\pi RT}\right)} \cdot \left(1 + \frac{\pi}{8} a\right) u \qquad (11.39)$$

where u = velocity of particle

$\quad\ a$ = coefficient of diffuse reflection (Millikan) or accommodation constant (Epstein)

when $a = 0$, all collisions are perfectly elastic

when $a = 1$, all collisions are diffuse.

Experimentally it has been found that "a" can be taken as 0·81.[420]

From equations (11.38) and (11.39) it was deduced by Waldmann[510] that the speed of very small particles in a thermal gradient is

$$u_t = -\frac{1}{5\left(1 + \dfrac{\pi}{8} a\right)} \frac{\varkappa_{g_{tr}}}{P} \cdot \frac{dT}{dx} \qquad (11.40)$$

This equation is similar to that by Einstein, with the assumption that the coefficient of diffuse reflection is zero and the constant $\frac{1}{5}$ is substituted by $\frac{1}{4}$. It has been shown[420] that for particles smaller than $\frac{1}{35}$ of the mean free path (i.e. $< \lambda/35$) with the coefficient of diffuse reflection taken as 0·8 to 1, equation (11.40) agrees well with experimental values (Fig. 11.8), while for particles of the size of λ, Epstein's equation is more applicable.

For particles of the size order of the mean free path λ or larger, the *thermal creep* theory of thermal precipitation can be used. This is based on the force set up at the gas–solid interface between a particle and the surrounding gas. When the gas temperature increases along the surface, the

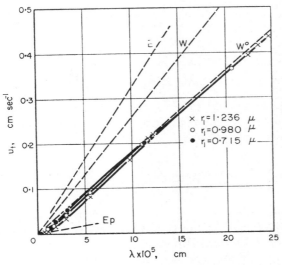

FIG. 11.8. Dependence of velocity of particle in thermal gradient on the mean free path of molecules. The experimental results of Schmitt are compared to the theories of Einstein, Epstein and Waldmann.[420]

$\left.\begin{array}{l}\times\\\bullet\\\bullet\end{array}\right\}$ Schmitt's experimental results – particles in argon.

E = Einstein's equation.
E_p = Epstein's equation (eqn. 11.42).

W = Waldmann's equation ($a = 0$) (eqn. 11.40).
W^0 = Waldmann's equation ($a = 1$) (eqn. 11.40).

molecules leaving the surface will have a greater component of velocity in the direction of the temperature increase than when they arrived at the surface. The net result is a creeping flow of gas from the colder to the warmer regions along the surface of the particle. In turn the surface experiences a force in the cold direction. Epstein[141] assumed the following in his derivation:

(a) The particle was large compared to the mean free path of the gas molecules.

(b) At a great distance from the particle the temperature gradient in the gas is uniform.

(c) Fourrier's equation for heat conduction without convection could be used, although this state did not exist because of the thermal creep.

Epstein then obtained an equation for the thermal force by considering the heat conduction problem, the equation for thermal creep and the equations of motion of the particle, neglecting the inertia terms, but using the creep velocity as the boundary conditions. The thermal force was then derived as the integral over the surface of the component of stress parallel to the direction of heat flow.

This gave

$$F_t = -\frac{9\pi d\mu^2}{2\varrho T(2 + \varkappa_g/\varkappa_p)} \frac{dT}{dx} \tag{11.41}$$

where $\varkappa_g$ = thermal conductivity of the gas

$\varkappa_p$ = thermal conductivity of the particle.

The resistance of the gas to the movement of the particle is given by Stokes' law (equation 4.22) including the Cunningham correction.

Then the velocity of the particle in the thermal gradient may be found from

$$u_t = -\frac{3C\mu}{2\varrho T(2 + \varkappa_g/\varkappa_p)} \cdot \frac{dT}{dx} \tag{11.42}$$

Einstein[133] also deduced an equation for large particles by substituting the product of the circumference of the particle by the mean free path for the area of the small particle. However, it has been shown that this modification gives only one third of the thermal force predicted by (11.42) (in which $\varkappa_g$ is made much smaller than $\varkappa_p$ to get equivalent equations).[405]

Good agreement was obtained between the particle velocity in a thermal gradient, calculated from Epstein's equation (11.42), and experimental velocities measured by a number of workers for tricresylphosphate,[405] paraffin oil, castor oil,[415] and stearic acid droplets.[417] The width of the dust free space which was accurately measured by Watson[517] for magnesium oxide smoke around a copper wire has also been calculated with reasonable precision[553] by combining the air velocity due to the convection currents with the thermal force velocity from Epstein's equation.

The particles for which good agreement has been obtained between experiment and theory all had low thermal conductivities (of the order of 10^{-4} cal/(cm.sec°K)), which is not so much different from that of air. For particles of sodium chloride and particularly iron[417] the agreement was much less, these particles being attracted to the cold surface by a force of 30 and 48 times the predicted value. It appears therefore that the theoretical relations presented, although reasonably successful for poor conductors, will give a conservative estimate of the force on the particles when these are good conductors.

The practical application of thermal precipitation to gas cleaning plant has only rarely been attempted. Blacktin experimented with the effect of drawing dirty gases through a heated gauze which repelled the particles originally in the gas. When the gauze was heated to 85 °C, efficiencies averaging 94 per cent (maximum 98 per cent) on a particle count basis, were obtained with gas velocities equivalent to 46·7 ft³/(ft²) (min) through the gauze surface.[52, 53]

Another patent suggests that the purification of air be carried out by passing it through the narrow channels between the hot and cold fins in a

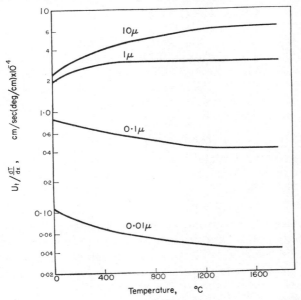

FIG. 11.9. Temperature dependence of thermal forces (calculated).[475]
(0.01 to 10 micron particles)

duct, the fins being attached to separate heating and cooling elements. The dust is subjected to a sharp temperature gradient and deposits on the cold fins.[440]

It has also been suggested that thermal precipitation may play a part in the deposition of particles from a hot gas when this is passed through a cold packed bed. The passages in the bed are narrow and so even a temperature difference of 50 °C may give rise to a temperature gradient of 1000 °C/cm in the passages. Calculations show that this would result in deposition of 98·8 per cent of the particles of 0·1 microns in a 9 in. deep bed at 500 °C.[473]

In such a system the temperature dependence of the thermal force is of considerable importance. This has not yet been investigated experimentally. However, it is possible to calculate this effect by determining the change in the ratio of the terminal velocity and the temperature gradient $u_t/(dT/dx)$

with the temperature, using Epstein's equation (11.42).[475] This shows (Fig. 11.9) that when particles are greater than 1 micron, the thermal precipitation velocity increases with temperature, while for particles smaller than 1 micron, it decreases with increasing temperature, independently of the thermal gradient.

11.7. SEPARATION OF PARTICLES IN A MAGNETIC FIELD

If a particle with no intrinsic magnetic properties is charged to a charge q by bombardment charging (equation 10.29) or ion diffusion charging (10.35), and is then introduced into the field of a magnet (field strength, $\mathbf{H}$ oersted), it will be acted on by a force at right angles to both the direction of the field and its direction of motion, and so will be diverted from its original path. The equation for the particle in a vacuum is:

$$\mathbf{H}qeu = mu^2/R$$

where m = mass of the particle
$\quad e$ = electronic charge
$\quad u$ = particle velocity
$\quad R$ = radius of circular path.

Consider the case when the particle, moving with the gas at a velocity u_g is given a velocity component at right angles to the gas stream equal to the terminal drift velocity, while passing through the field of a narrow magnet. The terminal drift velocity may be obtained by equating the magnetic force to the resistance of the gas, calculated from the Stokes–Cunningham law:

$$u_t = \frac{C\mathbf{H}qeu_g}{3\pi\mu d} \tag{11.43}$$

Here u_t is a function of u_g and higher gas velocities would favour higher particle velocities out of the gas stream. To the author's knowledge this phenomenon has not yet been utilized for gas cleaning plant.

If small magnetic particles were introduced into a magnetic field a different case would exist. As the particles are free to rotate, it may be assumed that they will align themselves in the magnetic field, their opposite ends being attracted to the two poles of the magnet. The net force on the particle in any particular position can be calculated by the algebraic addition of the attractive and repulsive forces. If the particle is midstream between the two poles, the forces will cancel out, and the particle will move straight through. Detailed calculation of the path of a particle and whether or not it will be collected would require a knowledge of the magnetic field distribution, the geometric configuration of the magnet and of the gas flow pattern.

APPENDIXES

I. EXAMPLE OF CALCULATION OF GAS FLOW RATE FROM FUEL CONSUMPTION AND COMPOSITION

A boiler is to produce 200,000 lb/hr of steam at 1600 lb/in². abs. and 900 °F from water at 68 °F. An efficiency of around 83 per cent can be expected. The fuel is coal of a gross calorific value of 13,040 B.t.u./lb and an ultimate analysis of 74 per cent carbon, 4·5 per cent hydrogen, 6·5 per cent oxygen, negligible nitrogen and sulphur, 7 per cent ash and 8 per cent moisture. The air supply will have an average temperature of 70 °F and an average relative humidity of 65 per cent. An excess air consumption of 50 per cent may be assumed. The flue gases will leave at 420 °F. What is the flow rate of flue gases to the gas cleaning device?

From steam tables, we get the following enthalpies,

Feed water at 68 °F	36·0 B.t.u./lb
Superheated steam at 1600 lb/in.² abs., 900 °F	1425·3 B.t.u./lb
∴ Enthalpy added	1389·3 B.t.u./lb

Assuming efficiency is based upon gross calorific value of fuel,
∴ Fuel consumption,

$$= 200,000 \times 1389 \cdot 3 \times \frac{100}{83} \times \frac{1}{13,040}$$

$$= 25,675 \text{ lb/hr} = 7 \cdot 132 \text{ lb/sec}$$

Assume complete combustion of the coal,

Basis: 100 lb of coal as fired.

Carbon in = 74 lb $= \dfrac{74}{12} = 6 \cdot 17$ lb moles

Hydrogen in = 4·5 lb $= \dfrac{4 \cdot 5}{2} = 2 \cdot 25$ lb moles

Oxygen in   = 6·5 lb $= \dfrac{6 \cdot 5}{32} = 0 \cdot 20$ lb moles

∴ Theoretical oxygen $= 6 \cdot 17 + \frac{1}{2}(2 \cdot 25) - 0 \cdot 20 = 7 \cdot 1$ lb moles

∴ Actual oxygen $= 7 \cdot 1 \times \dfrac{150}{100} = 10 \cdot 65$ lb moles

423

∴ Nitrogen in with air,

$$= 10.65 \times \frac{79}{21} = 40.06 \text{ lb moles}$$

∴ Flue gas will consist of,

(i) Carbon dioxide = 6.17 lb moles
(ii) Oxygen = 3.55 lb moles
(iii) Nitrogen = 40.06 lb moles
(iv) Water

    (a) from moisture in coal

$$= 8 \text{ lb} = \frac{8}{18} = 0.44 \text{ lb moles}$$

    (b) from combustion of hydrogen = 2.25 lb moles
    (c) in with combustion air.
        From a psychrometric chart, absolute humidity of air
        = 0.01 lb Water/lb dry air.

$$= 0.01 \times \frac{29}{18} = 0.016 \text{ moles Water/mole dry air}$$

∴ Water in = (0.016) (10.65 + 40.06) = 0.81 lb moles
∴ Total Water in flue gases = 3.5 lb moles
∴ Total flue gas,

$$= 6.17 + 3.55 + 40.06 + 3.5$$

$$= 53.28 \text{ lb moles/100 lb of coal}$$

$$= \frac{53.28}{100} \times 7.132 = 3.80 \text{ lb moles/sec}$$

Assuming that gases are at 1 atm pressure, Volume flow rate,

$$= 3.80 \times 359 \times \frac{880}{492}$$

$$= 2443 \text{ ft}^3/\text{sec}$$

$$= 146,000 \text{ ft}^3/\text{min.}$$

II. EXAMPLE OF SUCTION PYROMETER CALCULATION

Find the gas temperature using a suction pyrometer with a double shield finned head. The refractory material of the head has a thermal conductivity of 0.015 cal/(°C) (cm) (sec), a wall thickness of 3 mm and an emissivity of about 0.4 at 1600 °C. The gases, when aspirated past the couple with a velocity of 300 ft/sec, give a temperature reading of 1635 °C, at zero velocity, of 1453 °C and at 75 ft/sec of 1562 °C.

Method 1

The ratio $w/\varkappa = 0\cdot30/0\cdot015 = 20$
From Table 2.6, at about $1600\,°C$,
$$f = 0\cdot7$$

From Table 2.7, with Emissivity $= 0\cdot4, f = 0\cdot7$
Effective number of simple metallic shields per refractory shield (without fin allowance)
$$= 2\cdot1$$

Fin allowance $= 1\cdot4$

$\therefore$ Equivalent total number $= 2\cdot1 \times 1\cdot4 \times 2$
$$= 5\cdot9$$

The aspiration velocity of 300 ft/sec, gives, from Table 2·3, an equivalent number of shields at 500 ft/sec.
No. of equivalent shields (500 ft/sec) $= 0\cdot82$
$\therefore$ Total equivalent (500 ft/sec) $= 5\cdot9 \times 0\cdot82 = 4\cdot8$
From Table 2.2, efficiency of pyrometer $= 81\%$
$\therefore$ Actual gas temperature $= 1453 + (1635 - 1453)/0\cdot81$
$$= 1678\,°C$$

Method 2

An approximate gas temperature can be found by first calculating the shape factor:
$$\text{Shape factor} = \frac{T_{max} - T_0}{T_{max} - T_{1/4}} = \frac{1635 - 1453}{1635 - 1562} = 2\cdot5$$

From Table 2.8, efficiency $= 80\%$.
Actual gas temperature $= 1453 + (1635 - 1453)/0\cdot80$
$$= 1681\,°C$$

III. METHODS OF EXPRESSING THE EFFICIENCY OF COLLECTION

1. *Gravimetric efficiency*

This is the efficiency of collection based on weight collected compared to the total passing through the system. It is usually expressed as a percentage.
$$\eta_T = \frac{\text{wt. of material collected}}{\text{total weight entering system}} \times 100 \text{ per cent}$$

This is the most common method used, and it is the easiest determined in practice.

2. *Fractional efficiency*

The variation of efficiency with particle size of a particle collection system is best expressed in the form of a fractional efficiency curve (sometimes called a grade efficiency curve). The abscissa is used for particle size and the ordinate for the efficiency of collection. A collector, under specific conditions of gas flow rate, temperature, particle composition and distribution will have a specific efficiency at each size.

A fractional efficiency curve is set up by considering the efficiency in a series of narrow ranges of the particle size spectrum. This can be obtained by analysing for particle size distribution the original dust and the dust collected. From this data the efficiency in each size range (say 0–5, 5–10 microns, etc.) can be found from

$$\eta_i = \frac{\text{fraction in range ``}i\text{'' collected}}{\text{quantity in range ``}i\text{'' entering system}} \times 100 \text{ per cent}$$

if m_i = quantity in range "i" entering the collection system

M = total quantity of dust entering system

The gravimetric efficiency for the system can then be deduced from the fractional efficiency data[495]

$$\eta_T = \frac{\sum_{i=1}^{n} m_i \eta_i}{M} \text{ per cent}$$

where n = number of size fractions in the sample.

The construction of a fractional efficiency curve is shown in Fig. A.3.1.

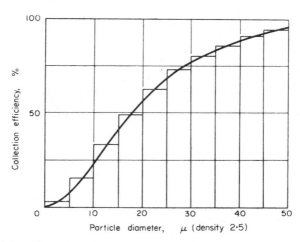

FIG. A.3.1. Construction of fractional efficiency curve from fractions collected in each size range.

Fractional efficiency curves are generally related to particles with a specific density. If it is necessary to obtain a fractional efficiency curve for particles with a different density, points on the curve have to be multiplied by the ratio $\sqrt{(\varrho_n/\varrho_0)}$, where ϱ_n is the new density, ϱ_0 the original density, in the case of cyclones, fibre filters, scrubbers or other devices where inertial impaction is the predominant collection mechanism; or ϱ_n/ϱ_0 for settling chambers and electrostatic precipitators.

The abscissa of a fractional efficiency curve is sometimes shown in terms of falling speeds of particles of stated density instead of particle size. This is very useful as it can be obtained directly from a particle size analysis based on aero- or hydrodynamic properties of the particles, and avoids the problems connected with non-spherical particles, where equivalent diameters have to be used. (See Chapter 4.)

3. Number fraction efficiency

Efficiency based on numbers of particles η_N

$$\eta_N = \frac{\text{no. of particles collected}}{\text{total number of particles entering collector}} \times 100 \text{ per cent}$$

4. Surface area efficiency[404]

Based on the surface area of particles. This is of great importance when obscuration is used as a measure of collection efficiency.

$$\eta_A = \frac{\text{surface area of particles collected}}{\text{total surface area of particles entering collector}}$$

5. Penetration P

This is the inverse of the efficiency of collection η_T. The penetration, in per cent, is given by

$$P = 100 - \eta_T.$$

6. Decontamination factor D.F.

This is a logarithmic scale of measuring efficiency

$$D.F. = [1 - \eta_T/100]^{-1}$$

The logarithm to the base 10 of the D.F. is known as the *decontamination index*.

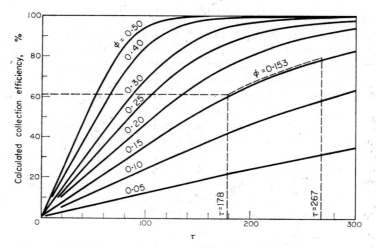

FIG. A 4.1. Efficiency of electrostatic precipitator with allowance for eddy
diffusion.[544]

Equation (10.56a) $\quad \tau = \left[4(N + 1)^2 \dfrac{D}{v_{av}L} \right] \dfrac{x}{L} \doteq 7{\cdot}41 \dfrac{x}{L}$

Equation (10.56b) $\quad \varphi = \left[2(N + 1) \dfrac{D}{v_{av}L} \right] \dfrac{w'}{v_{av}} \doteq 5{\cdot}67 \dfrac{w'}{v_{av}}$

($D/v_{av}L = 0{\cdot}0035$ and $(N = 20)$)

IV. CALCULATION OF EFFICIENCY OF ELECTROSTATIC PRECIPITATORS WITH EDDY DIFFUSION ALLOWANCE

The method suggested by Williams and Jackson[544] (discussed on page 359) can be used as follows. Two dimensionless parameters, representing a distance function (τ) and a velocity function (φ) are calculated, and the efficiency can then be obtained from Fig. A.4.1. The functions can be found from:

$$\tau = 7{\cdot}41 \frac{x}{L}$$

where x = path length in precipitator

L = distance between wire and plate (plate-type precipitator) or wire and tube (tube-type precipitator)

$$\varphi = 5{\cdot}67 \frac{\omega'}{v_{av}}$$

where ω' = apparent drift velocity

v_{av} = stream velocity.

The apparent drift velocity is best determined from test results for a precipitator with similar dimensions, and stream velocity. If this is not available, then the former can be estimated from measured efficiencies at various gas velocities.

The following problem given by Williams and Jackson illustrates this.

Problem. A parallel-plate precipitator with gas passages 12 ft long, having a wire to plate distance of 6 in., is found to have collection efficiencies of 61, 49, 40 and 35 per cent for gas stream velocities of 3, 4, 5 and 6 ft/sec, respectively. What would be the effect of increasing the length of the gas passages to 15 ft and reducing the wire to plate distance to 5 in., keeping the other operating conditions constant?

Solution. The parameter τ for the 12 ft long precipitator ($x = 12$) with wire to plate distance 6 in. ($L = 0.5$) is:

$$\tau = \frac{7.41 \times 12}{0.5} = 178.$$

From a vertical line drawn at $\tau = 178$ the values of φ for the given collection efficiencies are found to be 0.153, 0.118, 0.0970, 0.0825. If the precipitator dimensions are altered to $x = 15$ ft and $L = 0.417$ ft, then $\tau = 267$, and the new efficiencies, for the same values of φ, are then 80, 67, 57 and 50 per cent. This is summarized in the following table:

Stream Velocity ft/sec	Efficiency % $\tau = 178$	φ	Efficiency % $\tau = 267$
3	61	0.153	80
4	49	0.118	67
5	40	0.0970	57
6	35	0.0825	50

V. DESIGN OF HOODS AND PIPELINES

For containing and extracting gases, fumes and ducts from processes, hoods of various types are required. The design of the hood and accompanying ductwork is a function of the type of process, the size of the plant and its situation in relation to the gas cleaning plant. Details of design of hoods and ducts are discussed elsewhere, and only a brief outline of major features is given here.

The hood should enclose the process as fully as possible compatible with plant operation, reducing the amount of air that is drawn in to a minimum, and in turn, minimizing the quantity of gas to be treated subsequently in the cleaning plant. In the case of an electric furnace, total enclosure is of ̇ ̇ ̇

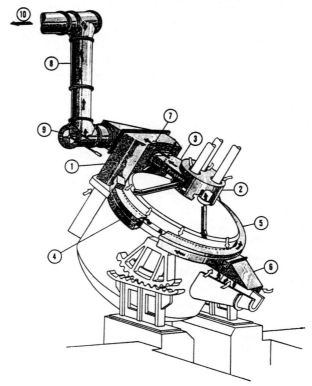

FIG. A.5.1. Total enclosure hood for arc furnace (frequent tilting).[360]

1. Distribution section and slag door hood.
2. Electrode hood and support arms (fastens to roof frame and moves with roof).
3. Connecting duct.
4. Manifold ring.
5. Manifold ring baffle.
6. Pouring spout hood.
7. Adjustable spring loaded damper.
8. Telescoping and swivel connection to exhaust system for continuous ventilation during furnace tilt.
9. Tempering damper.
10. Ducto dust collector.

feasible with a hood of the type shown in Fig. A.5.1, which permits tilting of the furnace without breaking the gas ducts. An alternative arrangement for enclosing a furnace is shown in Fig. A.5.2, although in this case the exhaust duct, which is water cooled, swings away from the furnace when this is being tilted for tapping. In steel making, where fumes during tapping

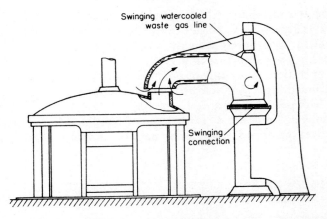

FIG. A.5.2. Total enclosure hood for arc furnace (water-cooled gas line).[192]

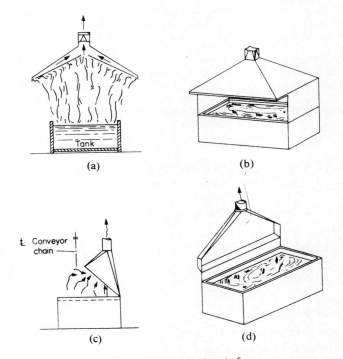

FIG. A.5.3. Various hoods:[6]

(a) Double hood.

(b) Canopy hood with sides.

(c) Semi-canopy hood.

(d) Low rear hood with slit entrance.

tend to be at a minimum,[474] this would not cause any difficulties. When considerable access has to be gained to a process, as in electrolytic plating, it is usual to have hoods which are open at one or more sides. Some typical designs are shown in Fig. A.5.3. When a hood is required for a grinding operation it may only be possible to draw air and dust away to one side, and much higher air velocities are necessary to ensure that the dust does not leak past the entrance to the duct.

Recommended practice as to the type of hood and the velocities of air required over the open face for a number of common processes is given in

TABLE A.5.1

Process	Usual type of hood	Face velocity ft/min
Pharmaceuticals coating pan	Narrow side hood	200–400
Pickling tanks	Canopy hood	250–300
Soldering	Enclosed—open at one side	150–200
Varnish kettle	Canopy type	250–300
	Slot type—2 in. slot	2,000
Dust from grain flour, wood	Canopy	500–600
	Slot (2–4 in. slot)	2,000
Aluminium furnaces	Enclosed hood—open one side	150–200
	Canopy hood	200–250
Brass furnaces	Enclosed hood—open one side	200–250
	Canopy hood	250–300

Table A.5.1. Gas velocities in ducts are generally in the range of 2,500 to 5,000 ft/min, which is well above the "pick up" velocities listed in Chapter 5.

The pressure loss in the ducts and pipelines can be estimated by the following:

1. In cylindrical pipes, the pressure drop per foot length, in in. W.G. is:

$$\Delta p = 7{\cdot}47 \times 10^{-7} f \frac{u}{D} \qquad (A.5.1)$$

where Δp = pressure drop per foot in in. W.G.

u = average pipe velocity (ft/min)

D = pipe diameter (in.)

f = friction factor, which is a function of the Reynolds Number

$$(Re = uD\varrho/\mu)$$

and can be obtained from the curve in Fig. A.5.4.

2. Rectangular ducts, cross section $a \times b$ replaces the diameter in equation (A.5.1) by the equivalent hydraulic diameter D_h where:

$$D_h = \frac{2ab}{a + b}$$

The pressure loss at a bend or fitting can be expressed in terms of a pipe length equivalent to a number of pipe diameters which are a function of the type of bend or fitting. Typical examples are given in Table A.5.2.

TABLE A.5.2 FRICTION LOSS OF FITTINGS, EXPRESSED IN TERMS OF EQUIVALENT PIPE DIAMETERS

90° elbow—standard radius	32
90° elbow—long sweep radius	20
180° close return bend	75
Tee—used as elbow entering run	60
Tee—used as elbow entering branch	90
Gate valve (open)	7
Globe valve (open)	300

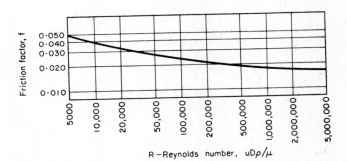

FIG. A.5.4. Relation between Reynolds number and friction factor f for pipes and ducts.[6]

* These values were taken from the 5th Edition of "*Technical Data on Fuels*" and were calculated from Sutherland's formula:

$$\text{gas viscosity} = \frac{KT^{3/2}}{T + C}$$

where T = absolute temperature and K, C = constants

The constants given at the foot of Table A.6.1. can be used for estimating gas viscosities when temperatures exceed 1000°C. The values calculated in this way can only be used as rough approximations.

Note: To obtain the values in f.p.s. units, multiply by 0·06720.

VI. VISCOSITY AND DENSITY DATA FOR GASES

TABLE A.6.1. DYNAMIC VISCOSITY OF GASES IN ABSOLUTE C.G.S. UNITS
(Data from "*Technical Data on Fuels*", Ed. Spiers)[452]

Temperature °C	Poise $\times 10^6$									
	Air	N_2	O_2	CO_2	CO	H_2	CH_4	C_2H_4	C_2H_6	Water vapour
−160	78·1	77·1	87·9		74·4	46·0	44·9			
−140	92·0	90·0	103		87·4	51·5	52·8			
−120	105	103	117		99·9	56·8	60·5			
−100	117	114	131		112	61·8	68·1	62		
− 80	129	126	144		124	66·5	75·1	68		
− 60	140	136	157	108	135	71·1	82·5	74		
− 40	151	147	169	118	145	75·6	89·3	81		
− 20	162	157	181	127	156	79·9	95·9	88		
0	172	166	192	137	166	84·1	102	94	86	
20	181	175	203	146	175	88·2	109	101	92	95·6
40	191	184	213	156	185	92·2	115	108	98	103
60	200	193	223	165	194	96·1	121	115	104	110
80	209	201	233	173	202	100·0	127	122	109	117
100	217	209	243	182	211	104	133	128	115	125
150	238	229	266	203	231	113	147	142	129	143
200	257	247	288	222	251	122	160	156	142	161
250	275	265	309	241	269	130	173	169	155	179
300	293	282	329	259	287	139	184	181	166	197
350	309	298	348	276	304	147	196	192	176	215
400	325	313	367	293	320	154	207	202	184	233
450	340	328	385	309	336	162	217	212	195	251
500	355	342	402	324	352	169	227	222	204	269
550	369	355	419	339	367	177	237			287
600	383	368	436	354	382	184	246		230*	306
650	396	381	452	368	396	191	256			327
700	409	393	468	382	410	198	265		249*	348
800	433	417	500	408	437	211	283		269*	387
900	457	440	530	434	464	223	300		283*	424
1000	479	461	559	459	490	235	316		299*	456
Sutherland* Equation factors										
$K = 10^{-7} \times$	150	143	176	158	135	66	—	—	—	—
C	124	110	131	240	102	72	—	—	—	—

See footnote p. 433.

TABLE A. 6.2. KINEMATIC VISCOSITY OF GASES IN STOKES
(Data from "Technical Data on Fuels", Ed. Spiers)[452]

μ/ϱ = Kinematic Viscosity — Stokes

Temperature °C	Air	N_2	O_2	CO_2	CO	H_2	CH_4	C_2H_4	C_2H_6	Water vapour
−160	0·0249	0·0252	0·0251			0·212				
−140	0·0346	0·0348	0·0348			0·279				
−120	0·0455	0·0458	0·0457			0·354	0·0466			
−100	0·0575	0·0577	0·0579			0·436	0·0599			
−80	0·0707	0·0709	0·0712			0·523	0·0738			
−60	0·0849	0·0849	0·0855		0·0839	0·618	0·0894			
−40	0·100	0·100	0·101	0·0506	0·0991	0·718	0·106	0·0374		
−20	0·116	0·116	0·117	0·0596	0·115	0·824	0·124	0·0456		
0	0·133	0·133	0·134	0·0693	0·133	0·936	0·143	0·0545		
20	0·151	0·151	0·152	0·0796	0·151	1·05	0·163	0·0644		5·53*
40	0·170	0·169	0·171	0·0905	0·169	1·18	0·184	0·0749	0·0635	2·01*
60	0·190	0·188	0·191	0·102	0·189	1·30	0·206	0·0860	0·0730	0·845*
80	0·210	0·208	0·211	0·114	0·209	1·44	0·230	0·0981	0·0833	0·400*
100	0·231	0·229	0·233	0·126	0·231	1·58	0·254	0·111	0·0941	0·208
150	0·287	0·283	0·289	0·160	0·287	1·95	0·318	0·125	0·105	0·272
200	0·346	0·343	0·349	0·196	0·348	2·35	0·388	0·140	0·117	0·344
250	0·410	0·406	0·414	0·235	0·413	2·78	0·462	0·177	0·148	0·424
300	0·478	0·474	0·483	0·277	0·482	3·23	0·540	0·216	0·184	0·512
350	0·549	0·545	0·557	0·321	0·555	3·72	0·622	0·258	0·221	0·608
400	0·623	0·618	0·633	0·367	0·632	4·23	0·711	0·302	0·260	0·713
450	0·701	0·695	0·714	0·416	0·713	4·77	0·801	0·350	0·299	0·825
500	0·782	0·774	0·798	0·467	0·797	5·33	0·898	0·399	0·342	0·946
550	0·865	0·856	0·886	0·521	0·885	5·92	0·999	0·449	0·385	1·07
600	0·951	0·942	0·977	0·576	0·976	6·53	1·10	0·502	0·430	1·22

TABLE A. 6.2 (continued)

μ/ϱ = Kinematic Viscosity—Stokes

Temperature °C	Air	N_2	O_2	CO_2	CO	H_2	CH_4	C_2H_4	C_2H_6	Water vapour
650	1·04	1·03	1·07	0·633	1·07	7·17	1·21			1·38
700	1·13	1·12	1·17	0·693	1·17	7·83	1·32			1·54
800	1·32	1·31	1·38	0·817	1·38	9·21	1·55			1·90
900	1·53	1·51	1·60	0·949	1·59	10·7	1·80			2·28
1000	1·74	1·72	1·82	1·09	1·83	12·2	2·06			2·70

Note: To convert the kinematic viscosities in the above table to f.p.s. units, multiply by 0·001076.
* for a pressure corresponding to that of saturated vapour.

TABLE A. 6.3. DENSITIES OF SOME COMMON GASES
(at 0 or 20°C, 760 mm Hg)

	g/cm³*	
Air	0·0012928	(20°C or 68°F)
Blast furnace gas	0·00121	(20°C or 68°F)
Coal gas		
Horizontal retort	0·00048	(20°C or 68°F)
Continuous vertical retort) (no steaming)	0·00052	(20°C or 68°F)
Continuous vertical retort (steaming)	0·00058	(20°C or 68°F)
Producer gas		
Coal (mechanical producer)	0·00105	(20°C or 68°F)
Coke (mechanical producer)	0·00108	(20°C or 68°F)
Carburetted water gas	0·00082	(20°C or 68°F)
Oxygen	0·001428	(0°C or 32°F)
Nitrogen	0·001257	(0°C or 32°F)
(Air)	0·001293	(0°C or 32°F)
Carbon dioxide	0·001963	(0°C or 32°F)
Carbon monoxide	0·001250	(0°C or 32°F)
Hydrogen	0·000090	(0°C or 32°F)
Methane	0·000715	(0°C or 32°F)
Ethane	0·001037	(0°C or 32°F)
Propane	0·002020	(0°C or 32°F)
Ethylene	0·001251	(0°C or 32°F)
Hydrogen sulphide	0·001521	(0°C or 32°F)
Sulphur dioxide	0·002927	(0°C or 32°F)
Sulphuric acid vapour	0·004380	(0°C or 32°F)
Ammonia	0·000771	(0°C or 32°F)
Hydrochloric acid gas	0·001639	(0°C or 32°F)
Fluorine	0·001696	(0°C or 32°F)
Chlorine	0·003214	(0°C or 32°F)
Argon	0·001783	(0°C or 32°F)

* 1 g/cm³ = 62·43 lb/ft³.

TABLE A. 6.4. CONVERSION FACTORS. MEASURES OF CONCENTRATION
(M = Molecular Weight)

To convert from	to	multiply by
g/m³	g/ft³	0·02832
	lb/1000 ft³	0·06243
	gr./ft³	0·43701
lb/1000 ft³	mg/m³	$16·018 \times 10^3$
	g/ft³	0·35314
	gr./ft³	7
gr./ft³	g/m³	2·288
gr./1000 ft³	mg/m³	2·288
ppm by volume	ppm by weight	$M/28·8$
	lb/ft³	$M/3·851 \times 10^8$

MEASURES OF PRESSURE

To convert from	to	multiply by
mm Hg	Atmospheres	0·001316
	Millibars	1·333
in. W.G. (water gauge) (60°F)	mm Hg (0°C)	1·8663

MEASURES OF VELOCITY

m/sec	ft/sec	3·281
	m.p.h.	2·237
	km/hr	3·6

BIBLIOGRAPHY

1. ABEL, E. and BARTH, H., *Arch. Eisenhüttenwesen*, **29**, 683 (1958).
2. Aerotec Industries Inc., South Norwalk, Conn. U.S.
3. AITKEN, J., *Trans. Roy. Soc.* (Edinburgh), **32**, 239 (1887).
4. Albany Felt Co., United States: Pat. No. 2,896,263 (July 1959).
5. ALBRECHT, F., *Physik., Z.* **32**, 48 (1931).
6. ALDEN, J. L., *Design of Industrial Exhaust Systems*, 3rd Edition, The Industrial Press, New York (1959).
7. ALEXANDER, R. McK., *Proc. Aust. Inst. Min. Met.* **152**, 203 (1949).
8. ALFORD, H. B., *Combustion*, **32**, 45 (1960).
9. ALLCUT, A. E., *Proc. Inst. Mech. Engrs.* **140**, 308 (1938).
10. ALLEN, C. H. and RUDNIK, I., *J. Acoust. Soc. Am.* **19**, 857 (1947).
11. ALLEN, H. S., *Phil. Mag.* **50**, 323, 519 (1900).
12. American Air Filter Co. Inc., Louisville, 8. Ky. U.S.
13. ANDERSON, E., from J. H. Perry, Ed., *Chemical Engineer's Handbook*, 1st Edition, p. 1548, McGraw-Hill, New York (1935).
14. ANDERSON, R. B., McCARTNEY, J. T., HALL, W. K., and HOFER, L. J. E., *Indust. Engng. Chem.* **39**, 1618 (1947).
15. ANDREASEN, A. H. M., *Staub.* **35**, 11 (1954).
16. ANON: *Times Review of Industry*, p. 80 (July 1954); *Brit. Chem. Engng.* **8**, 319 (1963).
17. ANON: *Engineering* **189**, 806 (1960).
18. ANON: *Chem. Engng.* **68**, No. 18, p. 84, Sept. 4th (1961).
19. APPLEBEY, M. P., *Trans. Soc. Chem. Ind.* **56**, 139 (1937).
20. ARENDT, P. and KALLMANN, H., *Z. Physik*, **35**, 421 (1925).
21. ARNOLD, H. D., *Phil. Mag.* **22**, 755 (1911).
22. ASHMAN, R., *Proc. Inst. Mech. Engrs.* **1 B**, 157 (1952).
23. AVY, A. P., *Staub.* **37**, 372 (1954).
24. AVY, A. P., in *Problems and Control of Air Pollution*, Ed. F. S. Malette p. 264, Reinhold, (1955).
25. Babcox and Wilcox, Ltd., London, E.C. 4. Bull. No. 1467/1.
26. BACHMANN, D., *Dechema Monographs*, **31**, (1959).
27. BADGER, W. L. and BANCHERO, J. T., *Introduction to Chemical Engineering*, p. 425, McGraw-Hill, New York (1955).
28. BADZIOCH, S., *J. Inst. Fuel.* **33**, 106 (1960).
29. BAINBRIDGE, C. A., *Chemical Processing*, November (1961) British Pat. 851, 555.
30. BALIFF, J., GREENBURG, L. and STERN, A. C., *Amer. Ind. Hyg. Assn. Quart.* **9**, 85 (1948).
31. BARBER, R., JACKSON, R., Land, T. and THURLOW, G. G., *J. Inst. Fuel.* **27**, 408 (1954).
32. BARKER, D. H., *Ph.D. Thesis*, University of Utah (1951).
33. BARNEBEY, H. L., *Heating Piping and Air Conditioning*, (March, 1958) p. 155.
34. BARTH, W., *Ver. Deut. Ing. Tagungsheft*, **3**, 11 (1954).
35. BARTH, W., *Brennstoff-Wärme-Kraft*, **8**, 1 (1956).
36. BARTH, W., *Staub.* **19**, 175 (1959).
37. BARTH, W., *Staub.* **21**, 382 (1961).
38. BASSA, G. and BEER, J., *Silikattechnik*, **5**, 529 (1954).
39. BAUM, K., *Berg- and Hüttenmännische Monatshefte*, **104**, No. 2, 41 (1959).

439

40. BECKER, H., RECHMANN, H. and TILLMANN, P., *Kolloid Z.* **169**, 34 (1960).
41. BECKER, H.A., *Canad. J. Chem. Engng.* **37**, 85 (1959).
42. BENARIE, M.M., *Staub.* **22**, 118 (1962).
43. BERG, G.J. VAN DEN, *Trans. Inst. Chem. Engng.* (London) **35**, 409 (1957).
44. BERG, R.H., *A.S.T.M. Special Technical Publication No. 234*, (1958) p. 245.
45. BEST, A.C., *J. Inst. Fuel.* **30**, 329 (1957).
46. BIENSTOCK, D., BRUNN, L.W., MURPHY, E.M. and BENSON, H.E., *Sulphur Dioxide, its Chemistry and Removal from Flue Gases*, U.S. Bureau of Mines Information Circular 7836 (1958).
47. BILLINGS, C.E., SILVERMAN, L. and SMALL, W.D., *J. Air Poll. Control Assn.* **5**, (3) 159 (1955).
48. BILLINGS, C.E., SILVERMAN, L., DENNIS, R. and LEVENBAUM, L.H., *J. Air Poll. Control Assn.* **10**, (4) 318 (1956).
49. BILLINGS, C.E., SILVERMAN, L. and KURKER, C., *J. Air Poll. Control Assn.* **8**, (3) 185 (1958).
50. BILLINGS, C.E., SILVERMAN, L. and KURKER, C., *Industrial Wastes*, (1959) (reprint).
51. BILLINGS, C.E., SILVERMAN, L., LEVENBAUM, L.H., KURKER, C. and HICKEY, E.C., *J. Air Poll. Control Assn.* **8**, (1) 53 (1958).
52. BLACKTIN, S.C., *Trans. J. Soc. Chem. Ind.* **58**, 334 (1939).
53. BLACKTIN, S.C., *Trans. J. Soc. Chem. Ind.* **59**, 153 (1940).
54. BLANKENBURG, R., *Staub.* **21**, 321 (1961).
55. BLANKENBURG, R., *Staub.* **21**, 426 (1961).
56. BLASEWITZ, A.G. and JUDSON, B.F., *Chem. Engng. Prog.* **51**, 6 (1955).
57. BLASEWITZ, A.G. and SCHMIDT, W.C., 2nd International Conference on *Peaceful Uses of Atomic Energy*, **18**, 184 (1958).
58. BOSANQUET, C.H., *Trans. Inst. Chem. Engng.* (London) **28**, 130 (1950). Appendix to paper by C.J.Stairmand.
59. BOSANQUET, C.H., CAREY, W.F. and HALTON, E.M., *Proc. Inst. Mech. Engng.* **162**, 355 (1950); BOSANQUET, C.H., *J. Inst. Fuel*, **30**, 322 (1957).
60. BOSANQUET, C.H. and PEARSON, J.L., *Trans. Faraday Soc.* **32**, 1249 (1936).
61. BOSTOCK, W., *J. Sci. Inst.* **29**, 209 (1952).
62. BOUCHER, R.M.G., *Z. Aerosol Forsch.* **6**, 26 (1957).
63. BOUCHER, R.M.G., *Chem. Engng.* **68**, (20) October 2nd (1961) p. 83.
64. ROZOVSKY, H., *Canad. Mining and Met. Bull.* **48**, 486 (1955).
65. BRADLEY, D. and PULLING, D.J., *Trans. Inst. Chem. Engng.* (London) **37**, 34 (1959).
66. BRANDT, O., FREUND, H. and HIEDEMANN, E., *Kolloid Z.* **77**, 103 (1936).
67. BRANDT, W., *Staub.* **21**, 392 (1961).
68. BRINK, J.A., Removal of Phosphoric Acid Mists in *Gas Purification Processes*, Ed. G. Nonhebel Chap. 15b, p. 720, Geo. Newnes, London (1964).
69. BRINK, J.A., *Air Pollution Control with Fibre Mist Eliminators*, Paper presented to the 1962 Annual Chemical Engineering Conference of the Chemical Institute of Canada — Sarnia, Ontario, October (1962) (reprint).
70. BRINK, J.A. and CONTANT, C.E., *Ind. Engng. Chem.* **50**, 1157 (1958).
71. BRINKMAN, H.C., *Appl. Sci. Research*, **A 1**, 27 (1949).
72. BRINKMAN, H.C., *J. Chem. Phys.* **20**, 571 (1952).
73. BRISSE, A.H., *A.S.M.E.* Preprint 50 PRI-16 April (1960).
74. British Standard, *Flow Measurement*, B.S. No. 1042 (1943–1957), British Standards Institution.
75. British Standard, *Code for the Sampling and Analysis of Flue Gases*. B.S. No. 1756 (1952), British Standards Institution.
76. British Standard, *Methods of Test for Air Filters used in Air Conditioning and General Ventilation*. B.S. No. 2831 (1957), British Standards Institution.

77. British Standard, *Code for the Continuous Sampling and Automatic Analysis of Flue Gases. Indicators and Recorders.* B.S. No. 3048 (1958), British Standards Institution.
78. British Standard, *Methods for the Sampling and Analysis of Fuel Gases* B.S. No. 3156 (1959), British Standards Institution.
79. BROOKS, S.H. and CALVERT, W.J., Iron and Steel Institute. Special Report No. 61 (1958) p. 5.
80. BRUNAUER, S., *Adsorption of Gases and Vapours,* Princetown University Press, Princetown. (1943).
81. Buell-van Tongeren Systems, Buell (1952), Ltd., 3 St. James Square, London S.W. 1.
82. BURGERS, J. M., *Proc. K. Ned. Akad. Wetensch.* **44,** 1045, 1177 (1941); *ibid.* **45,** 9, 126 (1942).
83. BURKE, E., *Chem. and Ind.,* 1312 (1955).
84. BUSBY, H. G. TREVOR and DARBY, K., *Colloques Internationaux du Centre National de la Recherche Scientifique,* Grenoble, September 27th (1960). (Editions du Centre National de la Recherche Scientifique – Paris, 1961).
85. CADLE, R.D., WILDER, A.G. and SCHADT, C.F., *Science,* **118,** 490 (1953).
86. CARMAN, P.C., *Trans. Inst. Chem. Engng.* (London) **15,** 150 (1937).
87. CARMAN, P.C., *Flow of Gases through Porous Media,* Butterworths, London (1956).
88. Casella, C.F. and Co., London, *Settlement Dust Counter,* Leaflet 778.
89. Casalla, C.F. and Co., London, *Thermal Precipitator,* Leaflet 804.
90. CAWOOD, W., *Trans. Farad. Soc.* **32,** 1068 (1936).
91. Chemical Construction Corpn., 525 West 43rd St., New York 36, New York.
92. CHEN, C.Y., *Chem. Revs.* **55,** 595 (1955).
93. CHEN, N.H., *Chem. Engng.* Feb. 5th. p. 109, (1962).
94. CHOWDHURY, K.C.R. and FRITZ, W., *Chem. Engng. Sci.* **11,** 92 (1959).
95. COBINE, J.D., *Gaseous Conductors,* Dover, New York (1958).
96. COBINE, J.D., *Gaseous Conductors,* p. 260, Dover, New York (1958).
97. COLLINS, T.T., SEABORNE, C.R. and ANTHONY, A.W., *Paper Trade Journal,* **26,** (3) 55 (1948).
98. Committee on *Permissible Doses for Internal Radiation,* Values recommended in the Report of: (1958 revision).
99. Continental Air Filter Inc., Louisville, Ky. U.S.
100. CORBETT, P.F. and CRANE, W.M., *B.C.U.R.A. Bull.* **16,** 1 (1952).
101. COTTRELL, F.G., *United States Pat.* 895,729 (1908), also *United States Patents* Nos. 866,843 and 945,717).
102. COTTRELL, F.G., *German Patent 230,570,* March 17th (1908).
103. COTTRELL, F.G., *J. Ind. Engng. Chem.* **3,** 542 (1911).
104. COULL, J., BISHOP, H. and GAYLORD, W.M., *Chem. Engng. Prog.* **45,** 525 (1949).
105. COXON, W.F., *Flow Measurement and Control,* Heywood, London (1959).
106. CRAGGS, J.M. and MEEK, J.D., *Electrical Breakdown in Gases,* The Clarendon Press, Oxford (1953).
107. CUMMINGS, W.G. and REDFERN, M.W., *J. Inst. Fuel* **30,** 628 (1957).
108. CUNNINGHAM, E., *Proc. Roy. Soc.* (London) **A 83,** 357 (1910).
109. CZAJA, A.T., *Staub.* **22,** 228 (1962).
110. DAESCHNER, H.W., SEIBERT, E.E. and PETERS, E.P., *A.S.T.M.* Special Pub. No. 234 (1958).
111. DALLA VALLA, J.M., *United States Technical Conference on Air Pollution,* Ed. L.C. McCabe, p. 341, McGraw-Hill, New York (1952).
112. DALMON, J. and LOWE, H.J., *Colloques Internationaux du Centre National de la Recherche Scientifique,* Grenoble, September 27th (1960). (Editions du Centre National de la Recherche Scientifique, Paris, 1961).
113. DANIELS, T.C., *The Engineer,* **203,** 358 (1957); (*See also* DAVIDSON, I.M.: *Proc. Inst. Mech. Engrs.* **160,** 243 (1949)).
114. DANSER, H.W., *Chem. Engng.* **57,** 158 (May 1950).

115. DAS, P.K., *Indian J. Met. Geophys.* **1,** 137 (1950).
116. Davidson & Co., Ltd., Belfast: *Publication Ref. No. 387/61.*
117. DAVIES, C.N., *Proc. Phys. Soc.* **57,** 259 (1945).
118. DAVIES, C.N., *Symposium on Particle Size Analysis, Trans. Inst. Chem. Engng. and Soc. Chem. Ind.* p. 25 (Feb. 1947).
119. DAVIES, C.N., *Proc. Phys. Soc.* **63 B,** 288 (1950).
120. DAVIES, C.N., *Proc. Inst. Mech. Engng.* **1B,** 185 (1952).
121. DAVIES, C.N., *Dust is Dangerous.* p. 21, Faber, London (1954).
122. DAVIES, C.N., *Dust is Dangerous.* p. 46, Faber, London (1954).
123. DECKER, W.A., SNOEK, E. and KRAMERS, H., *Chem. Engng. Sci.* **11,** 61 (1959).
124. DENNIS, R., SAMPLES, W.R., ANDERSON, D.M. and SILVERMAN, L., *Ind. Engng. Chem.* **49,** 294 (1957).
125. DENNIS, R. *et al.*: *Air Cleaning Studies Progress Report,* October 1956, p. 13, NYO–4611: Air Cleaning Laboratory, School of Public Health, Harvard University: Boston, Mass.
126. DEUTSCH, W., *Ann. Phys.* (Lpzg). **68,** 335 (1922).
127. DONOGHUE. J.K., *Trans. Inst. Chem. Engng.* (London) **33,** 72 (1955).
128. DOWIS, E., *The Refrigeration and Air Conditioning Business,* July 1959 (reprint).
129. DOYLE, H. and BROOKS, A.F.: *Ind. Engng. Chem.* **49** (12), 57A (1957).
130. EBBENHORST-TENGBERGEN, H.J.VAN: *Problems and Control of Air Pollution.* Ed. Mallette p. 255; Reinhold, (1955).
131. EINSTEIN, A., Investigations on the theory of Brownian movement, p. 75, Dover (1956), from *Z. Electrochemie* **14,** 235 (1908).
132. EINSTEIN, A., *Ann. Phys.* (Lpzg). **19,** 289 (1906); *ibid.* **34,** 591 (1911).
133. EINSTEIN, A., *Z. Physik.* **27,** 1 (1924).
134. ELKINS, H.B., *The Chemistry of Industrial Toxicology,* 2nd ed. Wiley New York (1959).
135. EMMETT, P.H., *Advances in Catalysis,* **I,** 65 (1948).
136. ENDRES, H.A. and VAN ORMAN, W.T., *Society Plastics Engineers Journal,* **9,** 26 (1953), Quoted by A. Winkel, *Staub.* **41,** 469 (1955).
137. ENDRES, H.A. and VAN ORMAN, W.T., *Heating, Piping and Air Conditioning,* p. 157 (Jan. 1952).
138. Engelhard Industries, Baker Platinum Division, London W.C.1.; Data Sheet.
139. ENGELS, L.H., *Staub.* **23,** 98 (1963).
140. EPSTEIN, P.S., *Phys. Rev.* **23,** 710 (1924).
141. EPSTEIN, P.S., *Z. Physik.* **54,** 537 (1929).
142. ESSENHIGH, R.H., *Safety in Mines Research Establishment,* Ministry of Fuel and Power. Report No. 120 (1955).
143. ETTRE, L.S., *J. Air Poll. Control Ass.* **11,** 34 (1961).
144. FAIRS, G.L., *Chem. and Ind.* **62,** 374 (1943).
145. FAIRS, G.L., *Trans. Inst. Chem. Engng.* (London) **22,** 110 (1944).
146. FAIRS, G.L., *Trans. Inst. Chem. Engng.* (London) **36,** 475 (1958).
147. FAXÉN, H., *Ann. Phys.* (Lpzg). **68,** 89 (1922).
148. FAXÉN, H., Quoted by P.G.W.HAWKSLEY, *B.C.U.R.A. Bull.* **15,** 105 (1951).
149. FEIFEL, E., *Ver. Deut. Ing. Forschungshefte,* **9,** 68 (1938); *ibid.* **10,** 212 (1939).
150. FEILD, R.B., Univ. Ill. Expt. Stat. Report No. 5. 1951. *Collection of Aerosol Particles by Atomised Sprays.*
151. FIRST, M.W., *A.S.M.E.* Preprint 49-A-27. Paper read at A.S.M.E. Conference, November (1949).
152. FIRST, M.W., JOHNSON, G.A., DENNIS, R., FRIEDLANDER, S. and SILVERMAN, L., *Performance Characteristics of Wet Collectors,* Harvard Air Cleaning Laboratory Report NYO 1587, April 22nd, 1953.
153. FIRST, M.W., MOSCHELLA, R., SILVERMAN, L. and BERLY, E., *Ind. Engng. Chem.* **43,** 1363 (1951).
154. FLEMING, E.P. and FITT, T.C., *Ind. Engng. Chem.* **42,** 2253 (1950).

155. FONDA, A. and HERNE, H., In Prepn. (quoted by H. Herne).[214]

156. FONTEIN, F. J., in *Cyclones in Industry*, Eds. K. Rietema and C. G. Verver, p. 118, Elsevier, Amsterdam (1961).

157. FORREST, J. S. and LOWE, H. J., *Mechanical Engineers Contribution to Clean Air, Inst. Mech. Engrs.* p. 42, (1957).

158. FORSTER, R. H. B., *Proc. Inst. Mech. Engrs.* **160**, 246 (1949).

159. FOWLER, J. L. and HERTEL, K. L., *J. App. Phys.* **11**, 496 (1940).

160. FRANCIS, A. W., *Physics* **4**, 403 (1933).

161. FRANCIS, W. and LEPPER, G. H., *Engineering*, **172**, 36 (1951).

162. FREDERICK, E. R., *Chem. Engng.* **68**, p. 107 (June 26, 1961).

163. FRIEDLANDER, S. K., *Amer. Inst. Chem. Engng. Jour.* **3**, 43 (1957); *Ind. Engng. Chem.* **50**, 1161 (1958).

164. FRIEDLANDER, S. K. and PASCERI, R. E., *Canad. J. Chem. Engng.* **38**, 212 (1960).

165. FRIEDMAN, S. J., GLUCKERT, F. A. and MARSHALL, W. R., *Chem. Engng. Prog.* **48**, 181 (1952).

166. FRIEDRICH, W., *Staub.* **19**, 281 (1959).

167. FURMIDGE, C. G. L., *Brit. J. App. Phys.* **12**, 268 (1961).

168. GANS, R., *Ann. Phys.* (Lpzg), **86**, 628 (1928).

169. GARNER, J. F. and OFFORD, R. S., *The Law on the Pollution of the Air*, Shaw & Sons, London (1957).

170. GARNETT, A., in *Air Pollution* Ed. M. W. Thring, p. 73, Butterworths, London (1957).

171. GILLESPIE, T., *J. Colloid Sci.* **10**, 299 (1955).

172. GILLESPIE, T. and LANGSTROTH, G. O., *Canad. J. Research.* **B 25**, 455 (1947).

173. GILLESPIE, T. and LANGSTROTH, G. O., *Canad. J. Chem.* **30**, 1003 (1952).

174. GILLESPIE, T. and RIDEAL, E., *J. Colloid Sci.* **10**, 281 (1955).

175. GILLILAND, E. R., *Ind. Engng. Chem.* **26**, 681 (1934).

176. GILLILAND, E. R. and SHERWOOD, T. K., *Ind. Engng. Chem.* **26**, 516 (1934).

177. GLASTONBURY, J. R., *Sydney Clean Air Conference*, Tech. Paper No. 18. N. S. W. University Press (1962).

178. GLAUERT, M., *Aeronautical Research Committee Report No. 2025* (London) H.M.S.O.

179. GLEDHILL, P. K., CARNALL, P. J. and SARGENT, K. H., *J. Iron and Steel Inst.* **186**, 198 (1957).

180. GOLLMAR, H. A., in *Chemistry of Coal Utilization*, Ed. H. H. Lowry, Vol. 2, p. 947, Wiley, New York (1945).

181. GOSLINE, C. A., FALK, L. L. and HELMERS, E. N. in *Air Pollution Handbook*, Ed. Magill *et al.*, Chapt. 5, p. 20, McGraw-Hill (1956).

182. GRANVILLE, R. A. and JAFFREY, W. G., *Engineering*, **187**, 285 (1959).

183. GREEN, H. L. and LANE, W. R., *Particulate Clouds, Dusts, Smokes and Mists*, p. 134, Spon, London (1957).

184. GREEN, H. L. and LANE, W. R., *Particulate Clouds, Dusts, Smokes and Mists*, p. 149, Spon, London (1957).

185. GREEN, H. L. and LANE, W. R., *Particulate Clouds, Dusts, Smokes and Mists*, p. 202, Spon, London (1957).

186. GREEN, H. L. and LANE, W. R., *Particulate Clouds, Dusts, Smokes and Mists*, p. 212, Spon, London (1957).

187. GREEN, H. L. and WOOTTEN, N. W., (Unpublished work quoted by Green, H. L. and Lane, W. R.: *Particulate Clouds, Dusts, Smokes and Mists*, p. 66, Spon, London (1957).

188. GREENBURG, L. and SMITH, C. W., *U.S. Bureau of Mines*, Report of Investigation 2392 (1922).

189. GREGG, S. J., *Symposium on Particle Size Analysis. Inst. Chem. Engng. and Soc. Chem. Ind.* (London) p. 27 (Feb. 1947).

190. GÜNTHEROTH, H., *Staub.* **21**, 430 (1961).

191. GUSTAVSSON, K. A., *Tekn. Tidskr.* **78**, 667 (1948).

192. GUTHMANN, K., *Stahl und Eisen*, **75**, 1571 (1955); *Staub.* **21**, 398 (1961).
193. HANSEN, K., *Fifth World Power Conference*, Vienna, **16**, 5829 (1956).
194. HANSEN, N.L. (1930), quoted by Rossaño and Silverman (1954) *(op. cit.)* and by Davies (1952) *(op. cit.)*.
195. HARR, R., WAGNER, K. and WILLMER, T.K., *Berg- und Hüttenmännische Monatshefte*, **104**, No. 2, 50 (1959).
196. HARRIS, W.B. and MASON, M.G., *Ind. Engng. Chem.* **47**, 2423 (1955).
197. HARTMANN, J. and LAZARUS, F., *Phil. Mag.* **29**, 140 (1940).
198. HASENCLEVER, D., *Staub.* **19**, 42 (1959).
199. HAUSBERG, G., *Staub.* **21**, 418 (1961).
200. HAUSBERG, G. quoting German Patent 521,697, November 15th (1925) in *Staub.* **21**, 418 (1961).
201. HAUT, H.VAN, *Staub.* **21**, 52 (1961).
202. HAWKSLEY, P.G.W., *B.C.U.R.A. Bull.* **15**, 105 (1951).
203. HAWKSLEY, P.G.W., in *Some Aspects of Fluid Flow. Inst. Physics Conference*, p. 114, Edward Arnold, London (1950).
204. HAWKSLEY, P.G.W., *Physics of Particle Size Analysis, Brit. J. App. Phys.* Supplement 3, S. 1 (1954).
205. HAWKSLEY, P.G.W., BADZIOCH, S. and BLACKETT, J.H., *J. Inst. Fuel*, **31**, 147 (1958).
206. HAWKSLEY, P.G.W., BADZIOCH, S. and BLACKETT, J.H., *Measurement of Solids in Flue Gases*, British Coal Utilization Research Association, Leatherhead (1961).
207. HEIMANN, H., *Air Pollution*, World Health Organization, p. 159, Geneva (1961).
208. HEINRICH, D.O., *J. Iron and Steel Inst.* **33**, 452 (1960).
209. HEINRICH, D.O., *Trans. Inst. Chem. Engng.* (London) **39**, 145 (1961).
210. HEINRICH, D.O., *Staub.* **22**, 360 (1962).
211. HEINRICH, D.O., *Staub.* **23**, 83 (1963).
212. HEINRICH, R.F. and ANDERSON, J.R., *Chemical Engineering Practice*, Ed. H.W.Cremer, vol. 3, p. 464, Butterworths, London (1957).
213. HEISS, J.F. and COULL, J., *Chem. Engng. Prog.* **48**, 133 (1952).
214. HELWIG, H.C. and GORDON, C.L., *Anal. Chem.* **30**, 1810 (1958).
215. HERNE, H., *Int. J. Air Poll.* **3**, 26 (1960).
216. HERSEY, H.J., *Ind. Chem.*, **31**, 138 (1955).
217. HIRSCHFELDER, J.O., CURTIS, C.F. and BIRD, R.B., *Molecular Theory of Gases and Liquids*, p. 539, Wiley, New York (1954).
218. HOCKING, L.M., *Quart. J. Roy. Met. Soc.* **85**, 44 (1959).
219. HOCKING, L.M., *Int. J. Air Poll.* **3**, 154 (1960).
220. HOHENBERGER, A., *Stahl und Eisen*, **81**, 1001 (1961).
221. HOUGHTON, H.G. in Perry, Ed., *Chemical Engineer's Handbook*, 3rd Edition, p. 840, McGraw-Hill, New York (1950).
222. Howden, James and Co. Ltd., 195, Scotland Street, Glasgow, C. 5.
223. Hubbard, E.H., *J. Inst. Fuel*, **30**, 564 (1957).
224. HUMPHREY, A.E. and GADEN, E.L., *Ind. Engng. Chem.* **47**, 924 (1955).
225. IBERALL, A.S., *J. Nat. Bur. St.* **45**, 398 (1950).
226. IHLEFELDT, H., *Staub.* **21**, 448 (1961).
227. INGLES, O.G., *Aust. J. App. Sci.* **9**, 120 (1958).
228. *International Critical Tables*, Ed. Washburn, E.W., McGraw-Hill, New York (1926).
229. JACKSON, R., *B.C.U.R.A. Bull.* **23**, 349 (1959).
230. JACKSON, R., *B.C.U.R.A. Bull.* **24**, 221 (1962).
231. JACKSON, R., THURLOW, G.G. and GOODRIDGE, A.M., *J. Sci. Inst.* **35**, 81 (1958).
232. JACKSON, R., THURLOW, G.G. and HOLLAND, R.E., *J. Inst. Fuel*, **33**, 180 (1960).
233. JACOBS, M.B., *The Chemical Analysis of Air Pollutants*, Interscience, New York (1960)
234. JAHN, R., *Radex Rundschau*, **7**, 625–631 (1952).
235. JARMAN, R.T., *J. Agric. Engng. Research*, **4**, 139 (1959).
236. JEANS, J.H., *The Dynamical Theory of Gases*, p. 316, Dover, New York (1954).

237. JENNINGS, R.F., *J. Iron and Steel Inst.* **164**, 305 (1950).
238. JOHNSON, G.A., FRIEDLANDER, S.K., DENNIS, R., FIRST, M.W. and SILVERMAN, L., *Chem. Engng. Prog.* **51**, 176 (1955).
239. JOHNSON, J.C. and GOODWIN, G.C., *Conference on the Mechanical Engineers Contribution to Clean Air*, Institution of Mechanical Engineers, London, February 20th, p. 60 1957.
240. JOHNSTONE, H.F., *Univ. Ill. Engng. Expt. Station*, Circular No. 20. (1929).
241. JOHNSTONE, H.F. and ECKMAN, F.O., *Ind. Engng. Chem.*, **43**, 1358 (1951).
242. JOHNSTONE, H.F., FEILD, R.B. and TASSLER, M.C., *Ind. Engng. Chem.* **46**, 1601 (1954).
243. JOHNSTONE, H.F. and ROBERTS, M.H., *Ind. Engng. Chem.* **41**, 2417 (1949).
244. JOHNSTONE, H.F. and SILOX, H.E., *Ind. Engng. Chem.* **39**, 808 (1947).
245. JOHNSTONE, H.F. and SINGH, A.D., *Univ. Ill. Engng. Expt. Station* Bull. No. 324, December 31st (1940).
246. JONES, W.P., *Ind. Engng. Chem.* **41**, 2424 (1949).
247. JONES, W.P. and ANTHONY, A.W., *United States Technical Conference on Air Pollution*, Ed. L.C. McCabe, p. 318, McGraw-Hill New York, (1952).
248. JOOS, E., *Staub.* **35**, 18 (1954).
249. Joy Manufacturing Co., Henry W. Oliver Blg., Pittsburg, 22. Pa. U.S. *Microdyne Collector.*
250. Jukes, Fredrk., Ltd., Garth Road, Surrey, England *(Pontifex Scrubber)*.
251. KALASCHNIKOW, S., *Z. Tech. Phys.* **9**, 267 (1934).
252. KAMAK, H.W., *Anal. Chem.* **23**, 844 (1950).
253. KANE, L.J., CHIDESTER, G.E. and SHALE, C.C., *United States Bureau of Mines, Report of Investigations*, No. **5672** (1960).
254. KANGRO, C., *Staub.* **21**, 275 (1961).
255. KATZ, M. and COLE, R.J., *Ind. Engng. Chem.* **42**, 2258 (1950).
256. KAY, K., *Anal. Chem.* **29**, 589 (1957); *ibid.* **31**, 633 (1959).
257. KELSALL, D.F., *Trans. Inst. Chem. Engng.* (London), **30**, 87 (1952).
258. KELSALL, D.F. and MCADAM, J.C.H., *Trans. Inst. Chem. Engng.* (London), **41**, 84 (1963).
259. KENNAWAY, T., Iron and Steel Institute Special Report No. 61, *"Air and Water Pollution in the Iron and Steel Industry"* (1958); *J. Air Poll. Control. Assn.* **7**, 266 (1958).
260. KIELBACK, A.W., *Chem. Engng. Prog. Symposium, Series No.* 35, **57** (1961) *"Pollution and Environmental Health"*, p. 51.
261. KING, L.V., *Proc. Roy. Soc.* (London) **A 147**, 233 (1934).
262. KING, R.A., *Ind. Engng. Chem.* **42**, 2241 (1950).
263. KIRKWOOD, J.B., Paper No. 14, *Clean Air Conference*, Univ. N.S.W. Press Sydney (1962).
264. KLEINSCHMIDT, R.V. and ANTHONY, A.W., *United States Technical Conference on Air Pollution*, Ed. L.C. McCabe, p. 310, McGraw-Hill, New York (1952).
265. Knit-Mesh Limited, 36, Victoria Street, London S.W.1.
266. KOGLIN, W., *Staub.* **22**, 189 (1962).
267. KOHL, A.L. and RIESENFELD, F.C., *Gas Purification*, McGraw-Hill, New York (1960).
268. KOLK, H. VAN DER, *Ver. Deut. Ing. Tagungsheft*, **3**, 23 (1954).
269. KOLK, H. VAN DER, *Ver. Deut. Ing. Berichte*, **7**, 25 (1955).
270. KOLK, H. VAN DER, in *Cyclones in Industry*. Chapt. 6, p. 77, Ed. K. Rietema and C.G. Verver, Elsevier (1961).
271. KOLLER, L.R. and FREMONT, H.A., *J. Appl. Phys.* **21**, 741 (1950).
272. KÖNIG, W., *Ann. Phys.* (Lpzg). **42**, 353 (1891).
273. KORDECKI, M.C. and ORR, C., *Arch. Env. Health*, **1**, 1 (1960).
274. KRAEMER, H.F. and JOHNSTONE, H.F., *Ind. Engng. Chem.* **47**, 2426 (1955).
275. KRIJGSMAN, M., *De Quantitative Bepaling van stoff in Hoogovengas*, p. 6. K.N.H.S. Centraal Laboratorium Report, March 28th (1955).

276. Krijgsman, M., *Stahl und Eisen*, **80**, 621 (1960).
277. Kristal, E., Dennis, R., Silverman, L., *T.I.D.* 7313, p. 203 U.S. Atomic Energy Commission, Technical Information Service, Oak Ridge, Tenn. (1956).
278. Kudlich, R., (revised by L.R. Burdick). *Ringelmann Smoke Chart.* United States Bureau of Mines, Information Circular **7718**, (1955).
279. Lachman, J.C., *Instr. and Control Systems*, **32**, 1030 (1959).
280. Ladenburg, R., *Ann. Phys.* (Lpzg). **4**, 863 (1930).
281. Ladenburg, R., *Der Chemie Ingenieur*, **I** (iv) 31 (1934).
282. Lagarias, J.S., *J. Air. Poll. Control. Assn.* **10** (iv) 271 (1960).
283. Lamb, H., *Hydrodynamics*, p. 601. Dover, New York (1945).
284. Lamb, H., *Hydrodynamics*, p. 612, Dover, New York (1945).
285. Land, T. and Barber, R., *Trans. Soc. Inst. Tech.* **6**, 112 (1954).
286. Land, T. and Barber, R., *J. Iron and Steel Inst.* **184**, 269 (1956).
287. Land Pyrometers Ltd., Sheffield, Technical Information, *Land Suction Pyrometer*, Type 4.
288. Land Pyrometers Ltd., Sheffield: *The Land Venturi Pneumatic Pyrometer—a first report*, Technical Note No. 72. May 15th (1962).
289. Landahl, H.D. and Herrmann, R.G., *J. Colloid Sci.* **4**, 103 (1949).
290. Landau, R. and Rosen, R., *Ind. Engng. Chem.* **39**, 281 (1947).
291. Landau, R. and Rosen, R., *Ind. Engng. Chem.* **40**, 1389 (1948).
292. Landolt-Börnstein, *Physikalisch-Chemische Tabellen*, J. Springer Verlag, Berlin, 1–6th Edition, (1923–1964).
293. Landt, E., *Gesundheits Ing.* **77**, 139 (1956).
294. Landt, E., *Staub.* **48**, 9 (1957).
295. Langmuir, I., O.S.R.D. Report No. 865 (1942).
296. Langmuir, I. and Blodgett, K.B., *General Electric Research Laboratory*, Schenectady, N.Y. Report R.L. 225 (1944–45).
297. Langmuir, I. and Blodgett, K., *Amer. Air Force Tech. Report*, 5418 (1946).
298. Lapple, C.E., in J.H. Perry, Ed. *Chemical Engineer's Handbook*, 3rd Edition, p. 1021, McGraw-Hill, New York (1950).
299. Lapple, C.E. and Kamack, H.J., *Chem. Engng. Prog.* **51**, 110 (1955).
300. Lauer, O., *Staub.* **20**, 69 (1960).
301. Lea, F.M. and Nurse, R.W., *Symposium on Particle Size Analysis. Inst. Chem. Engng. and Soc. Chem. Ind.* p. 47, February (1947).
302. Lederc, E., *Air Pollution*, World Health Organization, Geneva, p. 279 (1961).
303. Lewis, H.C., Edwards, D.G., Goglia, M.J., Rice, R.I. and Smith, L.W., *Indust. Engng. Chem.* **40**, 67 (1948).
304. Lewis, W.K., Gilliland, E.R. and Bauer, W.C., *Indust. Engng. Chem.* **41**, 1104 (1949).
305. Liebster, H., *Ann. Phys.* (Lpzg). **82**, 541 (1927).
306. Ter Linden, A.J., *Engineering*, **167**, 167 (1949).
307. Ter Linden, A.J., *Proc. Inst. Mech. Engng.* **160**, 233 (1949).
308. Ter Linden. A.J., *Tonindustrie-Zeitung*, **22** (iii) 49 (1953).
309. Ter Linden, A.J., in *Problems and Control of Air Pollution*, Ed. F.S. Mallette, p. 236, Reinhold (1955).
310. Ter Linden, A.J. and Van Dongen, J.R.J., *Trans. A.S.M.E.* **80**, 245 (1958).
311. Little, A., *Trans. Inst. Chem. Engng.* (London), **34**, 259 (1956).
312. Little, A.D., *Report for U.S. Public Health Service*, Robert A. Taft Sanitary Engineering Centre Technical Report No. A61–34.
313. Lobo, W.E., Friend, L., Hashmall, F. and Zenz, F.A., *Trans. Amer. Inst. Chem. Engng.* **41**, 693 (1945).
314. Lodge, O., *Nature* (London) **28**, 297 (1883).
315. Lorenz, H., *Abh. th. Physik.* **1**, 23 (1906).
316. Lowe, H.J. and Lucas, D.H., *Brit. J. App. Phys.* **4**, S 40 (1953).

317. LUNDE, K.E., *Ind. Engng. Chem.* **50,** 293 (1958).
318. LUNNON, R.G., *Proc. Roy. Soc.* (London) **A 110,** 319 (1926).
319. LUNNON, R.G., *Proc. Roy. Soc.* (London) **A 118,** 680 (1928).
320. McCABE, L.C., *Ind. Engng. Chem.* **44 (11)** 123A, November (1952).
321. McNOWN, J.S., LEE, H.M., McPHERSON, M.B. and ENGEZ, S.M., *7th Int. Congress App. Mech. Proc.* **7 II (i)** 17 (1948).
322. McNOWN, J.S. and MALAIKA, J., *Trans. Amer. Geophys. Union,* **31,** 74 (1950).
323. McWILLIAMS, J.A., PRATT, H.R.C., DELL, F.R. and JONES, D.A., *Trans. Inst. Chem. Engng.* (London) **34,** 17 (1956).
324. MACZEWSKI-ROWINSKI, B., quoted by Boucher, R.M.G., also *International Clean Air Conference,* National Society for Clean Air London, p. 160 (1959).
325. MAGILL, P.L., HOLDEN, F.R. and ACKLEY, C., *Air Pollution Handbook,* p. 13–96, Table 13–22, McGraw-Hill, New York (1956).
326. MANTELL, C.L., *Adsorption,* McGraw-Hill, New York (1945): also in Perry, Ed., *Chemical Engineers Handbook,* 3nd Ed. Sect. 14. p. 885 (1950).
327. MARSHALL, W.R., *Atomization and Spray Drying, Chem. Engng. Prog. Monograph,* Series No. 2, Vol. 50 (1954), Chaps. I–IX.
328. MARSHALL, W.R. and SELTZER, E., *Chem. Engng. Prog.* **46,** 501 (1950).
329. MARTIN, A.E., REID, A.M. and SMART, J., *Control,* **2,** (18) 108 (1959); *ibid.* **3,** (19) 91 (1960).
330. MARTIN, A.H., *Mining Sci.* **63,** 337 (1910).
331. MARZOCCHI, A., LACHUT, F. and WILLIS, W.H., *J. Air Poll. Control Assn.* **12,** (1) 38 (1962).
332. MASSEY, O.D., *Chem. Engng.* **66,** (No. 14) p. 143, July 13th (1959).
333. MASSON, H., *Staub.* **21,** 459 (1961).
334. MATTERN, C.F.T., BRACKETT, F.S. and OLSON, B.J., *J. Appl. Physiol.* **10,** 56 (1957).
335. MAY, K.R., *J. Sci. Instr.* **22,** 187 (1945).
336. MEDLOCK, R.S., *Instrument Engineer,* I (1) 3 (1952).
337. MEISSNER, H.P. and MICKLEY, H.S., *Ind. Engng. Chem.* **41,** 1238 (1949).
338. Menardi and Company: 1220 East Grand Ave., El Segundo, Calif. U.S.A.
339. MIERDEL, G., *Z. Tech. Phys.* **8,** 564 (1932).
340. MITCHELL, R.I. and PILCHER, J.M., *5th A.E.C. Air Cleaning Conference. T.I.D.* 7551 U.S. Atomic Energy Commission, Technical Information Service, Oak Ridge, Tenn. p. 67. (1957)
341. MÖLLER, W., *Phys. Z.* **39,** 57 (1938).
342. MORGAN, B.B., *Research,* **10,** 271 (1957).
343. MORGAN, B.B. and MEYER, E.W., *J. Sci. Instr.* **36,** 492 (1959).
344. MORRIS, G.A. and JACKSON, J., *Absorption Towers,* Butterworth, London (1953).
345. MULCASTER, K.D., *Staub.* **21,** 302 (1961).
345.a. MULDER, H., Reported by A.J.ter Linden. *Proc. Inst. Mech. Engng.* **160,** 233 (1949).
346. MÜLLER, P., *Chemie Ing. Technik.* **31,** 345 (1959).
347. NAGEL, R., *Ver. Deut. Ing. Tagungsheft.* **3,** 25 (1954).
348. NATANSON, G.L., *Dok. Akad. Nauk. S.S.R. Physical Chemistry Section,* **112,** 100 (1957).
349. NEUMANN, E.P. and NORTON, J.L., "*Ultrasonics—two Symposia*"—*Chem. Engng. Prog.* Symposium Series No. 1. **47,** p. 4 (1951).
350. NONHEBEL, G., *Air Pollution,* Chapt. 1. p. 3 Ed. M.W.Thring. Butterworth (1957).
351. NONHEBEL, G. and HAWKINS, J.E., *J. Inst. Fuel,* **28,** 530 (1955).
352. NORD, M., *Chem. Engng.* **57,** p. 116, October (1950).
353. Nordac, Ltd., Middlesex, England: Private Communication (1962).
354. NORMAN, W.S., *Absorption, Distillation and Cooling Towers,* Longman's, London (1961).
355. NORMAN, W.S., *Absorption, Distillation and Cooling Towers,* p. 67, Longman's, London (1961).

356. NUKIYAMA, S. and TANASAWA, Y., *Trans. Soc. Mech. Engng. (Japan)* **4**, (14) 86 (1938) quoted by Lewis, H.C. *et al. Ind., Engng. Chem.* **40**, 67 (1948).
357. OAKES, B., *Int. J. Air Pol.* **3**, 179 (1960).
358. Oxy-Catalyst Inc., (Berwyn. Penn.): *Basic Engineering Principles of the Oxy cat.*, p. 18.
359. PALLINGER, J., *Staub.* **22**, 270 (1962).
360. Pangborn Corporation, Hagerstown, Maryland, U.S.A. Bull. No. 921, 923A and 924.
361. PARKER, A., *Air Pollution Legislation* in *Air Pollution*, p. 365, World Health Organization, Geneva (1961).
362. PARKINGTON, J.W. and WALKER, LAURIE S., *Colloque Internationaux du Centre National de la Recherche Scientifique*, Grenoble, Septembre 27th, p. 351, (1960). Editions du Centre National de la Recherche Scientifique, Paris (1961).
363. PAUTHENIER, M.M. and MOREAU-HANOT, M., *J. Phys. et Rad.* Series 7; **3**, 590 (1932).
364. PAUTHENIER, M.M. and MOREAU-HANOT, M., *J. Phys. et Rad.* Series 7; **6**, 257 (1935).
365. PEARCEY, T. and HILL, G.W., *Quart. J. Roy. Met. Soc.* **83**, 77 (1957).
366. PEARSON, J.L., NONHEBEL, G. and ULANDER, P.H.N., *J. Inst. Fuel*, **8**, 119 (1935).
367. PEMBERTON, C.S., *Int. J. Air Poll.* **3**, 168 (1960).
368. PETROLL, J., *Freiberger Forschungshefte*, **A 204**, 94 (1961).
369. PETROLL, J. and LANGHAMMER, K., *Freiberger Forschungshefte*, **A 220**, 175 (1962).
370. PETTYJOHN, E.S. and CHRISTIANSEN, E.B., *Chem. Engng. Prog.* **44**, 157 (1948).
371. PICKNETT, R.G., *Int. J. Air Poll.* **3**, 160 (1960).
372. PIGFORD, R.L. and COLBURN, A.P., in Perry, J.H. Ed. *Chemical Engineers Handbook*, 3rd Edition (p. 675), McGraw-Hill, New York (1950).
373. PIGFORD, R.L. and PYLE, C., *Ind. Engng. Chem.* **43**, 1649 (1951).
374. POWELL, A.R., in *Chemistry of Coal Utilization*, Ed. H.H.Lowry, Vol. 2, p. 921, Wiley, New York (1945).
375. POZIN, M.E., MUKHLENOV, I.P., TARAT, E.YA., *J. Appl. Chem. U.S.S.R.* **30**, 293 (1957).
376. Prat-Daniel (Stroud) Ltd. Private communication.
377. PRESSLER, A.F., *Ph. D. Thesis*, Iowa State College, Iowa (1956).
378. PRIESTLEY, C.H.B., *Private communication*, (1959). Based on *Quart. J. Roy. Met. Soc.* **82**, 165 (1956).
379. PRING, R.T., *Air Repair*, **4**, No. 1. May (1954); *ibid.* **4**, No. 3. November (1954) (reprinted).
380. PROCKAT, F., *Glaser's Ann.* **106**, 73 (1930).
381. PROCKAT, F., *Glaser's Ann.* **107**, 43, 47 (1930).
382. Pulverising Machinery Ltd., Parnall Road, Fishponds, Bristol.
383. RADUSHKEVICH, L.V., *J. Phys. Chem. U.S.S.R.* **32**, 282 (1958).
384. RAMMLER, E. and BREITLING, K., *Freiberger Forschungshefte*, **A 56**, 5 (1957).
385. RANZ, W.E., *Tech. Report* No. 8. January 1st (1953) Univ. Illinios. Engng. Expt. Station.
386. RANZ, W.E. and JOHNSTONE, H.F., *J. Appl. Phys.* **26**, 244 (1956).
387. RANZ, W.E. and WONG, J.B., *Ind. Engng. Chem.* **44**, 1371 (1952).
388. RAY, A.B., *United States Technical Conference on Air Pollution*, Ed. L.C.McCabe. p. 355, McGraw-Hill, New York (1952).
389. RAYLEIGH, E. LORD, *Proc. Roy. Soc.* (London) **34**, 414 (1882–3).
390. RAYLEIGH, E. LORD, *Phil. Mag.* (5) **B 4**, 59 (1892).
391. REED, R.M. and UPDEGRAFF, N.C., *Ind. Engng. Chem.* **42**, 2269 (1950).
392.(a) REES, R.LL., *J. Inst. Fuel*, **25**, 350 (1953).
392.(b) REES, R.LL. *Institution of Mechanical Engineers Conference on The Mechanical Engineers Contribution to Clean Air*, p. 34, (1957).
393. REEVE, L., *J. Inst. Fuel*, **31**, 319 (1958); GREGORY, S.A., *Brit. Chem. Engng.* **5**, 340 (1960).
394. RICHARDSON, J.F. and ZAKI, W.N., *Chem. Engng. Sci.*, **3**, 65 (1954).

395. RICHARDSON, J.F. and ZAKI, W.N., *Trans. Inst. Chem. Engng.* (London) **32**, 35 (1954).
396. RIETEMA, K., *Cyclones in Industry*, Ed. K.Rietema and C.G.Verver, pp. 46 and 85, Elsevier, Amsterdam.
397. RILEY, H.L., *Iron and Steel Inst. Special Report*, **61**, p. 129 (1958).
398. ROGERS, S.M. and EDELMAN, S., *A Digest of State Air Pollution Laws*, U.S. Department of Health, Education and Welfare, Washington, 25 D.C. (1962).
399. ROHMANN, H., *Z. Physik.* **17**, 253 (1923).
400. ROSCOE, R., *Brit. J. Appl. Phys.* **3**, 267 (1952).
401. ROSE, A.H., STEPHAN, D.G. and STENBURG, R.L., in *Air Pollution*, p. 307, World Health Organization, Geneva (1961).
402. ROSE, H.E., *J. Appl. Chem.* **2**, 217 (1952).
403. ROSE, H.E. and SULLIVAN, R.M.E., *Nature*, **184**, 47 (1959).
404. ROSE, H.E. and WOOD, A.J., *An Introduction to Electrostatic Precipitation in Theory and Practice*, Constable, London (1956).
405. ROSENBLATT, P. and LA MER, V.K., *Phys. Rev.* **70**, 385 (1946).
406. ROSIN, P., RAMMLER, E. and INTELMANN, W., *Zeit. Ver. Deut. Ing.* **76**, 433 (1932).
407. ROSSANO, A.T. and SILVERMAN, L., *Heating and Ventilating*, p. 102, May (1945).
408. RUCKELSHAUSEN, K., *Über die Beseitigung von Staubansätzen auf technisch glatten Oberflächen durch Klopfen oder Vibrieren*, Dr. Ing. Thesis, Technische Hochschule, Stuttgart (1957).
409. RUFF, R.J., *Chem. Engng. Prog.* **53**, 377 (1957). *Industrial Gas*, (October, 1955) (reprint).
410. RUFF, R.J., in *Air Pollution*, Ed. A.C. Stern. Vol. 2, p. 356, Academic Press, New York (1962).
411. ST.CLAIR, H.W., *Rev. Sci. Insts.* **12**, 250 (1941).
412. ST.CLAIR, H.W., *Ind. Engng. Chem.* **41**, 2434 (1949).
413. ST.CLAIR, H.W., in *United States Technical Conference on Air Pollution*, Ed. McCabe, p. 382, McGraw-Hill, New York (1952).
414. ST.CLAIR, H.W., SPENDLOVE, M.J. and POTTER, E.V., *United States Bureau of Mines, Report of Investigation* No. 4218 (March 1948).
415. SAXTON, R.L. and RANZ, W.E., *J. Appl. Phys.* **23**, 917 (1952).
416. SAYERS, J.E., *Howden Quarterly*, (James Howden & Co, Glasgow **45**, p. 21 (1961).
417. SCHADT, C.F. and CADLE, R.D., *J. Colloid Sci.* **12**, 356 (1957).
418. SCHIELE, O., *Ver. Deut. Ing. Tagungsheft*, **3**, 20 (1954).
419. SCHILLER, L. and NAUMANN, A., *Zeit. Ver. Deut. Ing.* **77**, 318 (1933).
420. SCHMITT, K.H., *Z. Naturforsch*, **14A**, 870 (1959).
421. SCHMIDT, W.A., *J. Ind. Engng. Chem.* **4**, 719 (1912).
422. SCHMIDT, W.A. and ANDERSON, E., *Elec. Engng.* **57**, 332, Aug. (1938) (reprint).
423. SCHMIEDEL, J., *Z. Phys.* **29**, 593 (1928).
424. SCHNITZLER, H., *Arch. Eisenhüttenwesen*, **24**, 199 (1953).
425. SCHNITZLER, H., *Staub.* **23**, 78 (1963).
426. SCHWARTZ, E. and WEPPLER, R., *Siemens Zeitschrift*, **31**, 607 (1957).
427. SCOTT, D.S. and GUTHRIE, D.A., *Canad. J. Chem. Engng.* **37**, 200 (1959).
428. SEAMENS, F.L., *Air Pollution Handbook*, Ed. Magill *et al.* Sect. 14, McGraw-Hill, New York (1956).
429. SEIDMAN, E.B., *Anal. Chem.* **30**, 1680 (1958).
430. SELL, W., *Ver. Deut. Ing. Forschungsheft*, **347**, (1931).
431. SEMRAU, K.T., *J. Air. Poll. Control. Assn.* **10**, (3) 200 (1960).
432. SEMRAU, K.T., *Staub.* **22**, 184 (1962).
433. SEMRAU, K.T., MARYNOWSKI, C.W., LUNDE, K.E. and LAPPLE, C.E., *Ind. Eng. Chem.* **50**, 1615 (1958).
434. SEPTIER, L.G., *Iron and Steel Inst. Special Report* **61**, p. 74 (1958).
435. SFINDEX, S.A. (Sarnen, Switzerland): *Brit. Pat. No. 697,918* (1950).

436. SHALE, C.C. and MOORE, A.S., *Combustion*, p. 42, December (1960).
437. SHAW, F.M., *Fuel Econ. Rev.* **37,** 41 (1959).
438. SHEPHERD, G.B. and LAPPLE, E.C., *Ind. Engng. Chem.* **31,** 972 (1939).
439. SHERLOCK, R.H. and STALKER, E.A., *Univ. Mich. Engng. Research Bull.* No. 29 (1941).
440. SHERWOOD, T.K., *United States Pat. No. 2,833,370.* (1958).
441. SHERWOOD, T.K. and PIGFORD, R.L., *Absorption and Extraction*, McGraw-Hill, New York (1952).
442. SHERWOOD, T.K. and PIGFORD, R.L., *Absorption and Extraction*, p. 270, McGraw-Hill, New York (1952).
443. SHERWOOD, T.K. and PIGFORD, R.L., *Absorption and Extraction*, p. 347, McGraw-Hill, New York (1952).
444. SHERWOOD, T.K. and PIGFORD, R.L., *Absorption and Extraction*, p. 368, McGraw-Hill, New York (1952).
445. SILVERMAN, L., CONNERS, E.W. and ANDERSON, D.M., *Ind. Engng. Chem.* **47,** 962 (1955).
446. SILVERMAN, L., CONNERS, E.W. and ANDERSON, D.M., *Electrostatic mechanisms in aerosol filtration by mechanically charged fabric media*, Harvard School of Public Health, Air Cleaning Laboratory, Report (1956).
447. SKINNER, D.G. and BOAS-TRAUBE, S., *Symposium on Particle Size Analysis. Inst. Chem. Engng. and Soc. Chem. Ind.* p. 44, February (1947).
448. Sly, W.W. Mfg. Co., Cleveland 1. Ohio. Bull. 104.
449. SMITH, SIR E., *Proceeding of the Conference on the Mechanical Engineers Contribution to Clean Air*, p. 1, London, February (1957).
450. SMOLUCHOWSKI, M. VON: *Physik. Z.* 557, 585 (1916); Z. *Physik Chemie* **92,** 129 (1918).
451. SPAITE, P.W., STEPHAN, D.J. and ROSE, A.H., *J. Air Poll. Control. Assn.* **11,** (5) 243 (1961).
452. SPIERS, H.M., Ed. *Technical Data on Fuels*, 6th Edition British National Committee of the World Power Conference, London (1961).
453. SPROULL, W.T., *Ind. Engng. Chem.* **47,** 940 (1955).
454. SPROULL, W.T., *A.I.E.E. Preprint, Winter General Meeting*, January 21–25 (1957) Paper No. CP. 57–46.
455. SPROULL, W.T., *J. Air Poll. Control. Assn.* **10,** 307 (1960).
456. SPROULL, W.T. and NAKADA, Y., *Ind. Engng. Chem.* **43,** 1350 (1951).
457. STAFFORD, E. and SMITH, W.J., *Ind. Engng. Chem.* **43,** 1346 (1951).
458. STAIRMAND, C.J., *Symposium on Particle Size Analysis, Inst. Chem. Engng. and Soc. Chem. Ind.* p. 77, Feb. 4th (1947).
459. STAIRMAND, C.J., *Engineering*, **168,** 409 (1949).
460. STAIRMAND, C.J., *Trans. Inst. Chem. Engng.* (London), **28,** 130 (1950).
461. STAIRMAND, C.J., *Engineering*, **171,** 585 (1951).
462. STAIRMAND, C.J., *Trans. Inst. Chem. Engng.* (London), **29,** 356 (1951).
463. STAIRMAND, C.J. and KELSEY, R.M., *Chem. and Ind.*, 1324 (1955).
464. Standard Filterbau G.m.b.H.: 44 Münster (Westf). Germany.
465. STEPHAN, D.G. and WALSH, G.W., *Ind. Engng. Chem.* **52,** 999 (1960).
466. STEPHENS, E.J. and MORRIS, G.A., *Chem. Engng. Prog.* **47,** 232 (1951).
467. STERLING, P.H. and Ho, H., *Ind. Engng. Chem.* **53,** (6) 52A (1961).
468. STERN, A.C., *Air Pollution Standards*, in *Air Pollution*, Ed. A.C. Stern, Vol. 2, p. 451, Academic Press, New York (1962).
469. STERN, S.C., ZELLER, H.W., SCHEKMAN, A.I., *J. Colloid Sci.* **15,** 546 (1960).
470. STOKES, C.A., *Chem. Engng. Prog.* **46,** 423 (1950).
471. STOKES, G.G., *Trans. Camb. Phil. Soc.* **9 (ii)** 8 (1850).
472. STRAUSS, W., *Unpublished Calculations*, (1957).
473. STRAUSS, W., *Ph. D. Thesis*, University of Sheffield (1959).

474. STRAUSS, W. and THRING M,.W., *J. Iron and Steel Inst.* **193**, 216 (1959); *ibid.* **196**, 62 (1960).

475. STRAUSS, W. and THRING, M.W., *Trans. Inst. Chem. Engng* **41**, 248 (1963).

476. STRAUSS, W. and WOODHOUSE, G., *British Chemical Engineering*, **3**, 620 (1958).

477. STROHM, G.H., *Atmospheric dispersion of stack Effluents* in *Air Pollution*, Ed. A.C. Stern, Vol. I, p. 119, Academic Press (1962).

478. Sturtevant Engineering Co. Ltd., Southern House, Cannon Street, London, E.C. 4 *Ludgate Collector.*

479. SULLIVAN, R.R. and HERTEL, K.L., *J. Appl. Phys.* **11**, 761 (1940).

480. SUTTON, O.G., *Quart. J. Roy. Meteor. Soc.* **73**, 426 (1947).

481. SUTTON, O.G., *J. Met.* **7**, 307 (1950).

482. Swift, James and Son, Ltd., London: *Leaflet on Graticules.*

483. TAGGART, A.F., *Handbook of Mineral Dressing*, p. 9–07, Chapman and Hall (1947).

484. TAYLOR, J.R., HASEGAWA, A., CHAMBERS, L.A., *Air Pollution*, p. 293 World Health Organization, Geneva (1961).

485. THEODORSEN, T. and REGIER, A., *N.A.C.A. Report*, 793 (1944).

486. THOM, A., *Proc. Roy. Soc.* (London) **41A**, 651 (1933).

487. THOMAS, D.G. and LAPPLE, C.E., *Amer. Inst. Chem. Engng. Jr.* **7**, 203 (1961).

488. THOMAS, J.W. and YODER, R.E., *A.M.A. Arch. Ind. Health*, **13**, 545, 550 (1956).

489. THOMAS, M.D., *Air Pollution*, p. 233, World Health Organization, Geneva (1961).

490. THRING, M.W., *J. Inst. Fuel*, **12**, S 58 (1938).

491. THRING, M.W., *Science of Flames and Furnaces*, 2nd Edition Chapman and Hall, London (1962).

492. TORGESON, Quoted by Stern, S.C., Zeller, H.W., Schekman, A.I., *J. Colloid Sci.* **15**, 546 (1960).

493. TOROBIN, L.B. and GAUVIN, W.H., *Canad. J. Chem. Engng.* **37**, 129, 167, 224 (1959); *ibid.* **38**, 142, 189 (1960); *ibid.* **39**, 113, (1961).

494. TOWNSEND, J.S., *Electricity in Gases*, p. 376, Oxford (1915).

495. TROOST, N., *Proc. Inst. Elect. Engrs.* **101**, 369 (1954).

496. TUORILA, P., *Kolloid. Chem. Beih.* **24**, 1 (1927).

497. TURK, A., in *Air Pollution*, Ed. A.C. Stern. Vol. 2, pag. 384, Academic Press, New York (1962).

498. TURNBULL, S.G., BENNING, A.F., FELDMANN, G.W., LYNCH, A.L., McHARNESS, R.C., and RICHARDS, M.K., *Ind. Engng. Chem.* **39**, 286 (1947).

499. TYNDALL, J., *Proc. Roy. Inst.* (London) **6**, 3 (1870).

500. UMNEY, L.E.R., *National Gas Turbine Est., Pyestock*, Report No. R. 33. (1948) (Quoted by Daniels, T.C.).

501. Union Carbide Corpn., Linde Division. Catalogue F-1026-B. *Linde Molecular Sieves.*

502. Union Carbide Corpn., National Carbon Division, Data Sheet, based on *Chem. Engng. Prog.* **48**, 89 (1952).

503. VALENTIN, F.H.H., *33rd Int. Congress Ind. Chemistry*, Toulouse: quoted by *Brit. Chem. Engng.*

504. VERMEULEN, T., in *Advances in Chemical Engineering*, Vol. 2, p. 148, Wiley, New York (1958).

505. Visco Engineering Co., Ltd., Stafford Road, Croydon, Surrey.

506. Vokes, Ltd., Henley Park, Guildford, Surrey, England.

507. VONNEGUT, B., *J. Acoust. Soc. Amer.* **26**, 18 (1954).

508. VONNEGUT, B., *J. Acoust. Soc. Amer.* **27**, 430 (1955).

509. WADELL, H., *J. Frank Inst.* **217**, 459 (1934).

510. WALDMANN, L., *Z. Naturforsch*, **14A**, 589 (1959).

511. WALLIS, E., *British Chemical Engineering*, **7**, 833 (1962).

512. WALTER, E., *Staub.* **42**, 678 (1955).

513. WALTER, E., *Staub.* **48**, 14 (1957).

514. WALTER, E., *Staub*. **53,** 88 (1957).
515. WALTON, W.H., *Symposium on Particle Size Analysis, Trans. Inst. Chem. Engng. and Soc. Chem. Ind.* p. 136, Feb. (1947).
516. WALTON, W.H. and WOOLCOCK, A., *Int. J. Air Poll. Control. Assn.* **3,** 129 (1960).
517. WATSON, H.H., *Trans. Faraday Soc.* **32,** 1073 (1936).
518. WEBB, R.L., *Paint Industry Magazine*, January (1958); *Paint Industry Magazine*, October (1958).
519. WEBER, E., *Staub*. **20,** 338 (1960).
520. WEBER, K., *Z. Naturforsch.* **1,** 217 (1946).
521. WEIDNER, G., *Ver. Deut. Ing. Tagungsheft*, **3,** 16 (1954).
522. WELLMAN, F., *Feuerungstechnik*, **26,** 137 (1938).
523. WESTERBOER, I., *Staub*. **21,** 466 (1961).
524. Western Precipitation Corpn., Los Angeles 54, Calif. U.S.A. Bull. WP–506th. Edition (1958).
525. Westinghouse Electric Corpn., Pittsburgh 30, Pa. U.S.A.
526. WHEELER, A., *Advances in Catalysis*, Vol. 3, p. 250, Ed. W.G. Frankenburg *et al.* Academic Press, New York (1951).
527. WHITE, C.M., *Proc. Roy. Soc.* (London) **A186,** 472 (1946).
528. WHITE, H.J., *Trans. A.I.E.E.* **70,** II 1186 (1951).
529. WHITE, H.J., *Trans. A.I.E.E.* **71.I,** 326 (1952).
530. WHITE, H.J., *Air Repair*, **3,** (2) 79 (1953).
531. WHITE, H.J., *Ind. Engng. Chem.* **47,** 932 (1955).
532. WHITE, H.J., *Chem. Engng. Prog.* **52,** 244 (1956).
533. WHITE, H.J., *J. Air. Poll Control. Assn.* Silver Jubilee Meeting, June (1957) Papers 57–35 (reprint).
534. WHITE, H.J., *Colloques Internationaux du Centre National de la Recherche Scientifique*, Grenoble, September 27th (1960). (Editions du Centre National de la Recherche Scientifique, Paris (1961).
535. WHITE, H.J., *Industrial Electrostatic Precipitation*, Addison-Wesley, Reading, Mass. (1963).
536. WHITE, H.J. and BAXTER, W.A., *A.S.M.E.* Paper No. 59-A-279 (1959).
537. WHITE, H.J. and COLE, W.H., *52nd Air Poll. Control. Assn. Meeting*, Paper 59–48, June 1959).
538. WHITELEY, A.B. and REED, L.E., *J. Inst. Fuel*, **32,** 316 (1959).
539. WHYNES, A.L., *Trans. Inst. Chem. Engng.* (London) **34,** 118 (1956); BROSHEER, J.C., LENESTY, F.A. and ELMORE, K.L., *Ind. Engng. Chem.* **39,** 423 (1947).
540. WHYTLAW-GREY, R. and PATTERSON, H.S., *Smoke*, Arnold, London (1932).
541. WIESELSBERGER, C., *Z. Phys.* **23,** 219 (1922).
542. WIGGINS, E.J., CAMPBELL, W.B. and MAASS, O., *Canad. J. Res.* **17,** 318 (1939).
543. WILKE, C.R. and HOUGEN, O.A., *Trans. Amer. Inst. Chem. Engng.* **41,** 445 (1945).
544. WILLIAMS, J.C. and JACKSON, R., Third Congress of the European Federation of Chemical Engineering—*Symposium, The Interaction between Fluids and Particles*, p. 282 June 22nd Inst. Chem. Eng. (1962).
545. WILSON, B.W., *Aust. J. Appl. Sci.* **4,** 47 (1953).
546. WINKEL, A. and SCHÜTZ, A., *Staub*. **22,** 343 (1962).
547. WOLF, E.F., VON HOHENLEITEN, H.L. and GORDON, M.B., *Int. Clean Air Conference*, p. 239. National Society for Clean Air London (1959)
548. WONG, J.B. and JOHNSTONE, H.F., *Univ. Ill. Engng. Exp. Station Tech. Report*, No. 11 (1953).
549. WOOD, C.W., *Trans. Inst. Chem. Engng.* (London) **38,** 54 (1960).
550. WOOLLAM, J.P.V. and JACKSON, A., *Chem. Engng. Group of Soc. Chem. Ind.* **27,** 43 (1945).
551. YOCOM, J.E., *Chem. Engng.*, **69** p. 103, July 23rd (1962).
552. ZAHN, R., *Staub*. **21,** 56, (1961).
553. ZERNIK, W., *Brit. J. Appl. Phys.* **8,** 117 (1957).

AUTHOR INDEX

SUBJECT INDEX

Bold figures denote major treatment of topic

OTHER TITLES IN THE SERIES IN
CHEMICAL ENGINEERING